Y0-BED-839

Awarded to

Thomas Granger Adams

For outstanding achievement

in physiology

June tenth, 1966

THE HUMAN BODY

Congratulations & best of luck,
It was a pleasure to have you in my classes.
your teacher and friend.

Phobs Karan
June 66.

A Chanticleer Press Edition

THE HUMAN BODY

by Fritz Kahn, M.D.

RANDOM HOUSE NEW YORK

© 1965, by Random House, Inc.

All rights reserved under International and Pan-American Copyright Conventions. Published in New York by Random House, Inc., and in Toronto, Canada, by Random House of Canada Limited. (U.S. copyright is not claimed for color plates on pages 33–64).

Acknowledgment

The author wishes to express his gratitude to Chanticleer Press, in particular to his friend Paul Steiner, the publisher, for his unfailing encouragement, to Milton Rugoff and Susan Grafman, editors, for their labors on the manuscript and captions, and to Ulrich Ruchti for his layout and design. I also wish to thank Dr. Abraham Jacobson, Clinical Assistant Professor of Medicine at Cornell University Medical School for his criticism of the manuscript and his many suggestions.
I am much indebted to the artists, Helga Van Roy, Liff Hansen, Finn Simonsen, Paul Reitzel and Sheila Levrant, who so ably executed the bulk of the drawings. Finally, my deepest appreciation goes to Ellen V. M. Fussing for her help and enthusiasm throughout.

Planned and produced by Chanticleer Press, New York

Library of Congress Catalog Card Number: 65–19637

Manufactured in the United States of America

Contents

Preface

Although it is impossible to keep abreast of all the advances being made in our knowledge of the human body, this book takes into account the electron microscope's revelation of the organelles in cells, new views of the role of the glands, new theories of nutrition, revolutionary progress in the study of genes and chromosomes, and our increasing realization of the interrelation of mind and body.

Although we still discuss the body in terms of various systems, we are thus more than ever aware that all the systems are interconnected and interdependent. We are aware, too, how that seemingly incorporeal system, the mind, influences all the other systems, and conversely, how the body, especially in accident and illness, affects one's state of mind. Modern medicine, especially in the fields of psychiatry and psychosomatics, has driven home the point that glands and emotions, nerves and digestion, mental states and blood pressure and heart condition, are indivisible—fused with inconceivable subtlety and complexity into a single wonderful organism, the human body.

Hardly less important have been the revelations in the biochemistry of the sources of continuing human life, the chromosomes and genes. Since these transmit hereditary factors and control all the systems of the body, the tracing of the role of DNA in the genes and of RNA in the nucleus and cytoplasm of the cell is among the triumphs of recent medicine and may eventually prove comparable in significance to the unlocking of atomic energy.

If the reader finds in these pages some clarification of these marvels and mysteries of the human body, this book will have amply fulfilled its purpose.

I

Protoplasm: The Stuff of Life

An inconceivably complex, self-renewing substance enables living things to move, breathe, eat, speak and think.

All organisms, whether plants or animals, are made up of a specific material called protoplasm. This is the "stuff of life." The word itself, from the Greek *protos* and *plasma,* means the first thing formed. It is familiar to us from our very first impressions. We first come to know it, in a way, in whatever we eat for we absorb it, so to speak, with our spinach, eggs, meat, fish, salad, and indeed, all our food. We build all our living substance from such food even though the food itself is dead protoplasm and the essence of protoplasm is that it is living.

This substance appears in different forms; as the viscid material inside an egg, as the relatively solid material of an apple or a nut. Also, it may appear in many colors—green as in plants, red or white as in meat, and so forth. It is thus not a simple substance but a complex mixture of many ingredients.

Protoplasm

Protoplasm is not a uniform material like aspirin or an alloy like steel; even the term "substance" is not adequate. We can get a better conception of it if we think of it as a machine, a machine made not of iron but the semifluid we call protoplasm. Since this machine helps us to perform an incredible number of functions such as moving, breathing, dancing, speaking, and thinking, it is almost impossible to grasp how complex it is and how many mechanisms it contains. If we are astonished at the complicated mechanisms in an auto—the ignition, carburetor, brakes, radiator, etc.—how much more astonishing are the self-energizing and self-renewing mechanisms of protoplasm that enable living things to swim, to fly, to walk, and to crawl. But the machine is there, and man is such a machine.

We can not see protoplasm with the naked eye. We can not see the fine details of this machine with a microscope, not even when magnified 200,000 times by one of our electron microscopes. We must have an instrument that magnifies a hundred million times, because protoplasm is a machine wherein the parts are molecules, or, even less than molecules—atoms! Protoplasm is, moreover, not a single machine, but—like an auto—an intricate combination of dozens of different kinds of systems of machines—a whole city of machines.

Perhaps the following will help make clear its

(Facing page) Protoplasm, the life substance, here assumes the form of secreting cells in the pancreas. (Dr. J.A.G. Rhodin, from his Atlas of Ultrastructure, W.B. Saunders Company. 1963)

8

staggering complexity: Imagine that we are in an airplane flying over Detroit—a city of hundreds of factories, steel mills, and offices, with thousands of families, with hospitals and schools, churches and police stations, with dogs and cats and the countless other objects that make up a metropolis. We do not see all these things from an airplane but we know they are there. Then the airplane rises and the city becomes smaller and smaller and finally shrinks to a mere speck. Detroit in a speck—that is protoplasm. It is an organization of a hundred million chemical compounds, every compound a molecule with a specific task, a specific peculiarity, all contributing to the society, all in action, dancing, clicking, whirring like the wheels inside a watch.

The parts are atoms, ions, electrons. And the atoms and ions do not stand still. Movement is their life, and movement in the world of atoms is unimaginably swift. A second on one of our clocks is as long as a millenium in the world of atoms. If an atom leaps from one compound to another—which we call a chemical reaction—the leap is performed in less than a millionth of a second. Therefore, the modern biophysicist does not count in seconds but in *nanoseconds*, or thousandths of the millionth part of a second. All events in the world of atoms unroll with atomic speed, and protoplasm is an organization of atoms unimaginable in number and in velocity of action. A second is as rich in events as a century in the life of mankind.

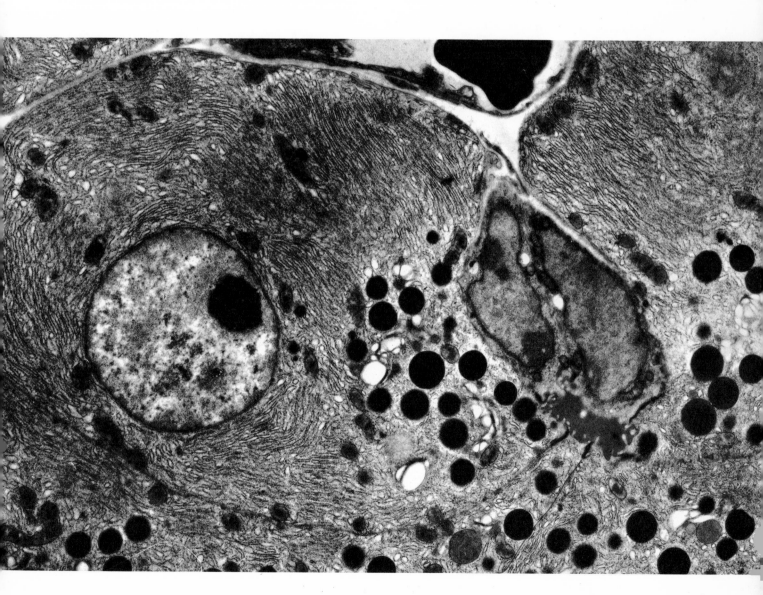

2

The Cell

All living tissue is made up of microscopic units that serve both as basic building blocks and miniature chemical factories.

Protoplasm is made up of units that have a distinct form. These units are called "cells." The cell was first described and given its name by an English scientist, Robert Hooke, as far back as 1665, when he studied a slice of cork under the microscope. But it was not until the early 19th century that it became clear that all living organisms are made up of cells, and it was as late as 1859 that the great German pathologist Rudolf Virchow first made the observation that "every cell arises from a pre-existing cell."

Animal cells are mostly small—very, very small, although the egg of a bird is, of course, quite large because it contains so much food material for the embryo to grow on.

When we gaze up at a starry sky we can see three thousand stars at the very most. Yet we are overwhelmed by their number. Now, if you prick your finger tip, squeeze out a drop of blood, and look at the drop through a microscope, you will see—five million cells! Of course we cannot count them because they are too densely crowded together; to see them as individual cells we have to dilute the blood two hundred times. The five quarts of blood coursing through the human blood vessels contain more than thirty million times one million red cells!

We can get some idea of the immensity of this number if we think of *Pithecanthropus erectus,* the first man-ape to walk erect. He lived about a million years ago. Measured in human generations this is about forty thousand generations ago—an inconceivably long time. Now if somehow one individual of the *Pithecanthropi* had remained alive through all the ages since that time but had lost one cell every second, he would altogether have lost less of his body than some ancient Roman statue with an arm or leg missing from it.

The protoplasm of which cells are made can take on and retain every kind of shape. Cells can be shaped like a ball, as in the human egg cell. The most numerous cells, the red blood cells, have a circular, slightly flattened form much like a doughnut, a shape suited for passing smoothly along the fine, pipelike blood vessels. The white corpuscles, or cells, of the blood are much less numerous than the red cells. While a drop of blood contains five million red cells, there are only five to ten thousand white cells present in it. The red cell generally maintains its overall

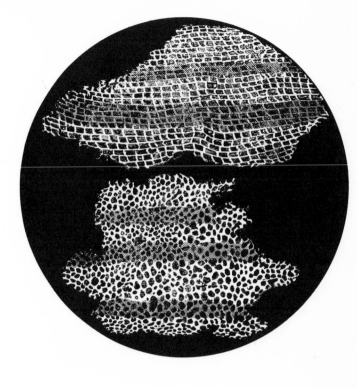

An 18th century microscope.

(Right) Illustration of cork cells from "Micrographia" (1665), a book by an English physicist Robert Hooke. Using a glass ball to concentrate light on thin slices of cork, Hooke was the first man to observe cells.

shape and goes only where the heart pump sends it within the arteries, capillaries and veins of the circulatory system unless there is a break or cut in a vessel. The white cell is capable of independent movement, and can move like an amoeba by varying its shape and sending out tentacles or pseudopods. It can slip out of the capillaries by crawling between the capillary cells, and it does so when a part of the body is infected—as with a boil—in order to fight the bacteria.

Man as a Community of Cells

Around the middle of the 19th century, two German scientists set forth the theory of man as a community of cells. They said just as man's dwellings are built of bricks, so man himself is composed of cells. If a single cell lives by itself, independently, as do bacteria or infusoria, we call the organism unicellular. Larger organisms, such as trees, worms, cattle and other animals, including man, are made

11

up of trillions of cells existing together. Man is a community of extraordinarily large numbers of cells.

Close-up of a Cell

It is hard to study protoplasm or a cell in its natural state because in terms of color it is, like the art form known as *en grisaille*, gray on gray. To study a cell the biologists developed a technique for staining microscopic objects. The career of the young biologist usually starts on the day his teacher demonstrates the study of microscopic preparations. The teacher brings in an onion, peels off one of its tissue-thin inner layers, and dips this in a dye of methylene blue. After a few minutes he spreads the "preparation" between two thin plates of glass and places the slide under a microscope. The dye stains the heart of the cell, the nucleus, differentiating it from the rest of the cell, the cytoplasm.

Just as every day in our society some individuals die while others are born, so in the human body the individual cells die after a specific interval and are replaced by new cells. If we study a section of human skin we see how the lowermost layers of cells, nourished by the blood vessels, constantly produce new cells and how the newcomers push the older cells toward the surface of the skin. These older cells, cut off from nourishment, gradually starve, their nuclei disappear, and the protoplasm becomes dry and flaky. Whenever we wash, some of the top layer of skin is sloughed off, but replacements keep coming up. So our skin is always fresh and "new."

In much the same way cells are replaced in every organ of the body. The blood corpuscles, which are products of the bone marrow, live only about three to four months. The liver cells, which work very hard, probably do not survive even as long as that.

The brain cells or bone cells apparently persist for an intermediate length of time. Since we have started a "population census" with the help of radioactive molecules, we may some day have more "life expectancy" tables for the cells. We can assume that about a billion divisions are always in process and that about twenty billion divisions are completed each day. No nation on earth can compete with the nation of body cells in birth rate.

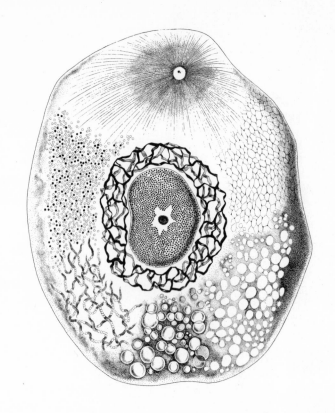

(Above) A human cell. Idealized, greatly magnified drawing of a cell as seen in an electron microscope. In the center is the nucleus filled with chromatin granules and a dark mass, the nucleolus. During cell division the chromatin and the nucleolus condense into the chromosomes. Surrounding the nucleus is the dark wreath of the Golgi body. At the top of the cell is the centrosome with strands radiating from it. To the left, seen here as black and white specks, are the microsomes and just below them the considerably larger mitochondria. At the bottom are the lysosomes.

(Right) Plant cell showing the rigid cell wall.

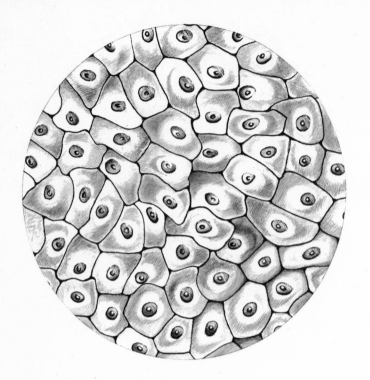

Cells replace themselves by a process called cell division. Sometimes this division is a simple process. The nucleus and the cytoplasm narrow centrally so that the cell takes on the shape of a dumbbell, and then the two halves separate. This kind of division, called amitosis, occurs only in simple cells, and takes place only rarely in the human body. Otherwise the division of all cells other than egg and sperm cells is that of mitosis and is a complex process.

Mitosis

Next to the nucleus lies a tiny body, the centrosome, and this is the first of the organelles—the specialized parts in the cell cytoplasm—that we will describe. This body acts like the ignition of a car: it starts the process of cell division. It contains two minute granules called centrioles. First the centrioles move apart, each with a sort of magnetic attraction sphere around it. As the two centrioles

Cell tissue. The human body is built up of tiny units, called cells, which serve both as building blocks (like those in the old wall above) and as chemical factories.

(Right) Types of human cells. From a simple egg-cell in the mother about two dozen types of cells develop, including (from top to bottom) the white blood, secretory, connective tissue and muscle fiber cells.

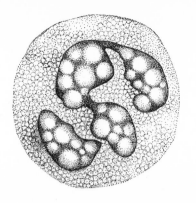

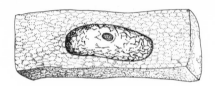

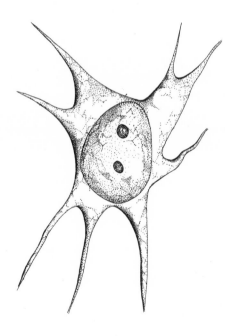

move to the opposite poles of the cell, rays form between them; these rays are strung out like the meridian lines on a globe and form a spindle between the centrioles.

The nucleus of the cell is filled with a substance which has a specific affinity with certain dyes and is therefore called chromatin, that is, the color substance. The chemical constituents of the chromatin form the genes that determine the traits and characteristics of every living thing. After it is stained, the chromatin of the nucleus becomes visible as dots and filaments. The chain of chromatin is as tangled as the earthworms in an angler's box.

As the spindles form during mitosis, the nuclear chromatin condenses into pieces, or rods, called chromosomes. The same number of chromosomes always appears in each species of plant or animal: eight in a fruit fly, fourteen in a garden pea, sixteen in an onion, forty in a mouse, forty-six in a man, or up to two hundred in some crayfish. We do not know the significance of the different numbers in each species: the number does not seem to be related to the number of hereditary traits. Even though we do not yet know the specific function of each chromosome, each of the forty-six chromosomes in man has its own particular structure. We do know which pair of chromosomes determines the sex of the offspring. And since certain hereditary factors, such as the ability of the blood to clot normally, are associated with the sex factor, we have a few clues concerning the location of certain factors.

Once the chromosomes have formed, each splits into two longitudinally, and the resulting two sets arrange themselves in an "equatorial" plate which hangs in the midst of the spindle. The chromosome halves in the "equatorial" plate begin to move apart, assuming the shape of hairpins, and the two sets of forty-six are separately drawn along the spindle rays toward each of the centrioles.

The cell now takes on the form of an hourglass and divides into two at the narrow mid-point. The mother cell has become two daughter cells. The chromosomes are no longer visible as such but stain only as chromatin. This wonderful ballet of the chromosomes takes place in every living plant and every animal. The process of division takes only about twenty minutes.

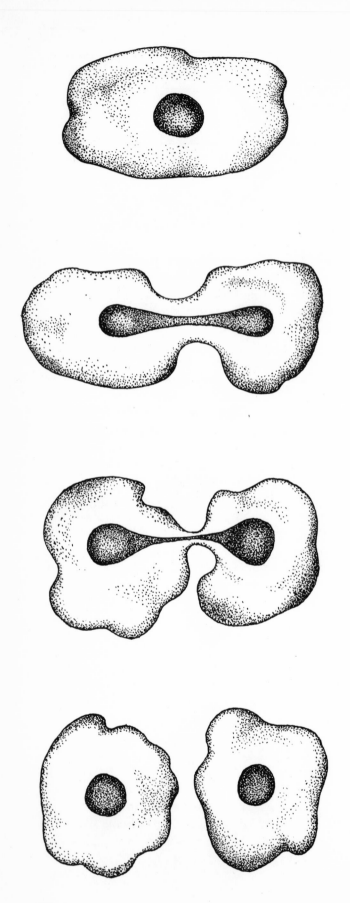

The Electron Microscope and the Organelles

One of the most spectacular inventions of the beginning of the 20th century was the electron microscope. Until then the scientists had used light-wave, or optical, microscopes. This microscope can magnify an object up to two thousand times but its power is limited by the length of light waves, since if two points are closer together than half the wave length of light they cannot be distinguished from one another, no matter what the magnification. Ultraviolet light has a smaller wave length than visible light and makes greater magnification possible, but it is still quite limited.

Then in 1924, Louis de Broglie discovered that electron particles behaved like waves, as does light. It turned out that their wave length is one hundred thousand times shorter than the wave length of ordinary light. As a result, electron microscopes were invented in the nineteen thirties, a stream of electrons taking the role of light beams and magnetic fields serving as lenses. With the electron microscope magnifications up to two hundred thousand times are common and, with photographic enlargements, we now view specimens magnified over one million times. This has literally opened up a new world to us.

We must not, however, lose sight of the price, so to speak, we pay for the miraculous magnification the electron microscope gives us. It limits our view to an infinitesimally small area. The naturalist of the 19th century saw the whole object: the entire infusoria or radiolaria, or the whole of a tiny crystal

The simplest form of cell division (amitotis). The nucleus and cytoplasm narrow at the center, take on a dumbbell shape and then split into two halves.

(Facing page) Mitosis. A plant cell (which lacks only the centrosome of an animal cell) shows most clearly the stages of mitosis. Reading from top to bottom, the nucleus breaks up into five distinct chromosomes. Lining up at the equator of the cell, they split into two sets, each moving to the opposite ends of the cell. Two new nuclei then form, each containing as many chromosomes as the parent cell. A wall will develop between the nuclei, creating two daughter cells. (Dr. A. H. Sparrow, Brookhaven National Laboratory)

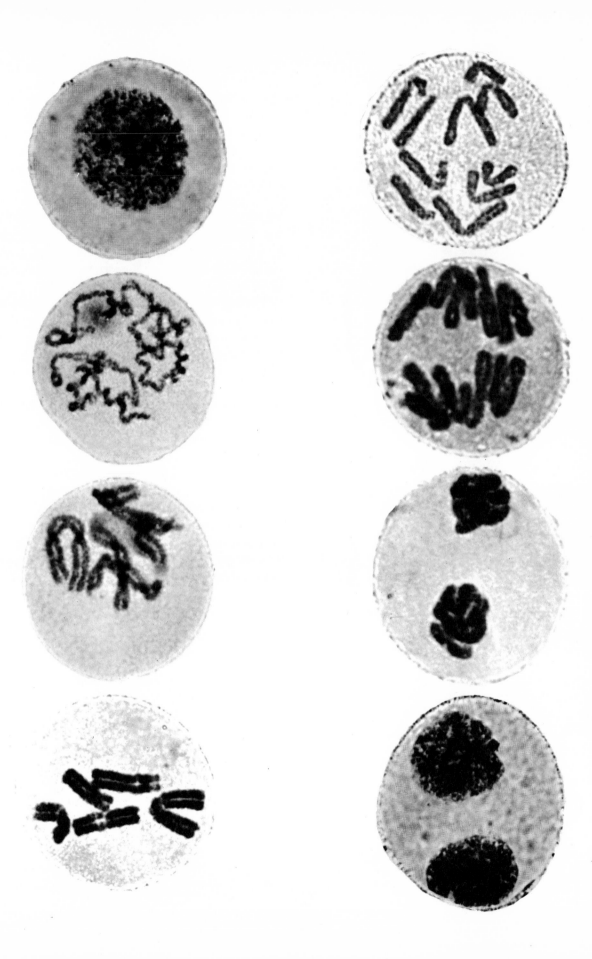

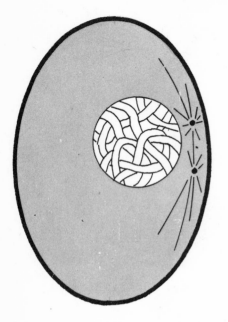 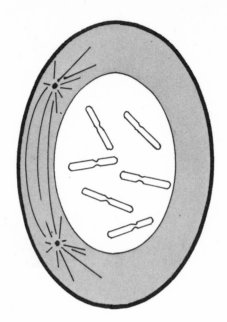 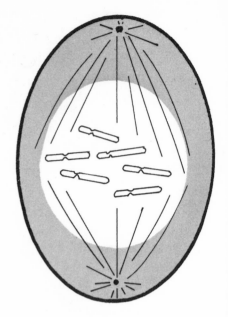

Human cell division, here shown in six scenes, might be called "the ballet of reproduction."

1. While the centrioles of the centrosome divide into two "stars" and form the spindle, the chromatin in the nucleus condenses into a tape or chain.

2. The chromatin tape divides into forty-six chromosomes of which only six are shown here. Although still joined at the center, each chromosome forms a double.

3. The centrioles travel to opposite poles of the cell and the chromosomes arrange themselves around the equator of the cell.

4. The nuclear membrane has disappeared, each of the chromosomes split in half and the doubled chromosomes are lined up in an equatorial plate.

5. The hairpin-shaped chromosome halves move apart, and each of the two sets is drawn along the spindle rays toward one of the centrioles. The cell elongates into an hourglass shape.

6. The cell divides at the center and becomes two cells. The chromosomes are no longer visible but stain only as chromatin. The process takes about twenty minutes and goes on constantly in about 100,000,000 body cells.

of snow. The biologist using the electron microscope to the fullest extent can not see even the whole of a single cell. But he has been able to identify the submicroscopic parts of protoplasm, the sub-organs called organelles.

Centrosomes and the Golgi Body

We have already mentioned one of these bodies, the centrosome, which acts as a center of energy in the process of mitosis during which the spindle is formed. The most prominent of the organelles is the Golgi body, or apparatus, first described in the last decade of the 19th century by the famous Italian microscopist Camillo Golgi. The exact function of the Golgi body is not yet known, but it is thought to be important in cell activities, particularly secretion. After the cell has been stained, it appears as a dark wreath near the nucleus; it is formed of paired membranes that become distended to form large spaces that are known as vacuoles,

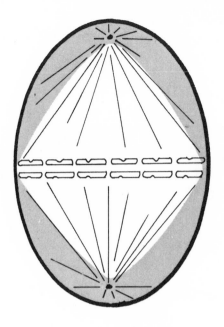 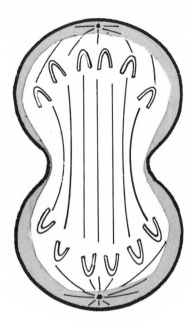 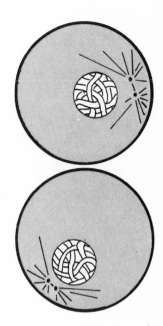

and it also contains small blebs called vesicles. The vacuoles become filled with granules which are enzymes and are probably formed in the microsomes.

Microsomes consist of countless minute grains scattered throughout the cytoplasm of the cell. They have multiple functions within the cell. Some microsomes rich in RNA (ribose nucleic acid), are called ribosomes and are involved in the synthesis of protein. Others contain enzymes with a variety of functions.

The Enzymes

The human body is a chemical factory with billions of cells that do the work, not by means of mechanical devices but with chemical reactions. The tools they use are certain specialized proteins called ferments or enzymes. For almost every act our body undertakes biochemically it uses a specific enzyme to increase the speed of the chemical reaction

tremendously. And what is peculiar about enzymes is that they are not used up when they finish speeding up a reaction but are available to do it again.

The most common foodstuff is sugar. Its energy is held in the banks of its molecules and we get this energy by opening the bonds and by oxidation. We speak of this breaking down of the sugar as "combustion"; if, however, we investigate this combustion we find that the decomposition of the sugar molecule takes place not in one explosion but in dozens of steps involving many enzymes. For example, only one kind of enzyme can carry the atom of hydrogen from one place to another. This enzyme is called the hydrogen-carrier, and in every second of our lives ten million hydrogen-carrying machines are moving hydrogen atoms. These reactions take place at the atomic speed of hundreds of millions of times per second; yet the moving of hydrogen atoms is only one of a thousand such processes inside the cell. There are, for example, nitrogen carriers, sulphur carriers, and hundreds of others. Compared with the human body, an

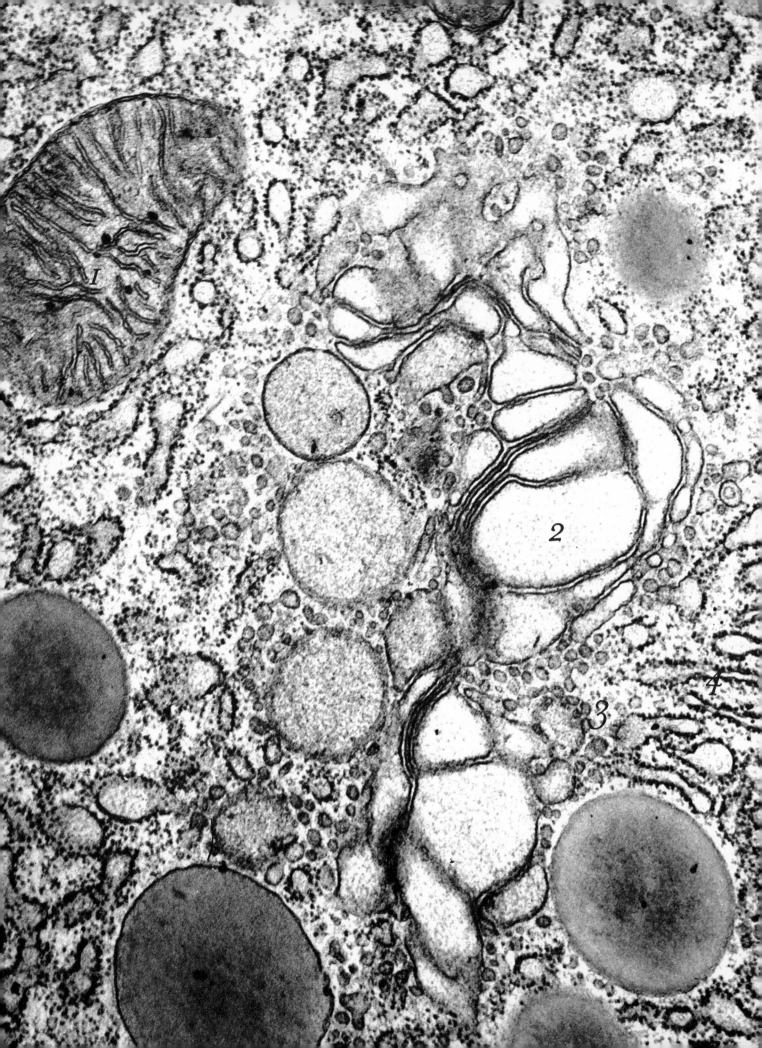

ordinary chemical factory seems almost like a sleepy place.

The Lysosomes

The lysosomes are tiny bags filled with digestive juices. They serve inside the protoplasm to break down particles that the cell engulfs (phagocytosis) and have therefore been called the digestive juice of the cells. Phagocytosis, for example, is what the white blood cells perform when they engulf bacteria or other foreign substances. Just as our mouth ingests food, the tiny particles are first ingested by the cell; the second stage is performed by the enzymes of the microsomes. But the investigation of this process is still in its early stages and conclusions must be accepted with certain reservations.

The Mitochondria

Beside the innumerable tiny microsomes, the cytoplasm contains considerably larger bodies called mitochondria. They serve to transform the chemical energy of our foodstuffs into the vital energy of living protoplasm and are termed "the powerhouse of the cell." Therefore they are especially numerous in muscle cells, kidney cells, and wherever else energy is required. Special enzymes are present in the mitochondria, particularly those necessary for oxidation. They also produce most of the ATP (adenosine triphosphate) of the cell, the compound that stores chemical energy. The amount of energy the molecule is able to transmit depends on the number of phosphoric molecules. The energy is located in the chemical bonds between each of the phosphoric acid molecules and the adenosine; as soon as we break the bond, the energy is released. After the release of the energy each molecule recharges itself.

(Left) The organelles. A greatly magnified photograph of the cell reveals such submicroscopic parts of the protoplasm as (1) the mitochondria; (2) the vacuoles; (3) the small vesicles of the Golgi body and (4) the ribosomes. (Dr. J. A. G. Rhodin, from his Atlas of Ultrastructure, W. B. Saunders Company, 1963)

Electron microscope. A stream of electrons acts like light rays, and magnetic fields serve as lenses to bend the rays. This instrument permits magnifications of over one million times. (Radio Corporation of America)

3
From Egg Cell to Embryo

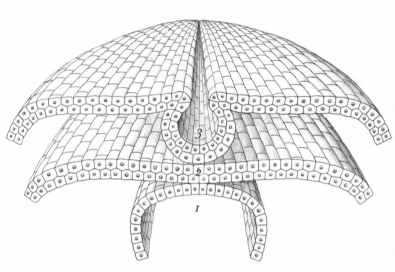

Out of the union of a single male cell, a spermatozoon, and a single female egg cell develops the embryo containing all the body organs.

Both the mature egg cells and the sperm cells of sexual reproduction are unique among cells. The sexual cells contain half the number of chromosomes found in the rest of the body cells, the somatic cells. Thus in the human body, eggs and sperms each have only twenty-three chromosomes in the nucleus, as against the forty-six present in somatic cells. This comes about through a process of cell division called meiosis, or reduction division.

During the early period of multiplication of the male and female sex cells, they still contain forty-six chromosomes, but they undergo a period of maturation. When this takes place, the chromosomes form and line up in pairs as they do initially in mitosis. The crucial difference is that each chromosome does *not* split in two. As a result, after the chromosomes line up at the equatorial plate, only one-half of the chromosomes, or twenty-three, are drawn along the spindle plates towards each of the centrioles. When the daughter cells separate, each has only one-half the number of chromosomes.

What is significant about meiosis is that it begins

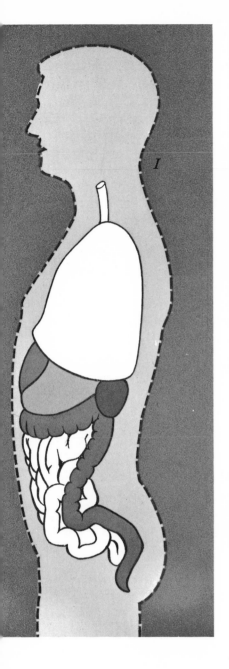
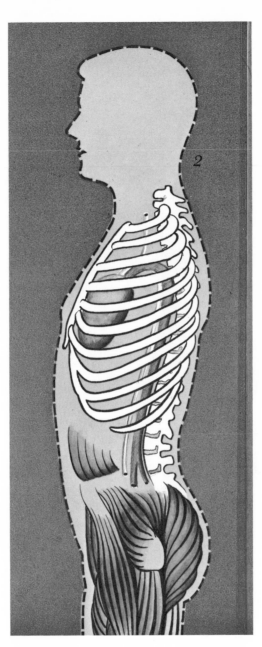

(Left above) The germ layers: (1) the inner layer (ento-derm), (2) middle layer (mesoderm) and (3) outer layer (ectoderm) from which the body organs develop.

The inner germ layer (shown above) forms the intestines and internal organs; the middle layer forms the connective tissue, such as fat, cartilage, bones, muscles, arteries and body fluids; and the external layer produces the skin, with the groove in this layer forming the nervous system.

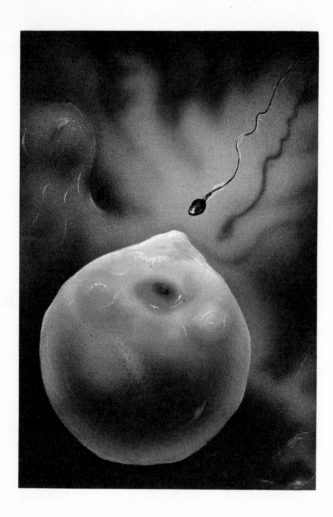

Fertilization of the egg cell. At the moment the father's spermatozoon fertilizes the mother's egg cell the qualities of paternal and maternal ancestors mix to form the future child.

(Facing page) The first stages of life: from egg cell to gastrula. Reading from top to bottom, the fertilized egg cell multiplies by division into a ball-shaped mass called the morula. After further division, the morula becomes a hollow sphere of cells containing a fluid-filled cavity. The sphere buckles inward and the gastrula forms.

the great game of chance which sexual reproduction represents. Thus the original sperm cell, containing forty-six chromosomes before meiosis, has a pair of sex chromosomes, X and Y. After meiosis, one of the two sperm cells contains only an X chromosome, the other only a Y chromosome. If the sperm cell containing the X chromosome succeeds in fertilizing an ovum, the offspring will be a girl; if the sperm cell containing the Y is successful, the offspring is a boy. This holds true for all traits, if the pair of chromosomes containing the traits are different. If they are identical, there is of course no variation possible. Otherwise meiosis is like the reshuffling of a deck of forty-six cards into two sets of twenty-three each, with all sorts of permutations and combinations possible.

The great event in the life of the egg cell is fertilization. A sperm cell of the father comes with twenty-three chromosomes of hereditary substance and penetrates an egg cell, which also contains twenty-three chromosomes. The two nuclei of the cells combine their chromosomes and the new cell with its forty-six chromosomes starts to grow by cell division and to transform into an embryo. The one cell becomes two, the two become four, and in a few hours the embryo is a ball. This stage of the embryo is called the mulberry or morula. The cells rearrange themselves to form a layer surrounding a cavity and the ball resembles a tennis ball, with the outside solid and the center hollow. It is now called the blastula.

The blastula then "caves in" and becomes cup-shaped. Since it now looks like a stomach it is known as a gastrula (from the Latin *gaster,* meaning stomach). The gastrula is a cup with an inner and an outer layer. Because their cells germinate and grow, these layers are called the germ layers. The inner layer (endoderm) produces the internal organs, the intestines and other viscera, while the outer layer (ectoderm) becomes our external organs, the skin, nervous system, and sensory apparatus. An intermediate layer develops between the two layers and is called the mesoderm. It produces the fat, cartilage and bones that give structure to the body, the connective tissue, the muscles that move the body, and finally the fluids, blood and lymph, that carry food to all organs and tissues.

The theory of the germ-layers is our guide through the labyrinth of the body's tissues and organs.

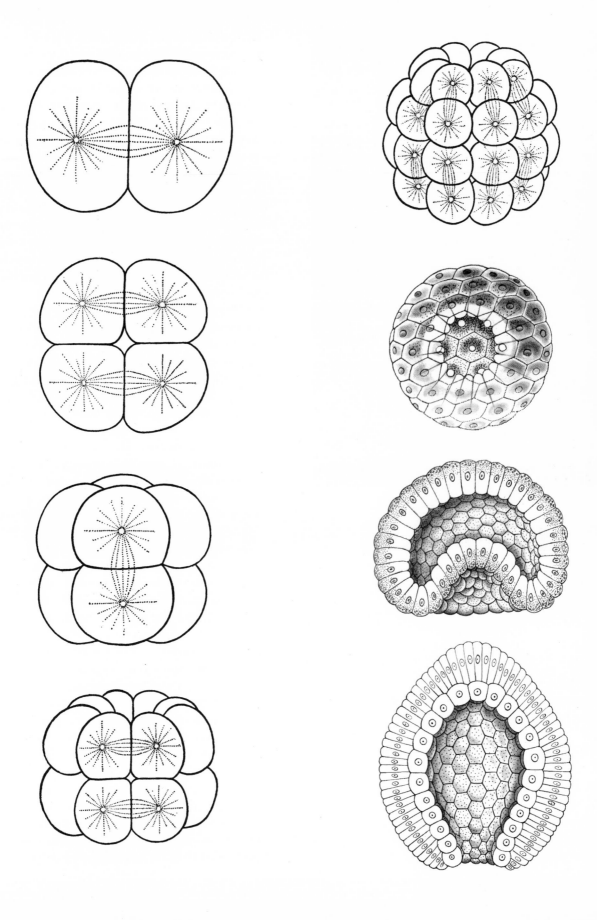

4

Genetics

Each individual is a combination of the traits carried by the twenty-three chromosomes in the father's sperm cell and the twenty-three chromosomes in a mother's egg cell.

The founder of the science of genetics, Gregor Mendel, was the son of poor Bohemian peasants. Since he showed signs of a gift for mathematics, he was entered in a religious order so that he could get a higher education. In his spare time he used the plants on the monastery grounds to make studies of the inheritance of color in garden peas and other flowers. He formulated the results in what we now know as the Mendelian Laws. Publishing his findings in a little pamphlet he sent it to all the academies and authorities, but got not one response. Deeply disappointed, he lost interest in his studies, grew enormously fat—without doubt for psychosomatic reasons—and died as prior of the cloister but without having had the slightest acknowledgement of his scientific achievements. Years later, three scientists, each working independently, also discovered the rules of heredity. Only when they published their findings did they learn that a monk had made these discoveries thirty-two years before.

Chromosomes—Bearers of Heredity

When the human egg cell is fertilized by the sperm cell, the twenty-three chromosomes contained in each sexual cell combine. The result is a new "child" cell that has a full complement of forty-six chromosomes, half from each of its parents.

Aside from the fact that the child inherits only half of the chromosomes of the father's sperm cell and the mother's egg cell, the sperm is only one of up to two hundred million sperm cells that the father ejaculates. And each of these sperm cells has a different group of chromosomes, depending on the extraordinarily large number of permutations and combinations that were possible when the reduction division from forty-six to twenty-three chromosomes took place during meiosis. Two hundred million chips are put down in the lottery of fertilization and only one wins! A pair of parents could combine their genetic heritage in billions of ways and every combination would result in a different offspring. And since over two billion human beings participate in this game of chance, the possible combinations of genetic traits in human personalities are inexhaustible. The results in individuals are sometimes frightening, sometimes wonderful but always unique. If the whole globe

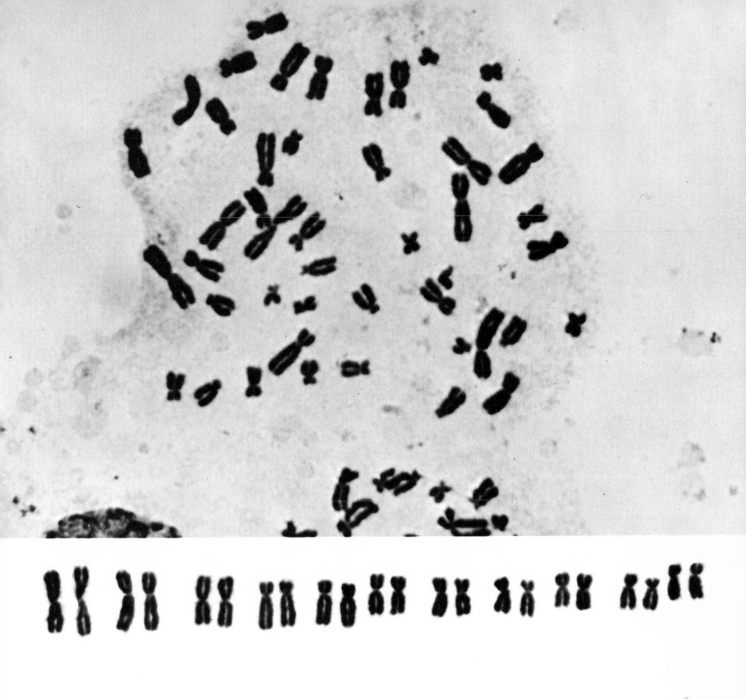

X

Chromosomes of human female from a white blood cell culture as seen under electron microscope.

In chromosome analysis (shown above), the cell is observed during mitosis when the doubled chromosomes are about to split at the equator of the cell. The chromosomes are identified by their length and the point at which the doubled strands are joined; except for the X and Y chromosomes, they are then numbered. (Dr. Grace Donnelly, Brookhaven National Laboratory)

were covered with bridge tables, each seating four persons, and they played bridge from morning to night, they could play a thousand years without getting the same combination of hands; so it is with the possible combinations of chromosomes in human beings.

At the time Mendel formulated his "laws," the chromosomes were not yet known to be the bearers of hereditary traits. It seems incredible that a Bohemian monk should have been able to make such discoveries as he did before the basic facts of the composition of cells had become known. Despite the fact that he did not know what carried the hereditary traits, Mendel declared that they were transmitted not by vague "spirits" or "forces" but by definite units.

As a result of his experiments with garden peas and their flowers he also declared that hereditary factors could be exactly defined. Peas with white and peas with red flowers which fertilize one another have three kinds of descendants: plants with white flowers, plants with red flowers, and plants with pink flowers. But in the pink flowers the original colors do not lose their identity, as happens when a painter mixes two colors on his palette, but retain their hereditary red and white factors and can transmit them to the following generation.

The other fundamental discovery was that the factors do not have equal force. One may prove stronger to the other, as with brown and blue eyes in human beings. A person may have the genetic trait for both brown eyes and blue eyes, having inherited the different traits from each of his parents, one through the sperm cell, one through the egg cell. In this case he is called heterozygous for the trait, but his eyes will be brown, because brown is stronger. It is only when both traits for eye color are blue that a person's eyes will be blue. He is then homozygous for the trait. The stronger characteristic is called the dominant, the weaker the recessive. The Mendelian rule of dominant and recessive characteristics is fundamental to an understanding of heredity.

Mutations

In the Netherlands, in 1848, twenty-five years after Mendel, another prodigy, Hugo van de Vries, was born. One day, young de Vries, strolling on the outskirts of Amsterdam, discovered some specimens of the weed Oenothera that were different from the normal species. An ordinary botanist would have wondered about it for a moment and then dismissed it. But not de Vries. He searched through his books but there was no mention of the specimen he had found. He hesitated to publish his finding because they contradicted the accepted dogma: *natura non facit saltus*—nature does not make abrupt changes. But in this case nature had apparently made a sudden change. For no detectable reason a new subspecies had appeared among well-known sisters and brothers.

De Vries decided that none of the forces described by Darwin—changes in climate, the struggle against new enemies, survival of the fittest—was involved. He concluded that there had been some unmotivated change in the genetic substance, and so he called it a mutation. Since several million genetic factors make up a child, any of several hundred deviations in the atoms may occur. If we may compare each human being to a printed book, none of us is without a printing error. But a mutation will become evident only if the deviation is marked. It may be that the mutation is so deleterious that the embryo cannot survive. The geneticist calls such a mutation a lethal factor: we do not know how often such a factor causes the death of an embryo.

The rediscovery of the Mendelian rules and the discovery of mutation by de Vries acted as a powerful stimulus to research, and the new science of genetics was born. Shortly after 1906, Thomas H. Morgan began experiments in heredity in California, using the fruitfly *Drosophila melanogaster*. Drosophila is convenient for such experiments because it brings forth a new generation in less than two weeks and its chromosomes are easy to trace because it has only eight in a cell. The characteristics of a fruitfly are, moreover, easily defined: color of body, color of eyes, patterns of wings, position of bristles, structure of legs, and so on. Morgan collected observations of the inherited characteristics of hundreds of thousands of fruitflies crossbred in all imaginable combinations. One outstanding result of this was his now famous charts of the fruitfly chromosomes. Another came to be known as "artificial mutation." Normally mutations in the

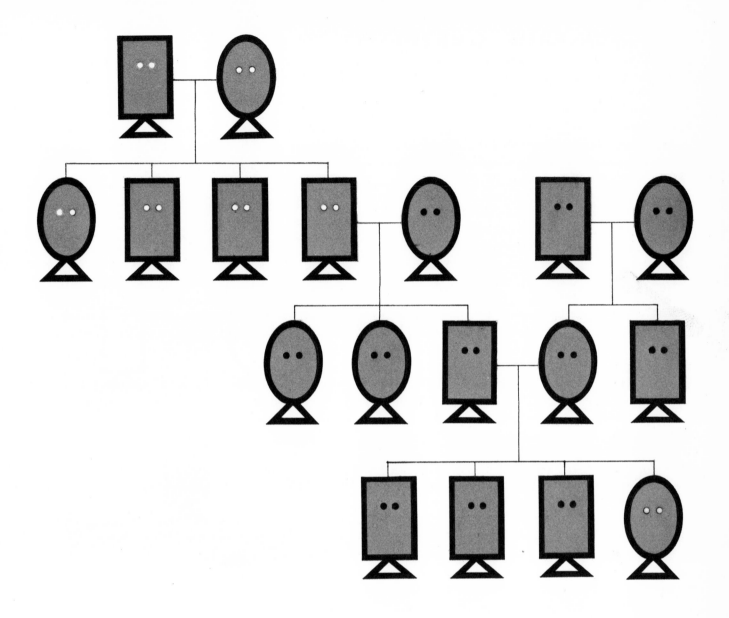

The genetic code. Each parent on the left of the chart has blue eyes; that is, both traits for eye color are blue, or homozygous. Their children inherit only blue-eye traits. One of these children marries a brown-eyed spouse, both of whose traits for eye color are brown. Each of their children has a blue-eye trait and a brown-eye trait (a heterozygous combination) but since the brown-eye trait is dominant, all of their children are brown-eyed. One of the children marries a brown-eyed spouse. Although a child of brown-eyed parents, this spouse is heterozygous for eye color, possessing one blue-eye trait and one brown-eye trait. As a rule, three out of four of their children will be brown-eyed and one blue-eyed.

Of the three brown-eyed children, one child will carry traits only for brown eyes and two will be heterozygous, carrying both brown-eye and blue-eye traits. The blue-eyed child will be homozygous for blue eyes only. An exception occurs when the irises of a blue-eyed person contain spots of brown pigment: if two such persons marry, they may have brown-eyed children.

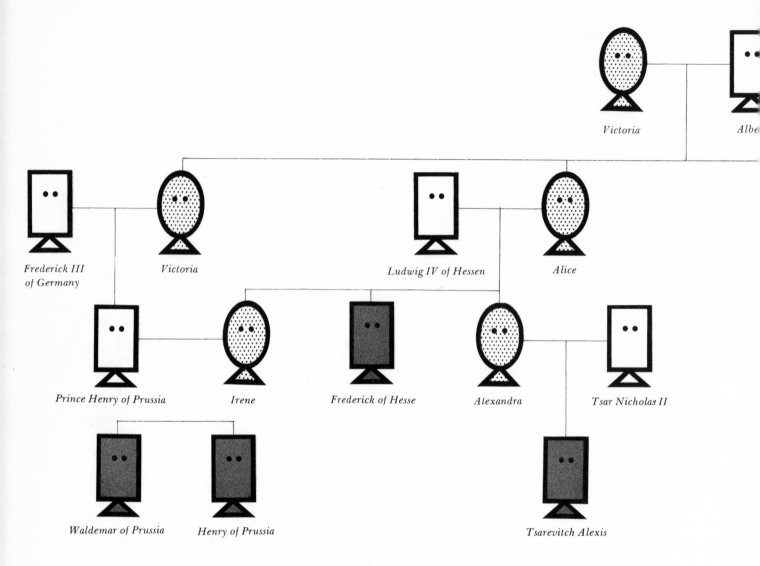

Victoria

Albe[rt]

Frederick III
of Germany

Victoria

Ludwig IV of Hessen

Alice

Prince Henry of Prussia

Irene

Frederick of Hesse

Alexandra

Tsar Nicholas II

Waldemar of Prussia

Henry of Prussia

Tsarevitch Alexis

structure of the chromosomes of fruitflies occur one in fifty thousand times. But if we expose the eggs of the fly to such chemicals as colchicine or to mustard gas the number of mutations are increased tenfold. One of the most interesting observations, made by the geneticist J. H. Muller, was the way x-rays increase mutations and produce crippled offspring.

Viruses

Looking about for other simple organisms to use in their studies, geneticists worked with bacteria, then with a microscopic fungus, and finally with viruses. Since a virus is little more than genetic

material wrapped in a sac of protein, its life cycle is extremely simple. First, a virus approaches its victim, which may be a bacterial cell, attaches itself to it, and injects its hereditary material into it. Inside the body the injected "chromosomes" proliferate, exploiting the protoplasm of their host. From the exhausted bacterial cell hundreds of new parasitic viruses are disseminated.

The Genetic Code

It took the efforts of hundreds of the best research scientists to begin decoding the hereditary or genetic substance. Fundamentally the gene in the

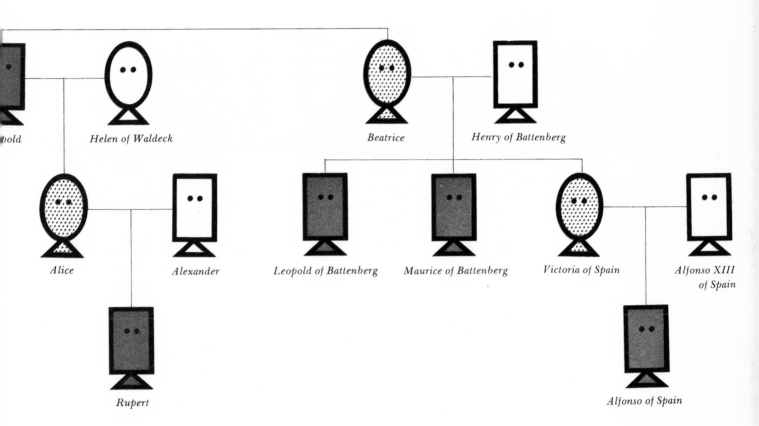

Labels in figure: pold · Helen of Waldeck · Beatrice · Henry of Battenberg · Alice · Alexander · Leopold of Battenberg · Maurice of Battenberg · Victoria of Spain · Alfonso XIII of Spain · Rupert · Alfonso of Spain

chromosome is a compound of proteins in the form of a double ladder of molecules. Chemically the ladders are made up of sugar, phosphoric acid and several organic compounds called bases. The sugar in the ladder is ribose but since it lacks one oxygen atom it is called deoxyribose. The phosphoric acid is the second link in the ladder, and it and the sugar make up alternating sides of the ladder. The sugar and phosphoric acid chains run, somewhat like the sides of a ladder, almost parallel (they are actually somewhat twisted) and are joined by rungs that are compounds of four bases: thymine, cytosine, guanine and adenine. Phosphoric acid and each of the bases constitute a nucleic acid, so the whole ladder is called deoxyribose nucleic acid, or DNA.

Queen Victoria's descendants are the most famous example of the transmission of an inherited sex-linked characteristic, hemophilia, or bleeders' disease. Only males (square) can contract the disease (dark gray) but a father transmits it only through his daughters (dotted ovals). Although females themselves cannot contract the disease, they can—but do not always—transmit it to their sons.

The composition of the sides of the ladder is constant, but the pattern of the horizontal rungs changes and constitutes what is called the genetic code. As with an unfamiliar secret code, we do not understand what it says but we know how significant it is. With every change in the arrangement of the molecules in the four code words, a different hereditary effect is created. Ultimately, all the extraordinary chemical processes that take place in our bodies are determined by the genetic code.

The present view is that DNA directs the manufacture of ribosenucleic acid (RNA) which serves as a messenger and leaves the nucleus to make its way to the ribosomes in the cytoplasm. There RNA directs the formation of proteins, particularly the enzymes. And it is the enzymes which in speeding up chemical reactions direct the metabolic functioning of the body. Genetic traits are only the chemical reactions peculiar to any one person.

Tumors—Benign and Malignant

Ultimately, the genes control the function and behavior of all cells in the body. The cells that make up an organ are normally restricted to that organ alone and develop it to the proper size. If some of the cells of an organ begin to multiply wildly, a tumor forms. If the tumor confines itself to that organ, it is called a benign tumor. If the abnormally multiplying cells spread to other parts of the body, the tumor is malignant—a cancer—and presents a threat to the entire body.

A tumor arises because something has gone awry within the genetic mechanism of the cells. We do not know precisely how this happens but we do know that excessive irritation or irradiation of cells can upset their genetic mechanism and create a tumor, sometimes benign, sometimes malignant. It is also believed that there is a hereditary tendency to develop certain tumors. Many scientists today suspect that tumors arise because certain viruses infect cells and derange the genetic mechanism. This has been shown to be true in animals infected by particular viruses. If we can identify the viruses that have the same effect on human beings, the day may come when many cancers can be prevented, just as we prevent poliomyelitis, measles and other diseases, by immunizing human beings against these viruses.

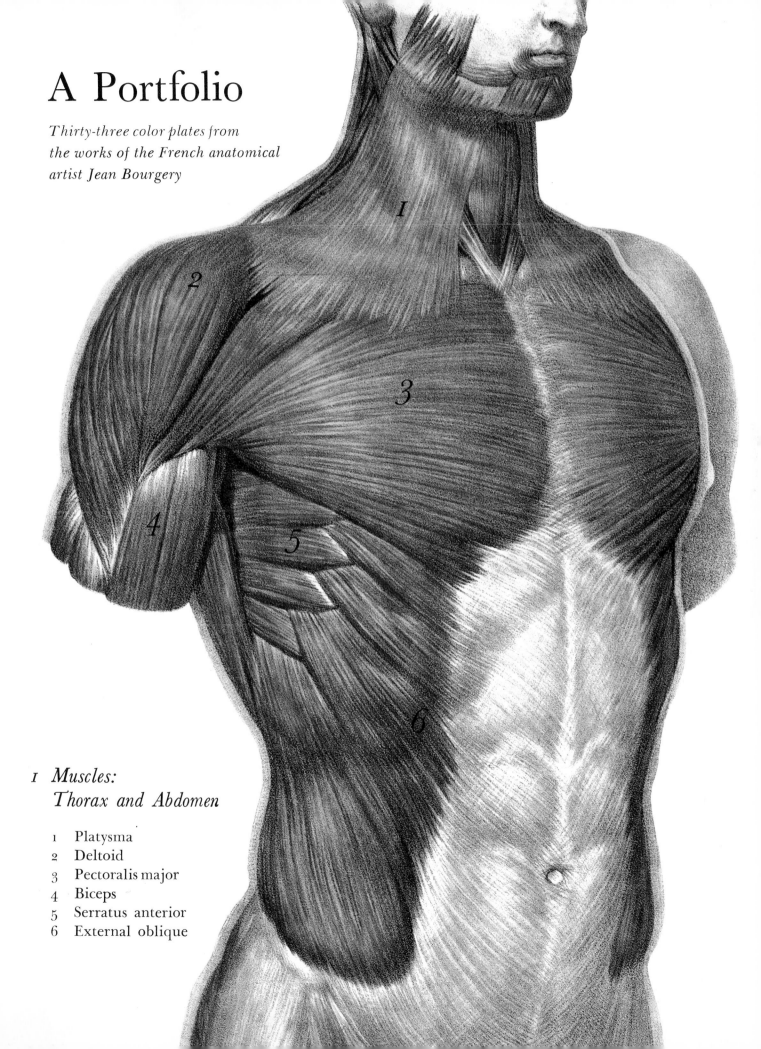

A Portfolio

*Thirty-three color plates from
the works of the French anatomical
artist Jean Bourgery*

1 **Muscles:
Thorax and Abdomen**

1 Platysma
2 Deltoid
3 Pectoralis major
4 Biceps
5 Serratus anterior
6 External oblique

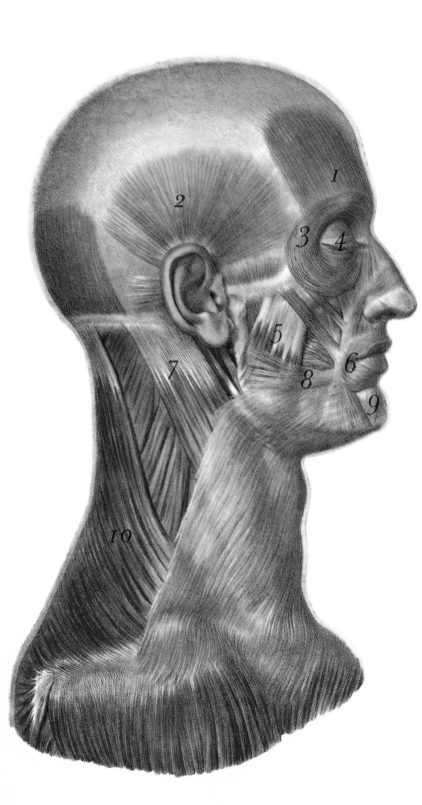

2 Muscles of the Head and Neck

These might be called the muscles of expression since they form smiles, frowns, looks of approval, scorn and so forth. Among the more important is the masseter, one of the muscles that moves the jaw, and the sternocleidomastoid, which bends the head and neck toward the shoulder and rotates the head.

1 Frontalis
2 Auricularis
3 Orbicularis oculi
4 Elevator muscle of eyelid
5 Masseter
6 Orbicularis oris
7 Sternocleidomastoid
8 Risorius
9 Quadratus labii inferioris
10 Trapezius

Facing page
3 Muscles of the Back

The trapezius and latissimus dorsi muscles are among those helping to connect the arm to the spinal column. The latissimus dorsi muscle draws the raised arm down and backward in a swimming motion. The trapezius helps draw the shoulder blade to the spine and turns it; it also helps draw the shoulder upward, bend the neck to one side and turn the face to the opposite side. The infraspinatus rotates the arm outward. The deltoid takes part in complex movements of the arm.

1 Trapezius
2 Shoulder blade area
3 Deltoid
4 Infraspinatus
5 Teres major
6 Latissimus dorsi
7 Gluteus

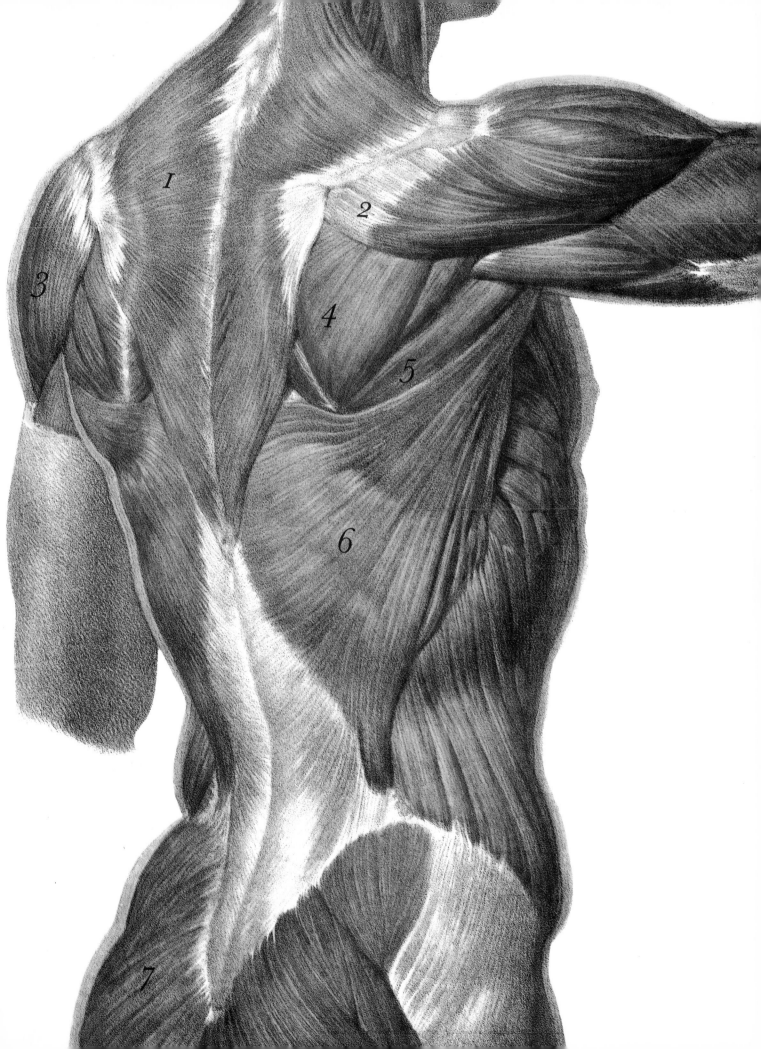

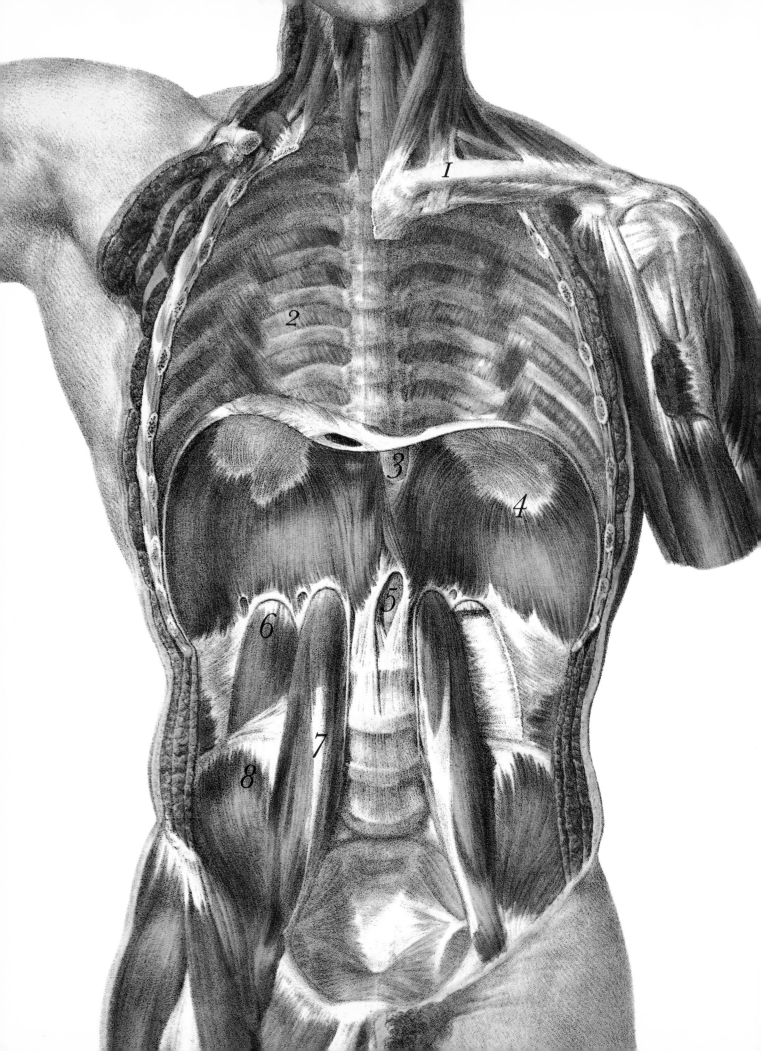

4 Posterior Muscles: Thorax and Abdomen

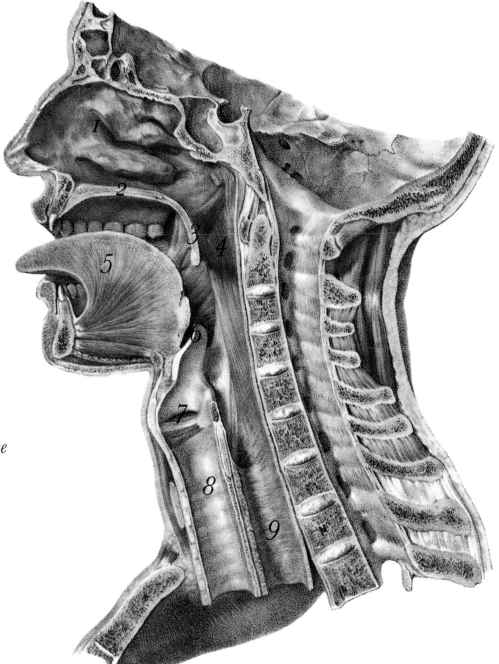

Facing page

The diaphragm separates the thorax and abdomen and with the intercostal muscles expands and contracts the thorax in breathing. The quadratus lumborum muscle flexes the spinal column to the side. The psoas and iliacus muscles flex the thigh at the hip.

1 Clavicle
2 Intercostal
3 Opening for esophagus
4 Left diaphragm
5 Opening for aorta
6 Quadratus lumborum
7 Psoas
8 Iliacus

5 Passageways of the Nose and Throat

1 Nasal cavity
2 Hard palate
3 Soft palate
4 Pharynx
5 Tongue
6 Epiglottis
7 Larynx
8 Trachea
9 Esophagus

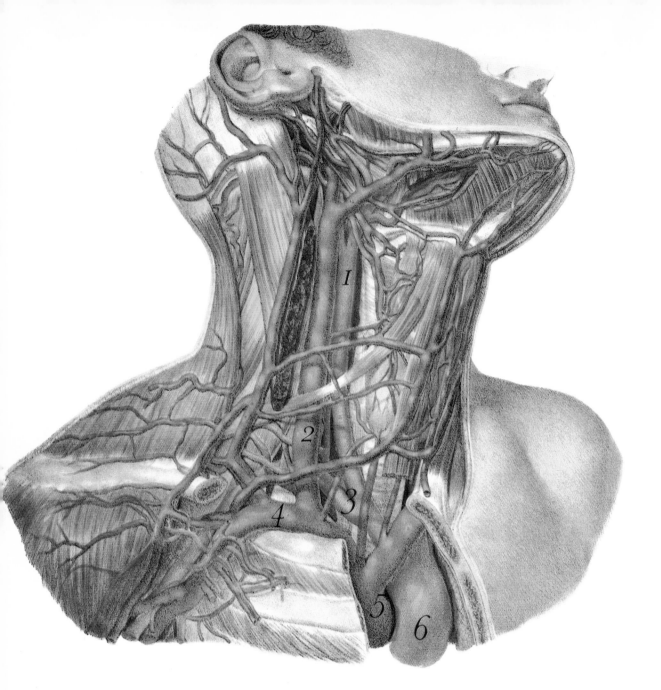

6 Veins and Arteries
of the Neck

1 Carotid artery
2 Internal jugular vein
3 Right subclavian artery
4 Right subclavian vein
5 Superior vena cava
6 Aorta

Facing page

7 The Heart
and Major Blood Vessels

1 Innominate artery
2 Thoracic aorta
3 Heart
4 Left diaphragm
5 Vena cava
6 Right kidney
7 Left kidney
8 Abdominal aorta

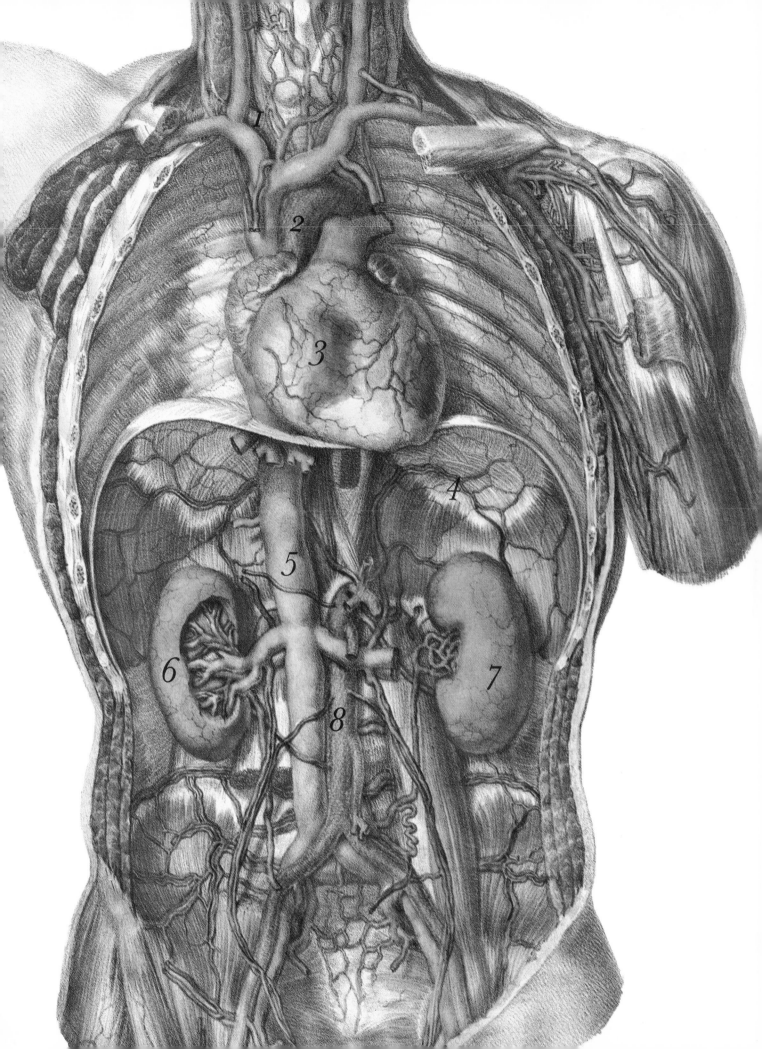

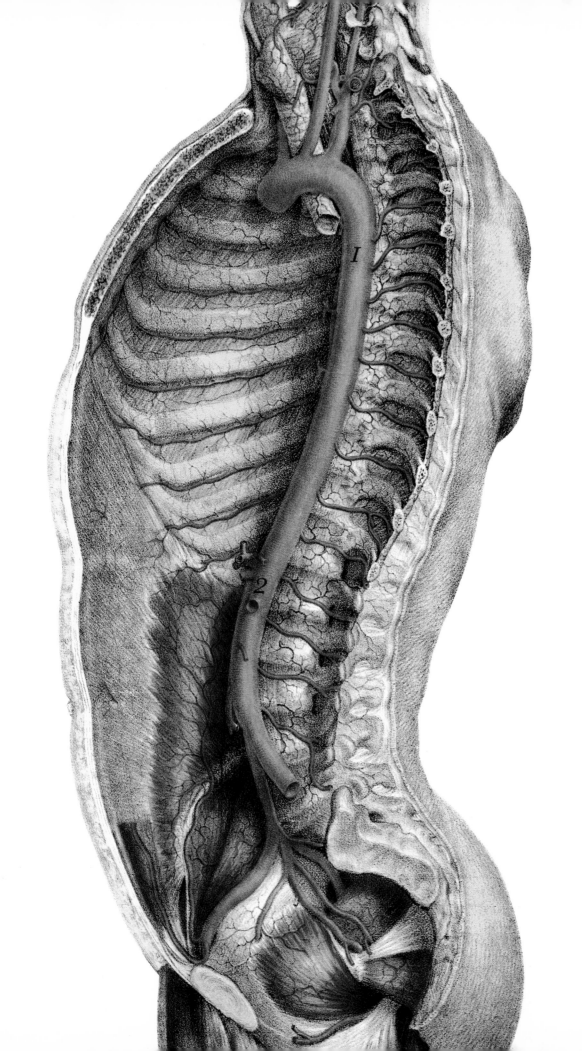

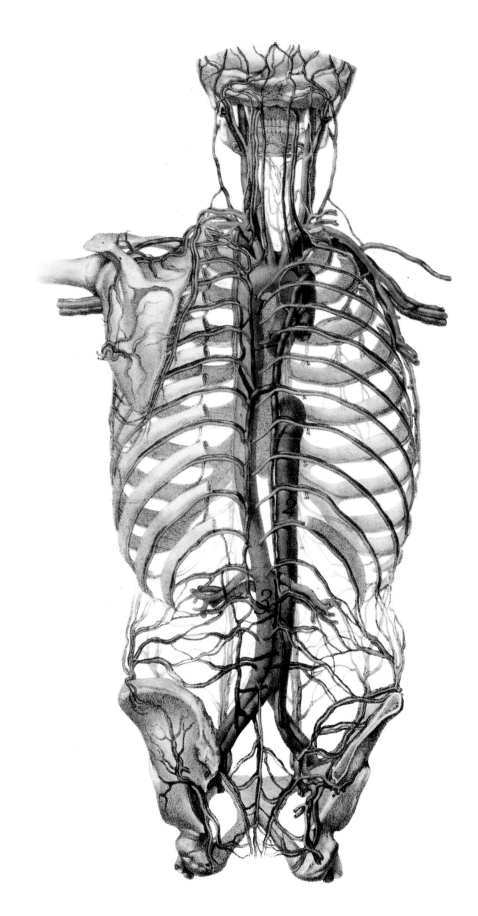

Facing page

8 *Major Arteries (side view)*

1 Thoracic aorta
2 Abdominal aorta

9 *Major Blood Vessels (rear view)*

1 Thoracic aorta
2 Vena cava
3 Abdominal aorta

1 Superior vena cava
2 Pulmonary artery
3 Branches of pulmonary artery
  to right lung
4 Branches of pulmonary artery
  to left lung
5 Aorta
6 Right auricle
7 Right ventricle

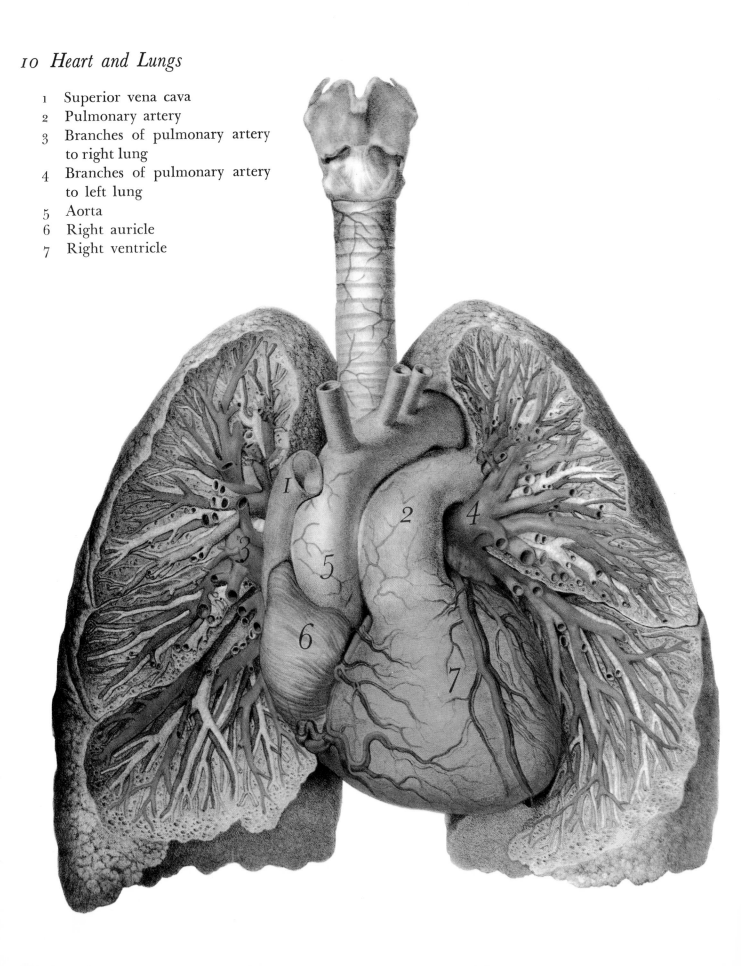

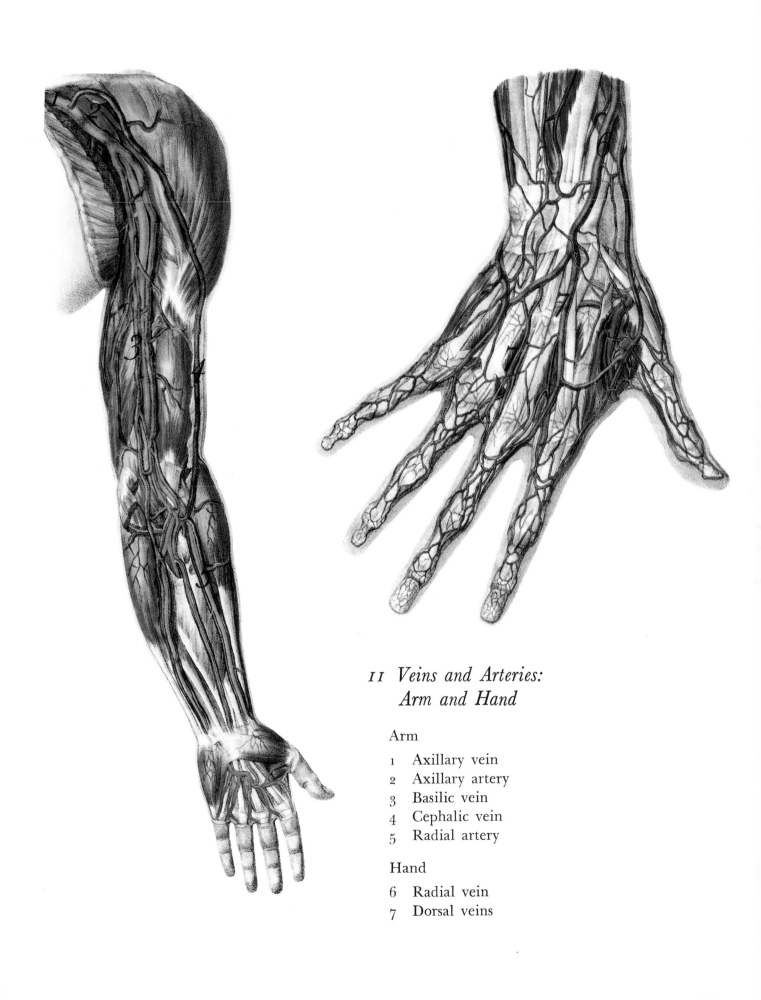

11 Veins and Arteries: Arm and Hand

Arm

1 Axillary vein
2 Axillary artery
3 Basilic vein
4 Cephalic vein
5 Radial artery

Hand

6 Radial vein
7 Dorsal veins

12 Veins and Arteries of the Leg

Back

1   Popliteal artery
2   Popliteal vein
3   Posterior tibial vein

Front

4   Anterior tibial artery
5   Anterior tibial vein

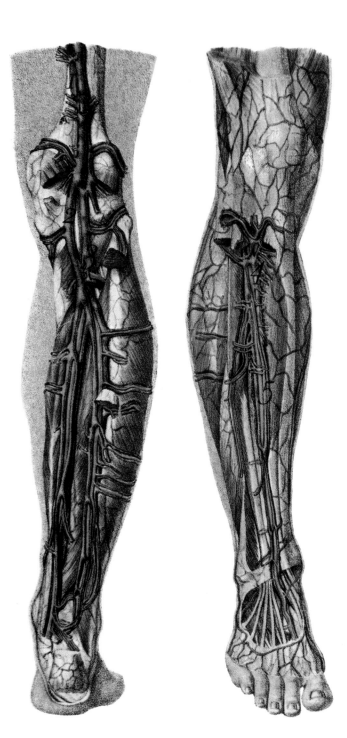

Facing page

13 Lymph System: Thorax and Abdomen

All the lymphatic vessels below the diaphragm empty into the thoracic duct, the main collecting unit of the lymphatic system. The duct finally empties into the left subclavian vein.

1   Left subclavian vein
2   Vena cava
3   Thoracic duct
4   Lower vena cava
5   Abdominal aorta

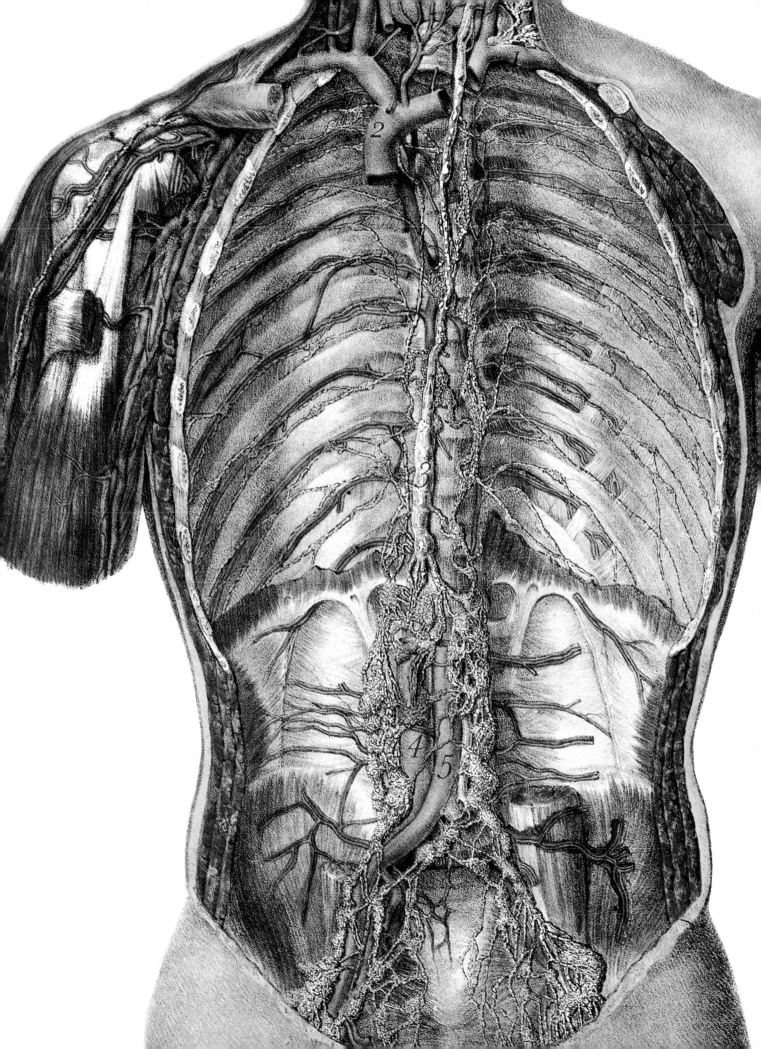

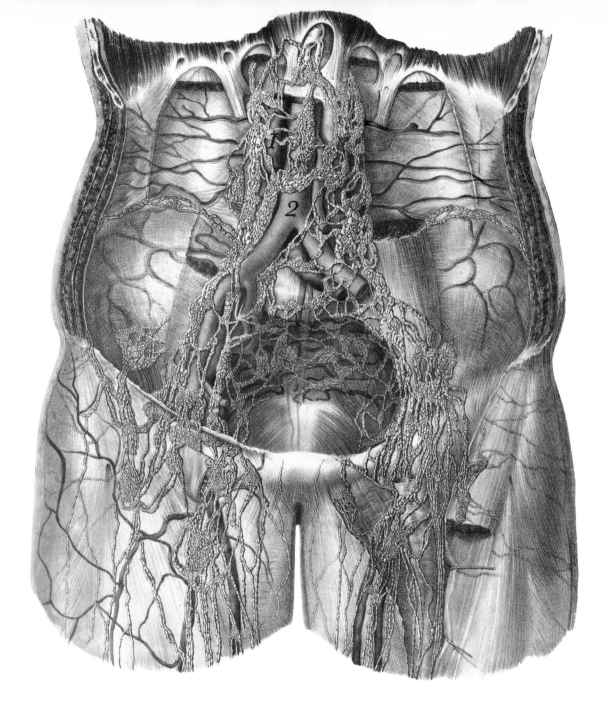

14 Lymph System: Abdomen

Lymph vessels (shown in silver) are
here seen running from the lower extremities into the abdomen. The lymphatic system collects the lymph after it
has bathed the cells and finally returns it
through the large lymphatic trunks into
the circulatory system.

1 Vena cava
2 Abdominal aorta

Facing page

15 Digestive Organs: Abdomen

1 Liver
2 Gall bladder
3 Stomach
4 Duodenum
5 Large intestine
6 Small intestine

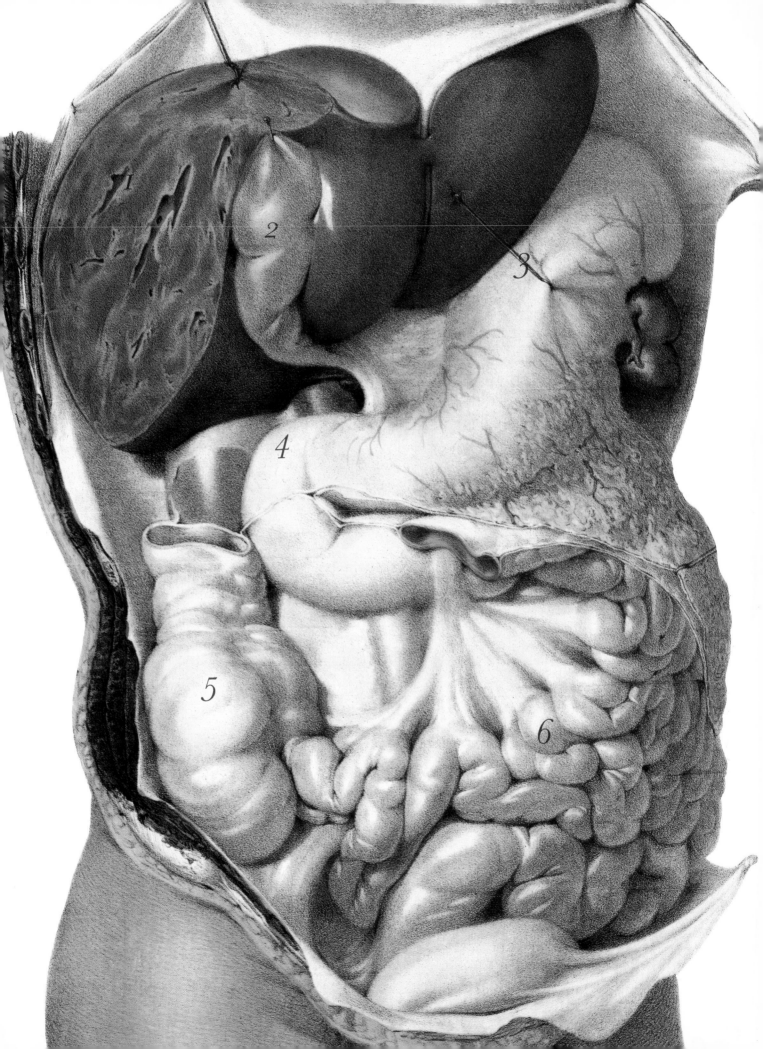

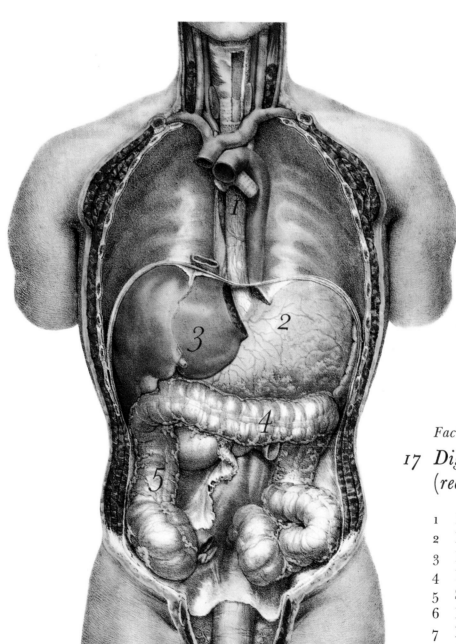

16 Digestive Organs

1   Esophagus
2   Stomach
3   Liver
4   Transverse colon
5   Ascending colon

Facing page

17 Digestive and Other Organs (*rear view*)

1   Pharynx
2   Esophagus
3   Left lung
4   Right lung
5   Spleen
6   Liver
7   Pancreas
8   Small intestine
9   Large intestine

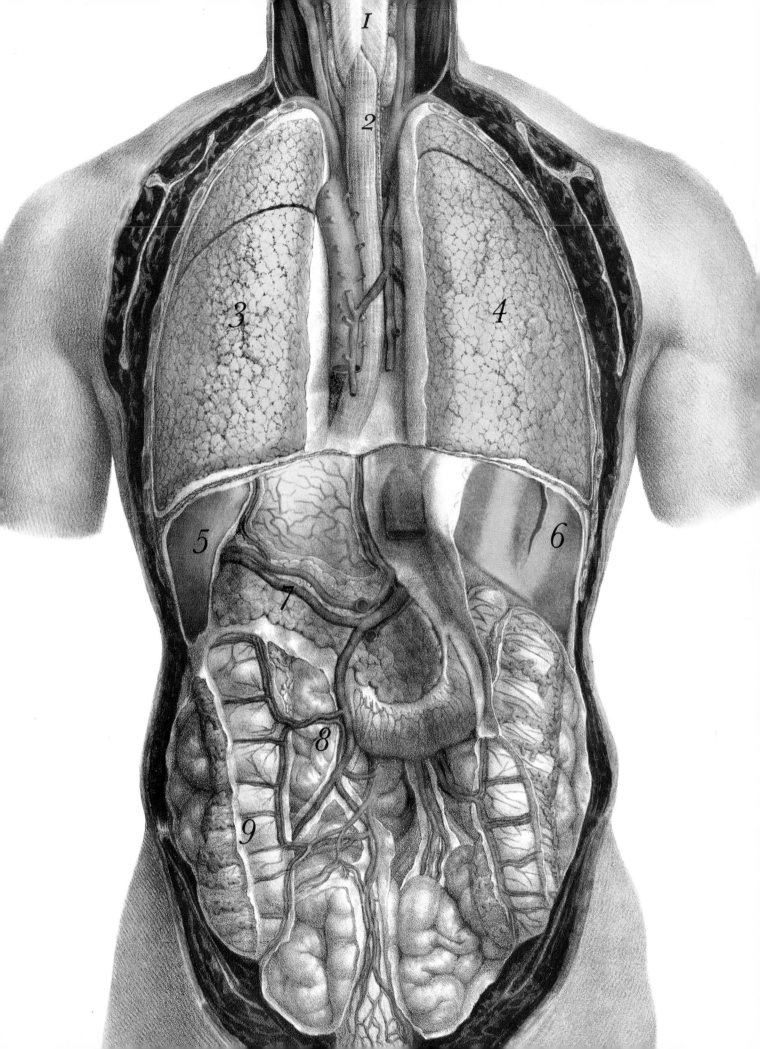

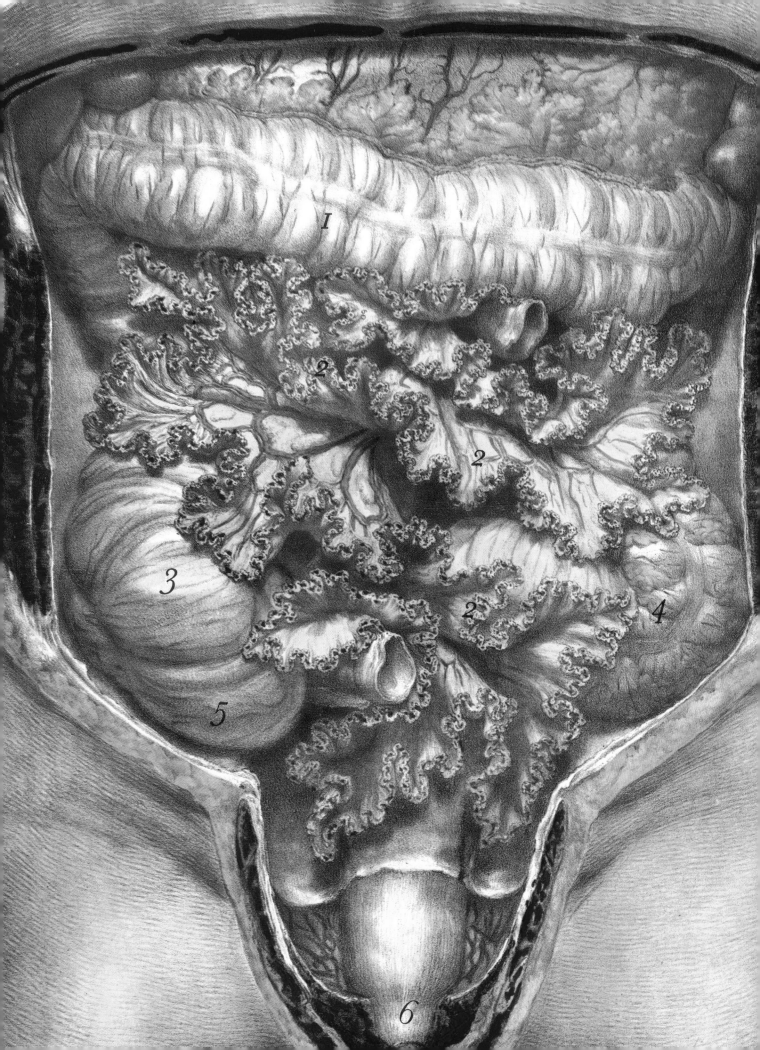

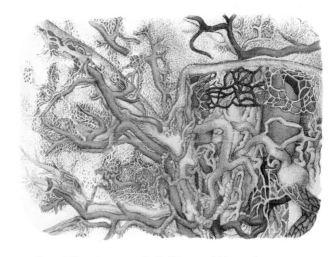

20 Capillaries and Biliary Vessels of Liver (*microscopic detail*)

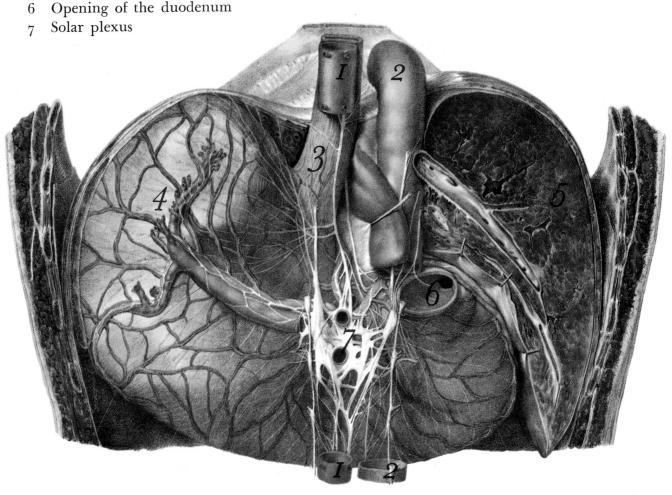

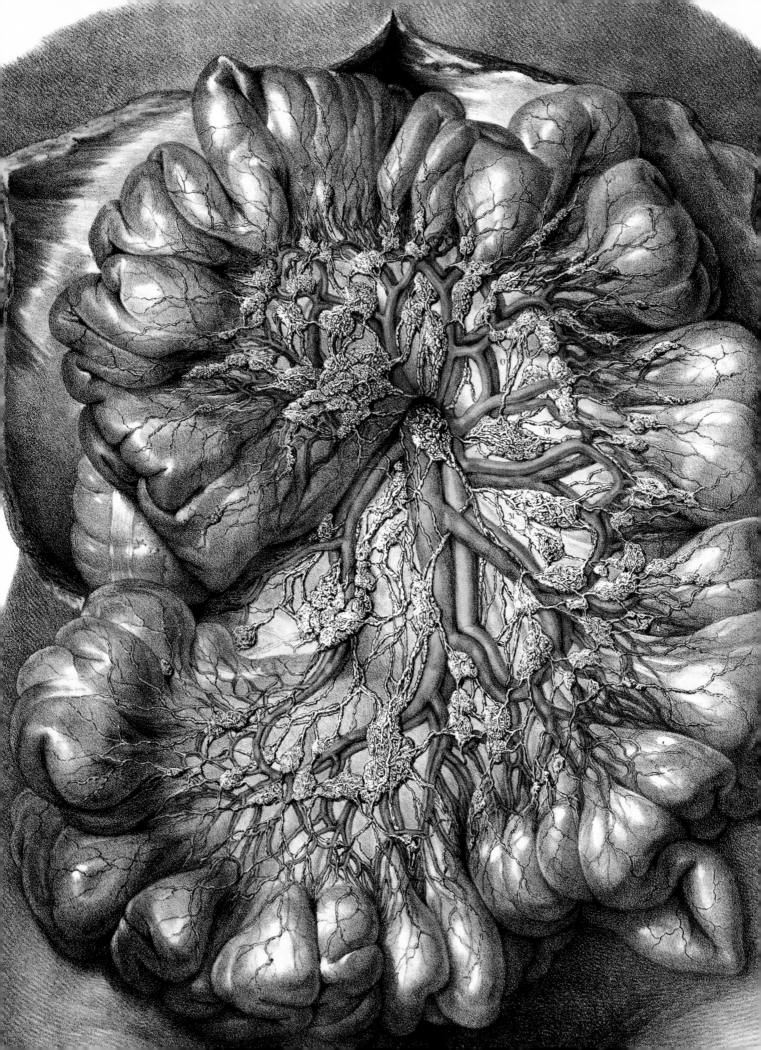

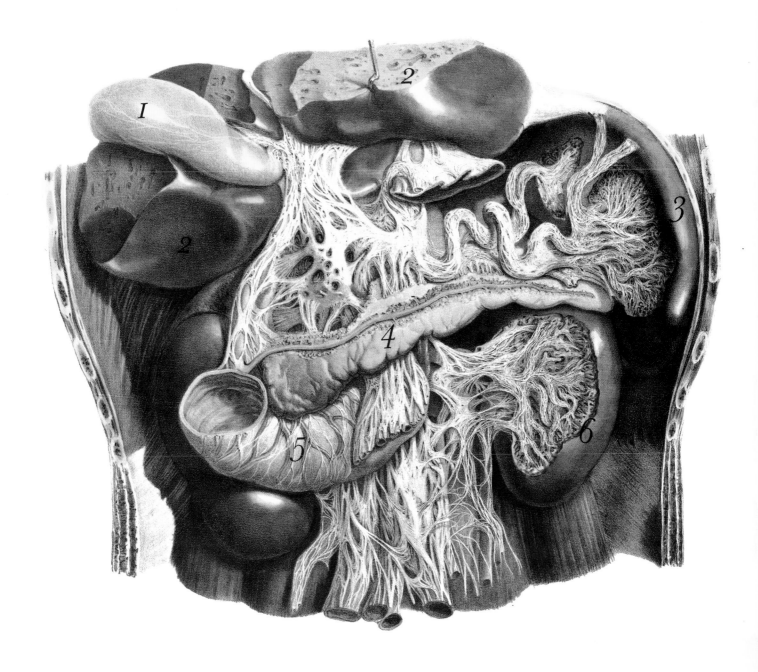

Facing page

21 *Small Intestines: Lymph and Blood Vessels*

The small intestines are enveloped in folds of membrane called the mesentery, which serves to support the intestines and vessels nourishing the intestines.

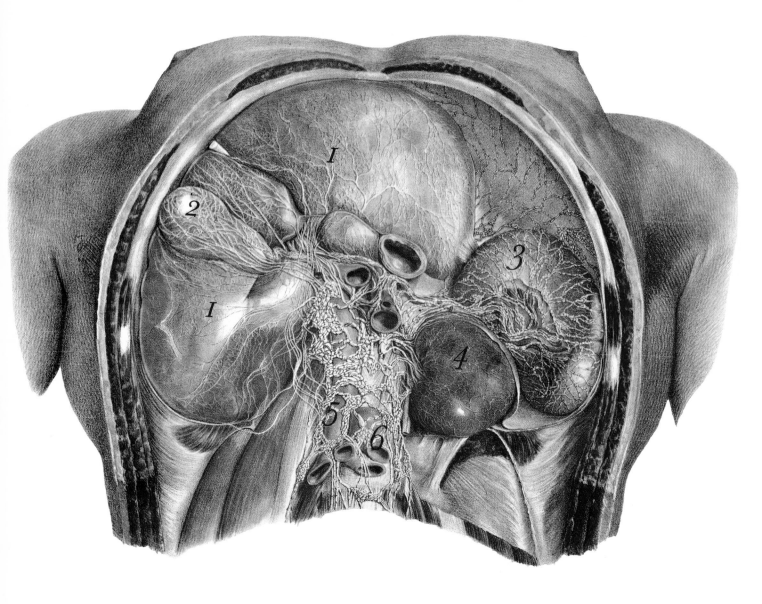

23 *Lymph Vessels: Liver,*
Spleen and Kidneys
(*from below*)

1 Liver
2 Gall bladder
3 Spleen
4 Left kidney
5 Vena cava
6 Aorta

Facing page

24 *Urinary Tract:*
Kidneys and Bladder

1 Vena cava
2 Renal veins
3 Right kidney
4 Left kidney
5 Right ureter
6 Aorta
7 Left ureter
8 Bladder
9 Urethra

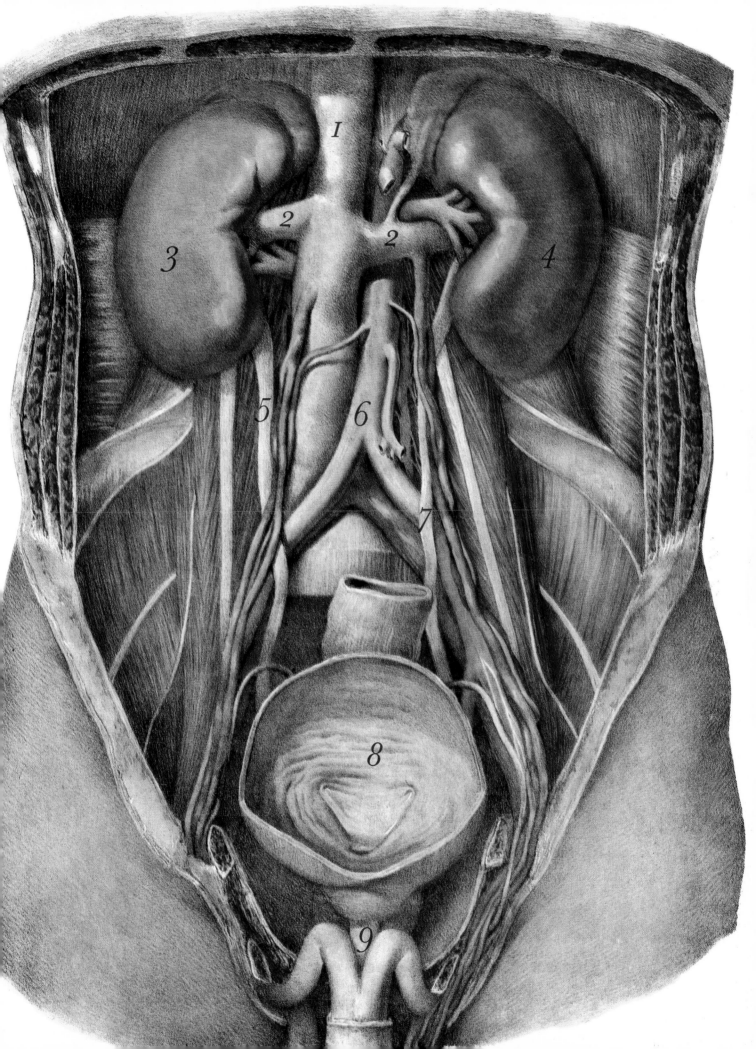

Facing page
26 *The Brain*

1   Olfactory tract
2   Pituitary body
3   Optic nerve
4   Medulla oblongata
5   Cerebellum

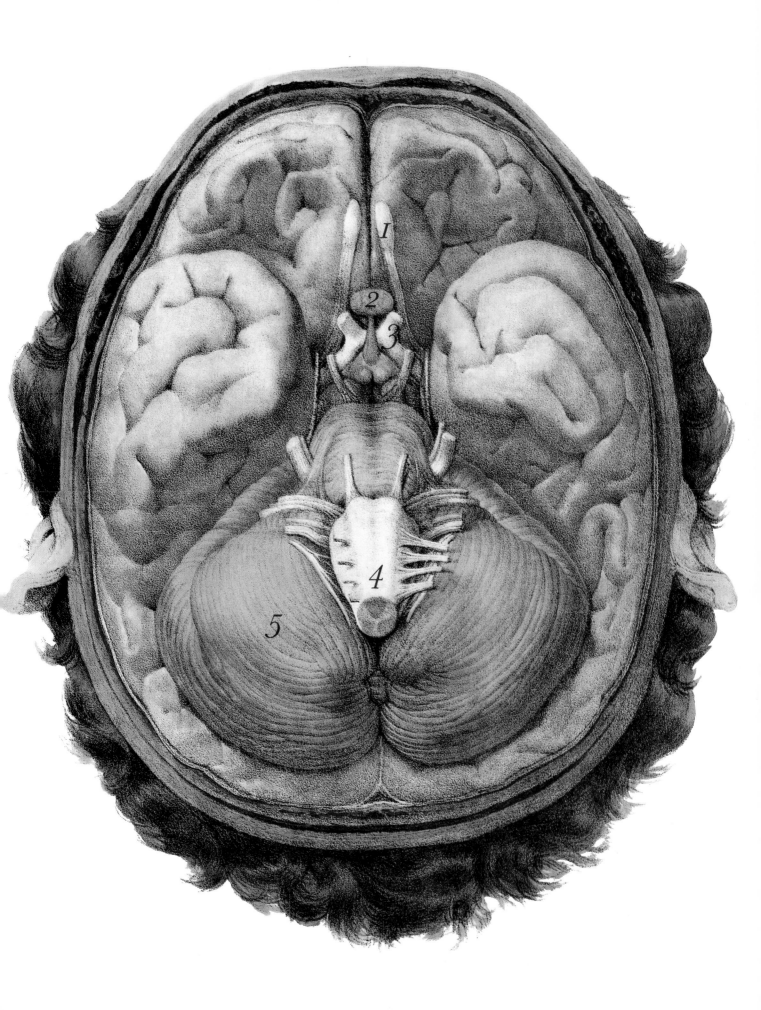

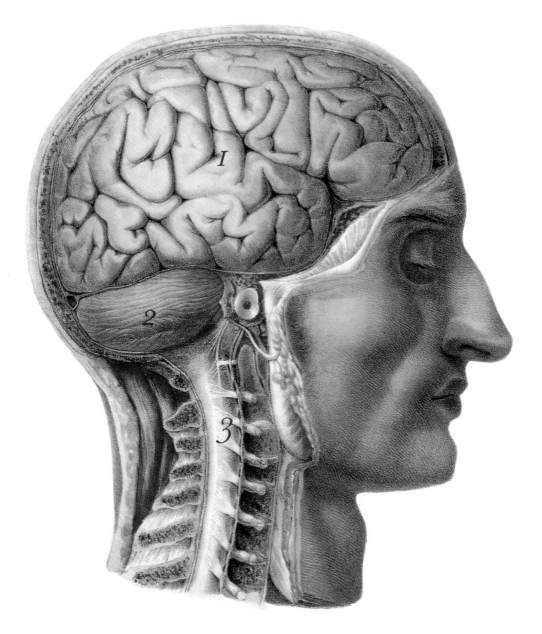

27 *Brain and Spinal Cord*

1   Cerebrum
2   Cerebellum
3   Spinal cord

Facing page
28 *The Brain*

1   Cerebrum
2   Pituitary body
3   Cerebellum
4   Medulla oblongata

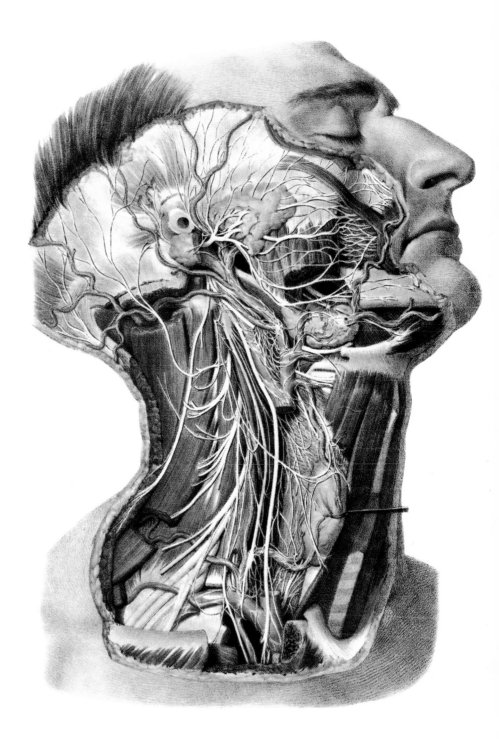

30 Autonomic Nervous System:
Head and Neck

In the deep structure of the neck, the
principle elements of the autonomic
nervous system—the parasympathetic
vagus nerve and sympathetic ganglia and
nerve fibers—are present.

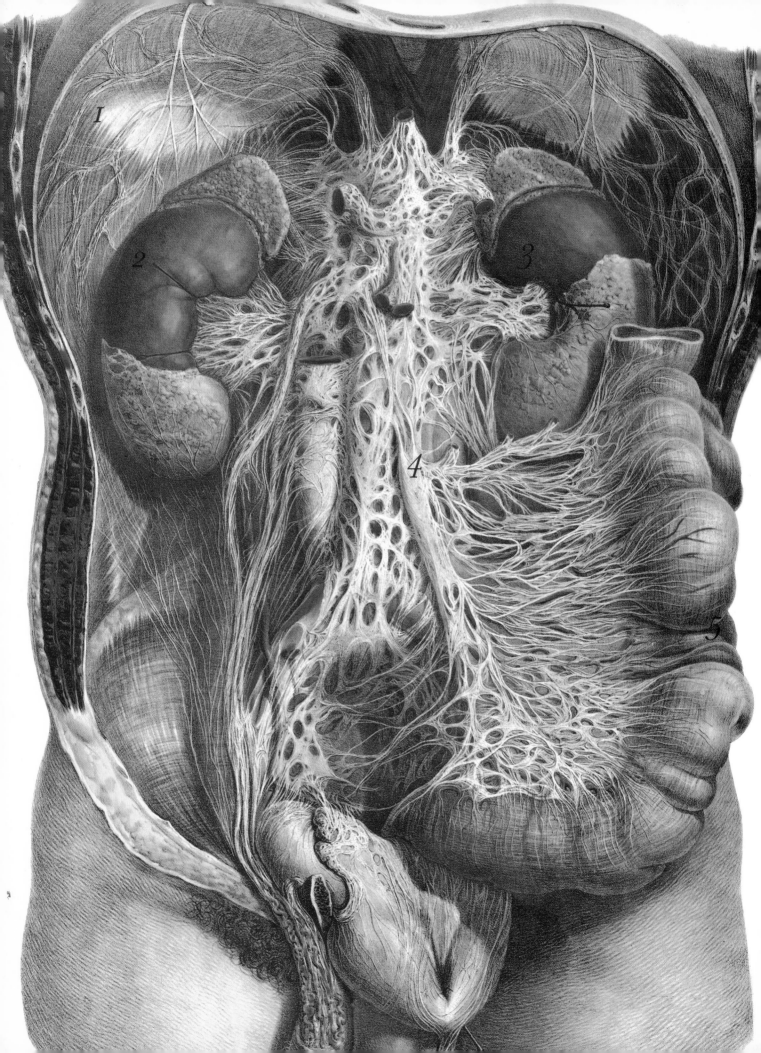

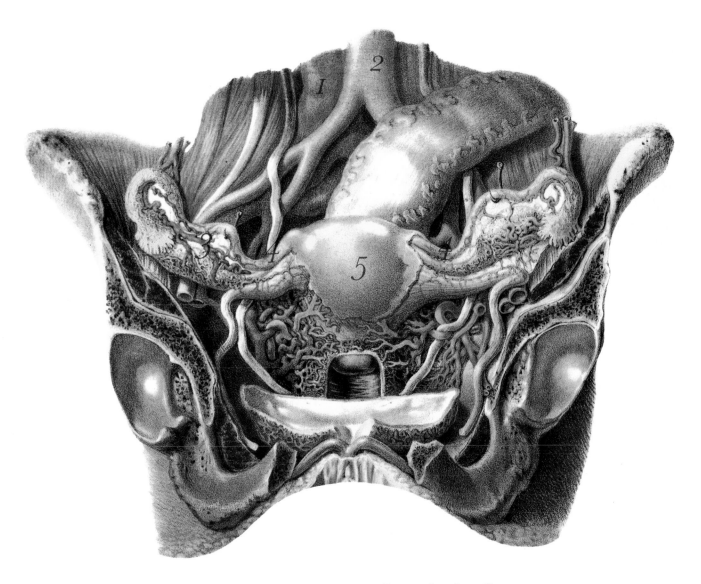

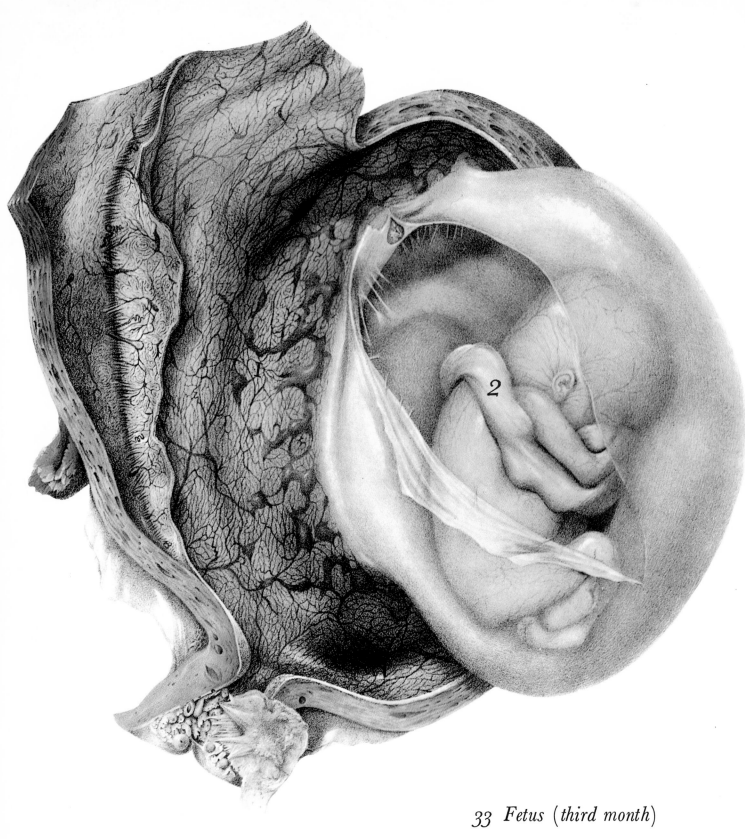

33 Fetus (third month)

By the end of the third month of pregnancy, the fetus is almost four inches long and less than an ounce in weight, but the structure is nonetheless clearly delineated.

1 Wall of uterus
2 Umbilical cord

5

Connective Tissue

Collections of connective tissue called ligaments, tendons or sinews bind the bones into the framework called the skeleton.

Historically the oldest and most simple tissue is the gelatinous tissue, called the mesenchyme. This tissue predominates in the earliest animals such as the jellyfishes or sponges. The human embryo also begins with considerable gelatinous tissue. The center of the eyeball remains gelatinous and is as transparent as glass but it is structureless and thus differs from the primitive mesenchyme. Examine an ox eye from a butcher shop and you will see a specimen of this structureless tissue.

The gelatinous tissue develops from the intermediate germ layer of the embryo. Its cells are irregular and star-shaped and interconnected by their branchlike extensions. The space between the cells is filled with the jelly-like intercellular substance. From these cells a variety of different structures arise: the blood and lymph, cartilage, bone and the fibrillous connective tissue itself.

Fibrillous Connective Tissue

The mesenchymal cells turn into many different cells, among them the fibroblast, which was given this name because it is believed to manufacture fibers. These fibers are the characteristic feature of connective tissue. There are three types of fibers: collagen fibers, which are white, flexible but nonelastic, and occur in bundles; elastic fibers, which are yellow, highly elastic and occur singly; and reticular fibers, which are very thin and highly branched.

At first the fibers are as loose as those in cotton; later they become more firm, and in some places dense. Our skin stays flexible and the features of our face retain their characteristic texture because these fibers retain their original tone. In time the fibers age and their elasticity decreases visibly. The skin below the chin begins to sag, "bags" develop under the eyes, "crow's feet" appear in the corners of the eye, the skin of the paunch grows slack, and the breasts droop. We may say that the first signs of aging show themselves in the connective tissue fibers.

Where the body requires it, the connective tissue produces fibers in great numbers and forms membranes. Around important organs these membranes become so firm that they develop capsules. The heart is surrounded by a sac, the pericardium, the

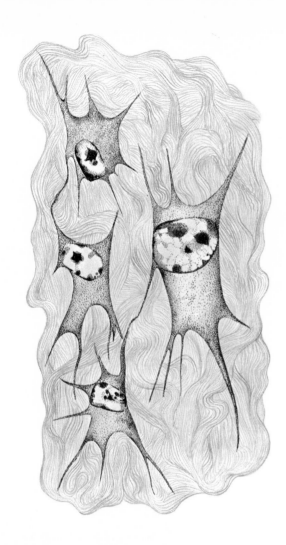

Gelatinous tissue, the most primitive kind of tissue, predominates not only in the human embryo but also in such simple organisms as the jellyfish.

(Left) Fiber in youth and age. In the young woman the connective fibers are taut and elastic; in an older woman, as represented in a sculpture by Rodin, they have lost much of their elasticity.

lungs by a thin envelope, the pleura, and the brain is protected by a case, the dura mater.

Ligaments, Tendons and Sinews

Where the connective tissue must do heavy duty, the fibers form ligaments. In some instances the ends of muscles develop into particularly strong ligaments called tendons. The most familiar of these is the Achilles tendon (so called because Achilles dragged the defeated Trojan hero, Hector, by this tendon around the walls of Ilion) connecting the bony part of the heel with the muscles of the calf. (It should not be confused with Achilles' heel, the one place where, according to legend, Achilles was vulnerable.)

Innumerable ligaments of all kinds bind the bones into the framework called the skeleton. Strong ligaments form the neck, which holds the skull erect on the trunk. The strongest ligaments are those that tie the trunk to the thigh bones so that we can balance on these audaciously constructed stilts, our legs. When the regicide Ravaillac stabbed Henry IV in Paris during the celebration of the monarch's wedding, the murderer was tortured to death. As the climax, the still quivering body was stretched between four horses and an attempt was made to "quarter" it. But the ligaments of the hips would not yield, and only by using axes was it possible to separate the limbs from the torso.

Ailments of the Connective Tissues

Chemically the collagen fibers of connective tissue consist of a relatively simple protein called collagen. By a magnification of fifty thousand times, the electron microscope reveals that the collagen fiber is woven of strands, and by an even greater magnification it has been found that each strand is made up of rows of molecules with a regular pattern. When collagen fibers are subjected to changes of temperature or of electrical potential, the pattern of the molecules is distorted. And, in fact, in boiling water, the collagen dissolves and is the source of animal glue or gelatin.

In modern medicine a whole group of diseases

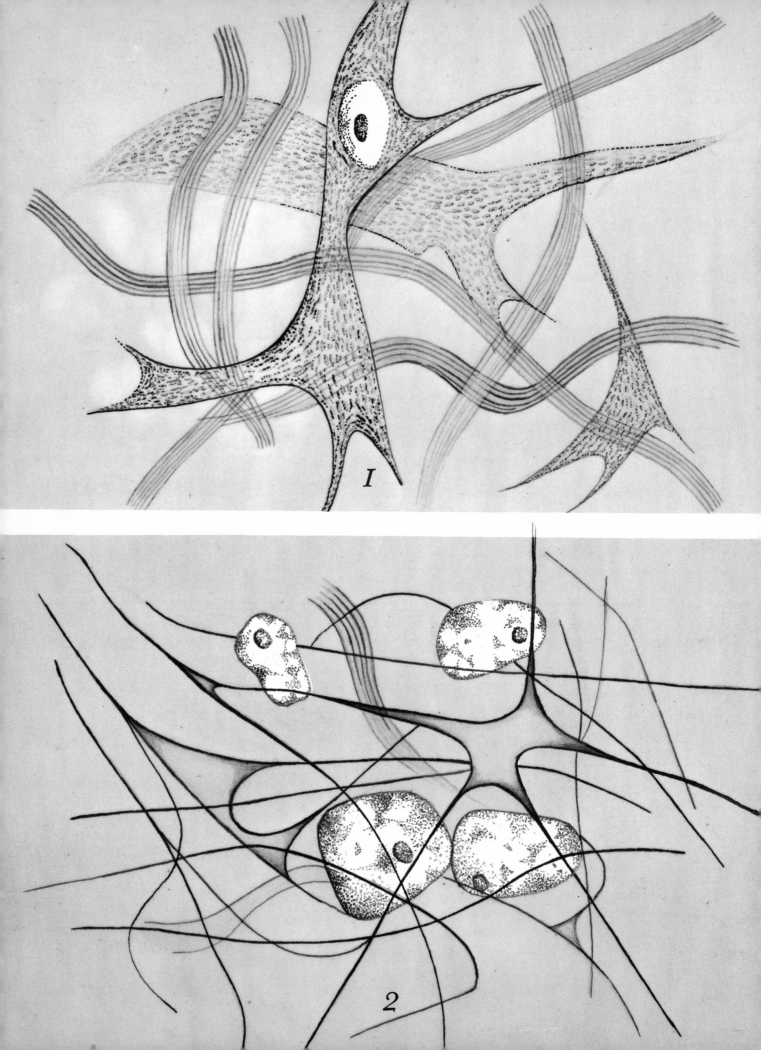

I

2

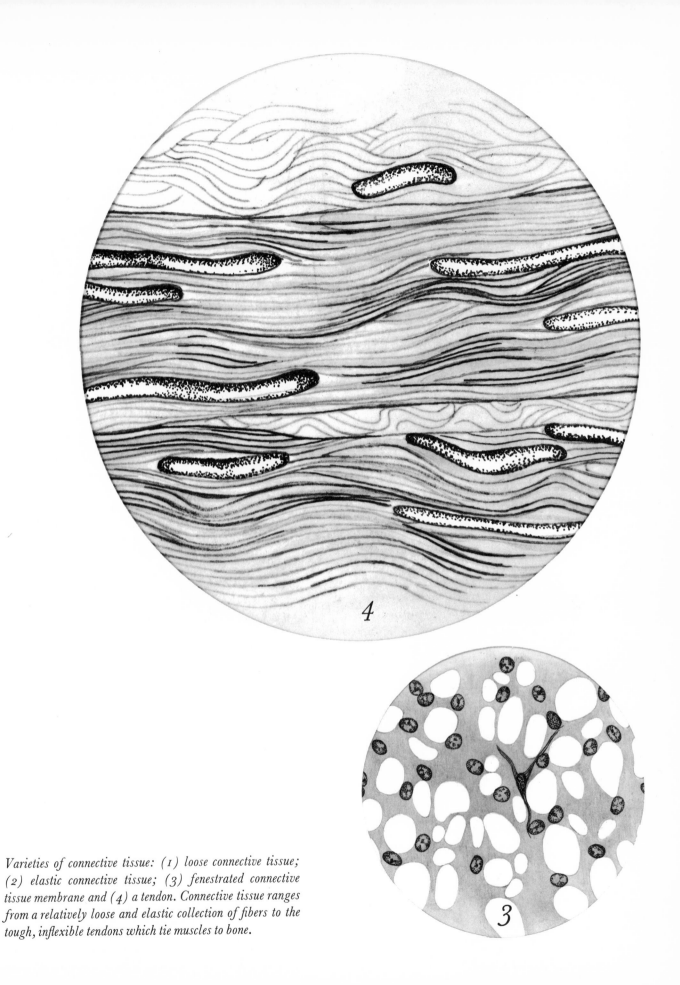

Varieties of connective tissue: (1) loose connective tissue; (2) elastic connective tissue; (3) fenestrated connective tissue membrane and (4) a tendon. Connective tissue ranges from a relatively loose and elastic collection of fibers to the tough, inflexible tendons which tie muscles to bone.

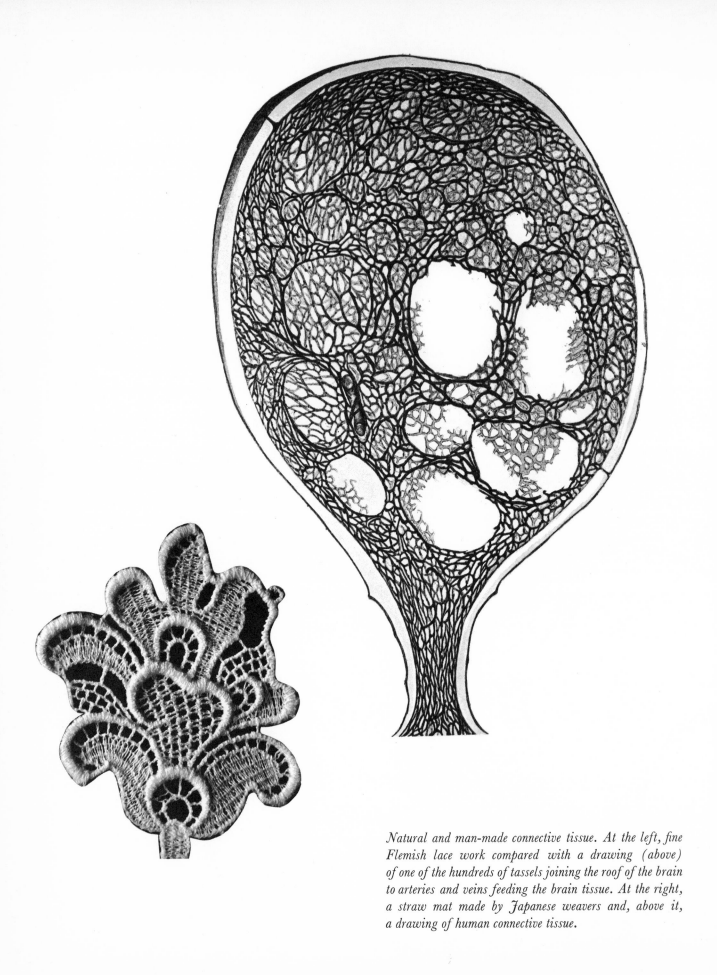

Natural and man-made connective tissue. At the left, fine Flemish lace work compared with a drawing (above) of one of the hundreds of tassels joining the roof of the brain to arteries and veins feeding the brain tissue. At the right, a straw mat made by Japanese weavers and, above it, a drawing of human connective tissue.

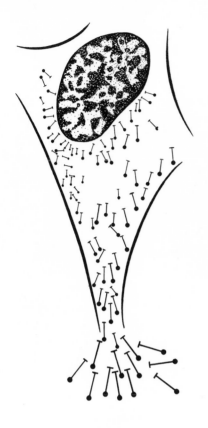

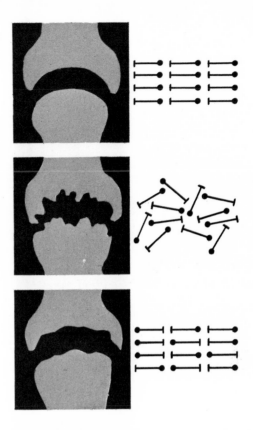

A connective tissue cell producing collagen molecules.

(Left) Collagen fibers. An electron microscope magnification of fibers composed of the protein glue called collagen. One of the most common products of the body, collagen comprises about fifteen percent of the body mass. (Dr. Jerome Gross)

(Right above) Arthritic joints caused by a disturbance of the molecular strands of the collagen. Top: the straight lines of the collagen molecules in the healthy body. Center: the disarrangement that occurs in an arthritic condition. Bottom: collagen molecules showing improvement after treatment.

are now described as diseases of collagen or the connective tissue disorders. Generally speaking, in all of these diseases, inflammation of the joints plays a part. But since connective tissue is part of the supporting structure of every organ of the body, any of these may be involved in the disorders. Some of these have bizarre names like *dermatomyositis* and *polyarthritis*, but the most common is *rheumatoid arthritis*, a disease that affects five million people in the United States alone. Signs of arthritis have been detected in the skeleton of prehistoric man—memorials of suffering a million years old.

Rheumatism is the most common malady of the human race. No other ailment can compete with it in the number of work days and the amount of income lost because of it—not to mention lowered efficiency. Although we do not know exactly what causes arthritis, we do know that people who overwork their joints, like seamstresses and carpenters, are subject to it. So are persons who work with water and in cold, damp conditions, such as sailors, fishermen, washwomen and masons. A cure for this malady would be truly a boon to mankind.

73

6

Fat

Fat tissue serves the human body as a reserve store of energy, as padding and protection, and as insulation against loss of heat. But too much fat may be dangerous.

The connective tissue cell is the parent of a whole family of cells. One of its descendants is the fat cell. First, tiny globules of fat appear in the protoplasm of a cell of connective tissue. These grow and blend until they fill the cell and it becomes a huge drop of fat, with hardly any cytoplasm, and with the nucleus flattened to one side.

Fat cells may appear wherever connective tissue is present, and where they crowd out other cells, we have fatty or adipose tissue. What is the function of adipose tissue? It is a kind of reserve store of "high octane fuel" for the body. It supports and protects body organs. And since it is a poor conductor, it is a good insulator against loss of heat. Sea lions, whales, and other mammals that inhabit cold seas have thick layers of fat as protection against loss of warmth.

The picture we have of the lean person is that he is, as a rule, quicker to react, more easily excited and more apt to be impulsive than the fat person. A classical contrast of thin and fat types is Don Quixote and Sancho Panza. And Shakespeare's Julius Caesar says: "Let me have men about me that are fat, sleek-headed men and such as sleep o'nights. Yond Cassius has a lean and hungry look.... Would he were fatter!"

The formation and distribution of fat is influenced by many factors but chiefly by the hormones. If the thyroid gland produces too great a quantity of its hormones, the body will store up and deposit only small amounts of fat. Therefore persons suffering from overproduction of thyroid hormones are generally lean. If the thyroid gland produces too little, metabolism slows down, fat settles in the tissues and the activity of the nervous system is reduced.

Fat as Protective Padding

The body uses fat as an elastic padding. We are protected by fat much as the hockey player is by the pads he wears. Because of this, the person who loses fat during a consuming illness, suffers, when he leaves his bed, from the loss of this protection. The pelvis, the "rocker" we sit on, loses its fat; thus, when the convalescent appears at the family table for the first time, we put a pillow under him. Even the eyeballs are generously padded, because

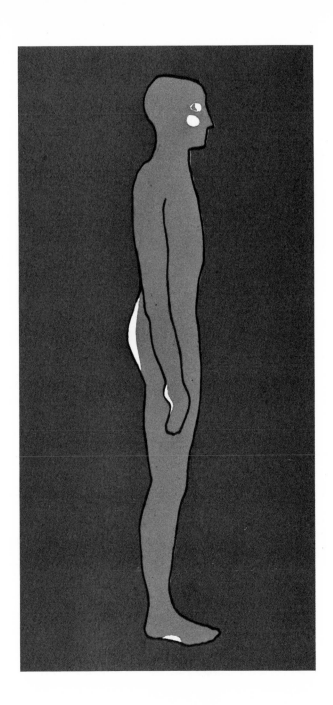

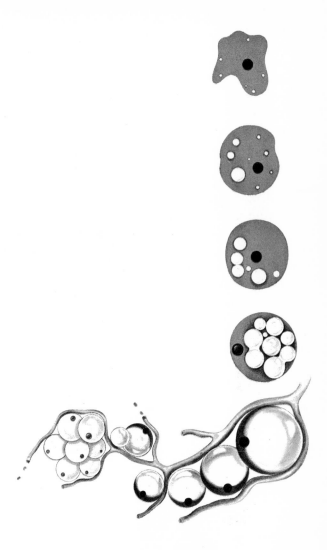

Layers of fat act as padding or as shock absorbers in the socket around the eyeball, in the cheeks, under the arch of the foot, and to cushion the palm and the buttocks.

(Right above) Development of a fat cell. First, tiny globules of fat appear in the cytoplasm of a connective tissue cell. These grow until they fill the cell and it becomes a huge drop of fat, with almost no cytoplasm and with the nucleus flattened to one side.

they roll inside the bony walls of the cavities of the eyes. Cushions of fat are present in the cheeks; if we lose fat during an illness, friends note that our cheeks are "hollow." The palms of our hands are also padded with thin layers of fat: we go through life wearing gloves on our palms.

The greatest accumulation of fat in the body is the omentum, an apron of fatty tissue that covers the intestines and protects them from cold. Because it has no other function besides protection it is delicate in structure, and, when it comes from a Christmas goose, is highly esteemed by gourmets.

Distribution of Fat

Fat is unevenly distributed. The genes that direct that distribution see to it that very little is deposited

75

around the joints. Moreover, more fat is formed in the female body than in the male and it is also differently distributed. Fat gives the specific female shape to many parts of the feminine form.

The attitude toward fat in relation to the esthetic and sexual appeal of women differs. Certain societies, such as the one visited by Mungo Park, the famous explorer of the Niger River, thought fatness in females so attractive that some of its girls were overfed to the point where they could no longer walk. And the Hottentots of Africa think the most desirable females are those with the largest buttocks, encouraging a condition known as steatopygy. In some early societies massive breasts, bellies and buttocks were doubtless prized because they were identified with fertility.

The fat we eat passes through the wall of the intestinal canal and into the lymph vessels and the blood stream. Some of the fat may be burned up in the release of energy, some may be converted into sugar, and some excreted by certain glands, but much of it reappears in the various tissues that serve as fat depots. Some fats go into the skin, others into the breasts, still others into the buttocks and the hips. Conscious of their figures, women in

Don Quixote and Sancho Panzo as classical examples of the lean person and the fat person. The lean man tends to have a quixotic and excitable personality while the stout individual usually seems placid and agreeable.

particular know where fat tends to accumulate on their bodies—generally the waist, thighs and hips.

For most people fat tends to accumulate more rapidly after the age of thirty-five or forty. Of course there are some who remain lean and find it difficult to gain even a pound or two.

Such tendencies are often hereditary. We are the product of the combined chromosomes of our parents—fat or lean, temperamental or phlegmatic, waistline or no waistline.

The causes of excess weight are complex. The average human body deposits around fifteen per cent of its weight as fat, or about twenty pounds in a 150-pound individual. The obese person deposits double or even triple that much. The fat person is like someone who moves about forever lugging a huge suitcase. That is why a fat man perspires more than a lean man on a hot summer day. Every rise in temperature increases the effort that must be made by blood, circulation, heart, and the respiratory system. The heart of the fat person must also pump more blood; additional blood vessels must be filled and emptied day in and day out. Worse than that, the fat person seems more susceptible than the lean person to the development of hardening of the arteries, or arteriosclerosis. This is particularly serious when it involves the coronary arteries, which supply the muscle of the heart with blood.

Every physician with a patient who is overweight and no longer young knows that in the patient's excess weight lurk such threats as heart attacks, coronary artery thrombosis and similar complications. Every pound counts and the treatment of a fat person usually starts with an attempt to reduce his weight.

Diet

When a patient over forty comes to a doctor and complains about a loss of agility or of his youthful physique, the doctor stands him on a scale and usually has to explain: "You are fifteen pounds overweight." The doctor then confers with the patient about his eating habits and puts him on a special diet. Strangely enough, despite the advances in the biological sciences, we have not yet developed a method of easily determining exactly how much of the body weight is fat, how much water, bone, and so forth.

Diet is a modern term. In old times the rich ate too much, and the masses, eternally hungry, filled their stomachs with "hearty" meals of cabbage, potatoes, and coarse bread. The plates heaped high with cabbage and potatoes are slowly disappearing, and the week-long wedding feasts such as that depicted in Breugel's paintings have become shorter and shorter. The whole philosophy of nutrition has changed fundamentally since the beginning of the twentieth century. Scientists discovered that food value depended on other factors besides calories and proteins. The triumvirate of proteins, carbohydrates and fats, which had reigned like dictators, were dethroned. Vitamins were discovered. The salad bowl began to compete with the soup bowl and the gravy bowl. Milk, cream, butter and eggs became plentiful and relatively inexpensive. Fruit juices came to be a regular overture to breakfast. Laboratory experiments on animals and humans demonstrated that the body does not thrive on more and more food, but that there is an optimum and that this optimum is astonishingly low. The Danish professor Hindhede fed himself and a group of students for months on half of the scientific "minimum."

The benefit of fresh air, sunlight, bathing in sea and lake, and daily exercise was recognized. At the same time, a new ideal of bodily beauty arose: no more the fleshy nymphs of Rubens or the voluptuous women of Titian; no more the men with big bellies that are supposed to prove how prosperous they are. The new ideal is the lean or athletic type.

7

Cartilage

In many parts of the body, such as the nose and ears, the connective tissue hardens into a gristle that simultaneously provides firmness and flexibility.

In those parts of the body where the connective tissue is exposed to shock or stress, the fibers fuse into gristle, an opaque substance called cartilage. In some places the fibers can still be distinguished, forming fibrocartilage.

In the beginning, when the embryo is no bigger than a bee, its skeleton is entirely cartilaginous. This primordial skeleton looks like a first rough sketch of a man. By fusing into gristle, the connective cells that form the cartilage are entombed like the tiny polyps in marine corals. From then on they must live as hermits in their compartments. No blood vessels enter the cartilage, the cells being nourished by lymph that permeates the cartilage by osmosis.

The Main Cartilaginous Parts

When the child leaves the mother's womb, the skeleton has assumed its permanent form but the bones are still soft; if not cartilaginous, they are still rich in cartilage and colloid tissue. This flexibility of the bones enables the child to squeeze through the narrow tunnel of the female reproductive organs. The hardening of the bones takes place very gradually, which explains why children rarely suffer from broken bones. That is also why they are so much more limber than adults and capable of all kinds of acrobatics. In families of acrobats the parents train the children from childhood in order to take advantage of this capacity.

Between the ages of five and fifteen the bones harden and the cartilage retreats to the ends of the bones. Only in the following areas does the cartilage remain and fulfill its special function.

The Ends of the Ribs

The chest of the human body is a cage encasing the two lungs. The lungs inhale and exhale air by the alternate expansion and contraction of the chest wall, which serves as a bellows. The bars of the cage are not iron but two dozen long, curved bones. The ends of all bones are capped with cartilage in order to withstand shock and to prevent chipping or breaking; the whole end section of each rib in the front of the chest is cartilaginous so that the

(Facing page) Cartilaginous parts (in black) of the skeleton. These provide flexibility: for example, in the nose and ear to protect from blows; in the larynx and windpipe to permit sound vibrations; at the ends of the ribs to permit movement in breathing; in the fibrous disks of the spine to cushion the vertebrae.

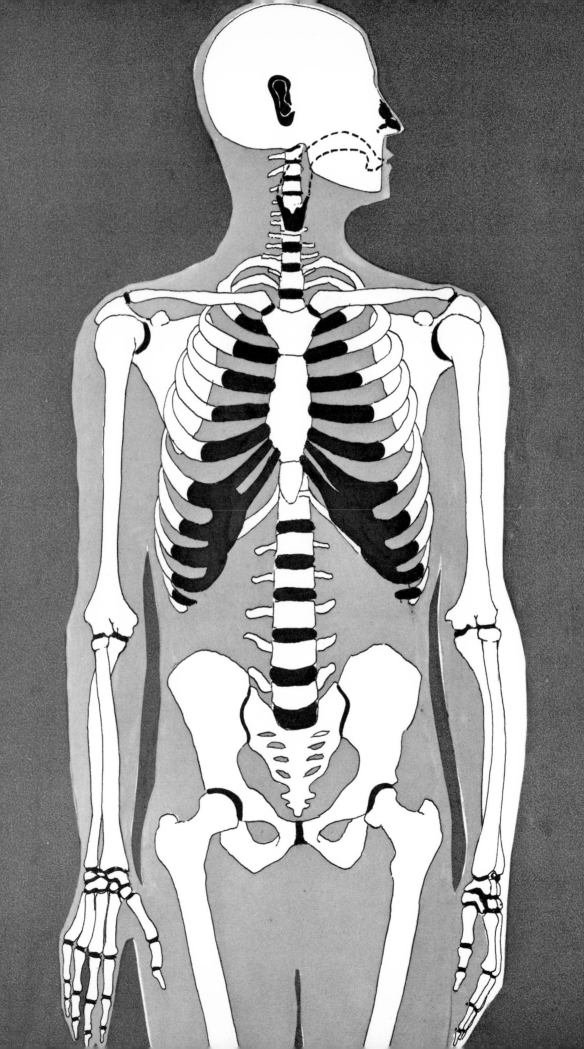

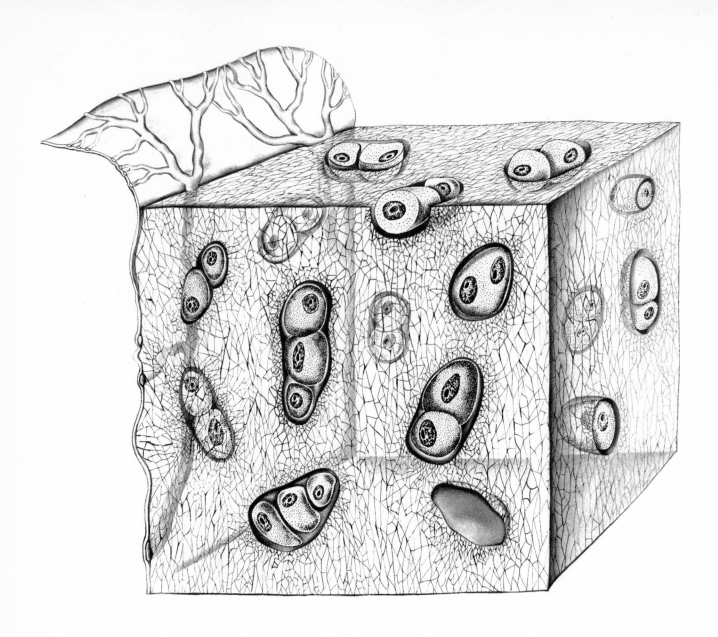

The microscopic structure of cartilage. A product of connective tissue cells, cartilage develops when fibers fuse and the cells are encased in hardening collagen. The isolated connective cells are nourished by lymph through osmosis; blood vessels do not enter cartilage.

(Facing page) Cartilaginous skeleton of the embryo. While the embryo is less than one half-inch long, its skeleton is almost all cartilaginous. The flexibility of cartilaginous bones enables the child to squeeze through the birth canal.

chest will have no difficulty expanding during the act of inhaling. This is the most important mass of cartilage in the body.

Vertebral Disks

A considerable amount of cartilage is also found in the so-called disks of the spine. The human spine is a column of some thirty bony rings, the vertebrae, cushioned one against the other by cartilaginous disks. These disks do not consist of pure cartilage but of fibrocartilage whose semifluid core is called the nucleus pulposus and bears a strong resemblance to the original gelatinous embryonic substance. Even though the spinal column is marvelously enveloped and held together by hundreds of ligaments, muscles and tendons, one or two of these fibrous disks do occasionally rupture, allowing the nucleus pulposus to slip out of place. Such dislocations, often very painful, can usually be corrected by massage, corsets, traction, or surgery.

Larynx and Windpipe

The largest single formation of cartilage in the body is the larynx. It is a rather complex, trumpet-shaped frame of plates and rings composed of cartilaginous pieces. In the central part of this trumpet are the two vocal cords; when air is exhaled through these cords, they vibrate, and these vibrations we hear as sound and speech. Short cords produce higher tones than long cords and that is why women's voices are higher pitched than men's and why children have shrill voices.

The larynx is the entrance to the windpipe, which conducts the air downward into the lungs. Its walls are held open by rings of cartilage, so that it cannot collapse. About the middle of the thorax it branches out, forming the cartilaginous skeleton of the lungs. As the branches become smaller, the tubes and their cartilaginous rings also become finer.

Nose and Ear

Among familiar formations of cartilage are those of the ears and the nose. They demonstrate the

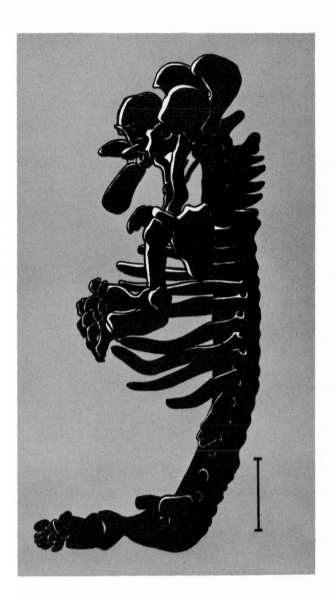

main qualities of cartilage—its strength and flexibility. If they were solid bone and thus rigid, they would soon be chipped or broken off, just as they are in antique marble busts. In our grandfather's time teachers gave pupils demonstrations of the flexibility of the cartilage of the ears: if a pupil's work was not satisfactory, the teacher would twist the ear as though it were a corkscrew rather than a sensitive organ. Since they consisted of cartilage they were none the worse for such harsh treatment.

The Pubic Symphysis

Inside the base of the trunk is a bony, basin-shaped structure, the pelvis. It is composed of two halves.

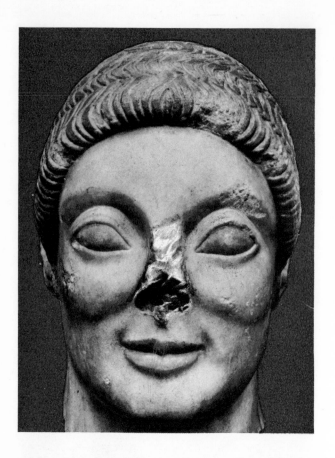

In the back the halves coalesce in a firm middle piece, the sacrum. In the front, however, the two halves of the pelvis remain open but the gap is bridged by cartilaginous tissue. This bridge, the pubic symphysis, is of supreme importance to a woman when she is giving birth. As the child descends from the womb, it can be pushed past the pelvic ring only with great effort on the part of the mother. The crucial additional space in the passageway is supplied by the cartilaginous substance of the symphysis. Softened by relaxin, a hormone produced late in a pregnancy, the cartilage yields a fraction of an inch during the passage of the child's head. If the pubic symphysis, as sometimes happens, becomes prematurely ossified, or if a woman bears her first child when past the years of youth, the cartilage may have become rigid and be a troublesome impediment.

The faces at which bones touch and move against each other at the joints are coated with a layer of cartilage that prevents them from grating. Lining the joint space is a membrane, the synovium, which secretes a clear, watery lubricant, the synovial fluid. Because of this lubrication, the cartilages can slide over each other without friction. In the larger joints, such as the knee, special disks, the *menisci*, act as shock absorbers and help prevent the bones from slipping out of their tracks or sockets. Like the springs, bumpers and shock absorbers of our automobiles, they are essential in helping us endure the shocks and blows we are subjected to. The hardening of the cartilaginous tissue as we grow older is one of the chief reasons for the remarkable difference in the way children jump about without worrying about the effects of falling while elderly persons must move slowly and carefully.

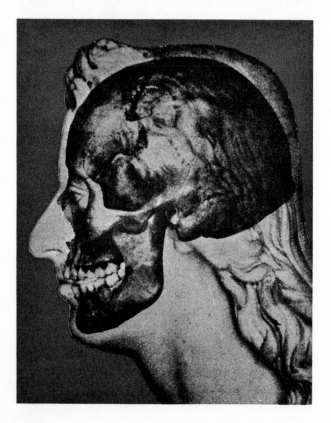

(Above) Marble vs. cartilage. Most excavated busts from ancient civilizations have lost their noses; these were made of marble which, unlike cartilage, is hard and brittle.

The skull of Schiller (dug out of a Potter's Field grave for reburial) here imposed on a bust of the poet shows how cartilaginous structures such as the nose soon fall away after death.

8

Bones

Cartilage changes into a relatively hard substance to provide a framework that will continue to grow without interrupting the activities of life.

In the first stage of embryonic life the bones appear as cartilage. Then comes one of the most remarkable chapters in the story of the human anatomy: the cartilage changes into bone. Cartilage is a relatively soft tissue and the arteries that nourish it do not enter it but creep along its outer cover like ivy on a wall. Then one day the cells of the cover become aggressive and invade the cartilage wall. It may be that a specific hormone gives the signal for their invasion. The cartilage cells multiply and line up in rows like soldiers defending themselves against invaders. The rebels use the arteries as supply lines and soon take over the cartilage cells. After their victory, they build up new and stronger bone cells and columns of bone. As glue they use a protein, "collagen," a soft, flexible substance that protects the bones from breaking easily. As cement they use calcium phosphate, forming the mineral material of bone. We can easily demonstrate the presence of these two ingredients in bone: if we put a bone into a fire, part of it, the collagen, will burn and be consumed, while the hard frame of calcium will remain. Contrariwise, if we put a bone into a weak acid, the calcium phosphate will dissolve and the collagen fibers will swell but remain in a form as flexible as a rope.

These two contrasting qualities combine in any living bone. In childhood the collagenous, that is, flexible character prevails; with the advance of age the flexibility wanes, and the rigidity of the calcium phosphate becomes more and more evident. We start out in life as, so to speak, a starfish but we end up as coral. The skeleton of a child is almost immune to fractures; the young adult has considerable resistance but a sharp blow will cause a fracture. The aged person loses both collagen and calcium from his bones and the bones are so weak that an ordinary fall is sufficient to fracture a major bone. Often the aging person slips in the bathtub and fractures a hip. Has anyone ever heard of a child breaking his hip in a bathtub? One of the greatest threats to the aged is the ever-increasing fragility of the bones; this is due both to decalcification and loss of the collagen substance.

After the successful rebellion against the cartilage, the new regime builds a new palace—the bony skeleton. The bone is not a simple replacement of the cartilage but a marvelous new construction. In this new structure hundreds of fine

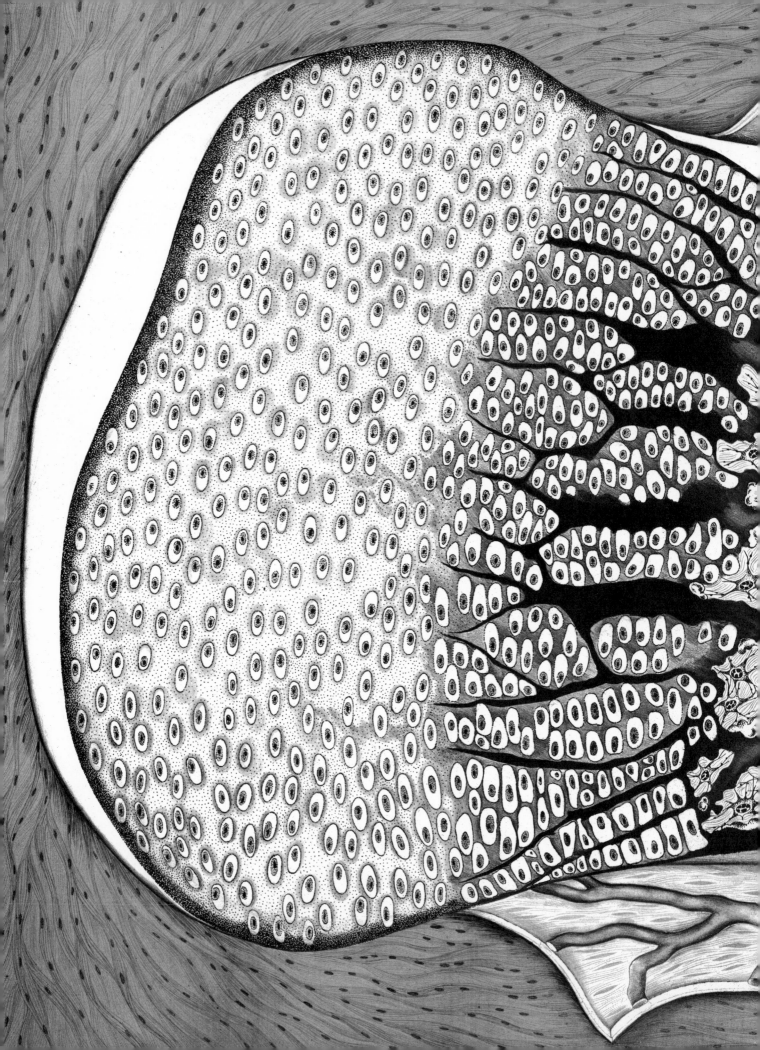

Origin of bone. Blood vessels, accompanied by bone-forming cells, invade and erode the cartilage; the cartilage cells line up but cannot stem the invasion. Blood plasma supplies calcium and phosphate and soon the bands between the cartilage cells begin to calcify. More blood vessels invade, cartilage cells are removed, and bone-forming cells begin to lay down bone.

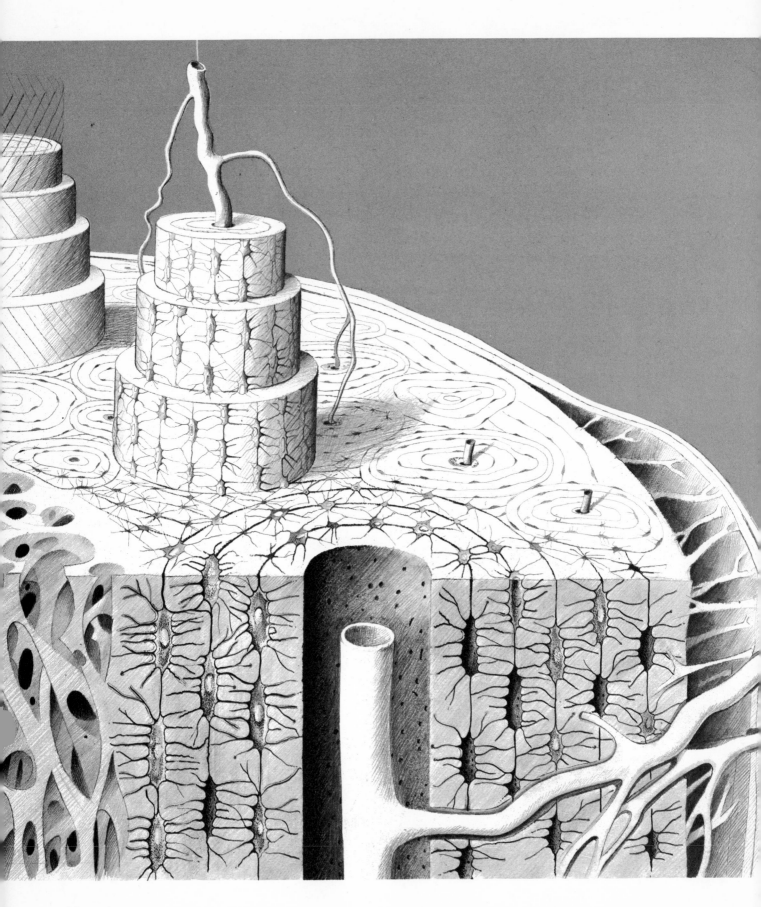

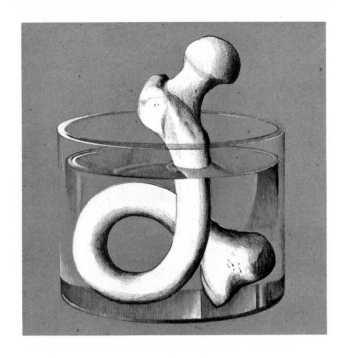

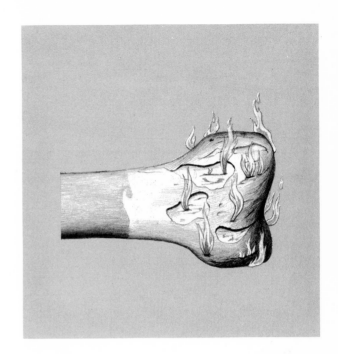

Bone substance. Bone is composed of a gluey substance, collagen, which gives it flexibility, and of calcium and phosphate, which give it rigidity. If a bone is kept in acid, the calcium phosphate dissolves and only the ropy collagen fibers remain. If, however, the collagen is burned away (right), the hard frame of calcium and phosphate remains.

(Left) The structure of bone is testimony to Nature's architectural genius. The nourishing blood vessels ascend in parallel lines, surrounded by connective tissue cells which form bone. The compact parts of bone are predominantly structural, like columns in a skyscraper, while the center, which contains the blood-producing marrow, is almost hollow.

arteries ascend in parallel lines, each artery surrounded by layers of connective tissue cells. They build up bone substance; the result is a kind of temple composed of many columns set very close together. Bone is relatively solid but if we saw a bone lengthwise, we see that it is not compact, and even partly hollow. The porous part serves as a safe-storage for the manufacture of blood cells.

In a few instances bone is formed directly from connective tissue, as in the skull cap.

The Inner Architecture

The bones have an outer and an inner architecture. The outer one consists of the arms and legs as columns, the pelvis as an arch, the vertebrae as blocks. The anatomists of the 18th and 19th centuries discovered that bones also have a wonderful inner architecture. The interior of a bone is reinforced by girder-like structures. Bones are continually undergoing reconstruction and the stresses to which they are subjected cause the formation

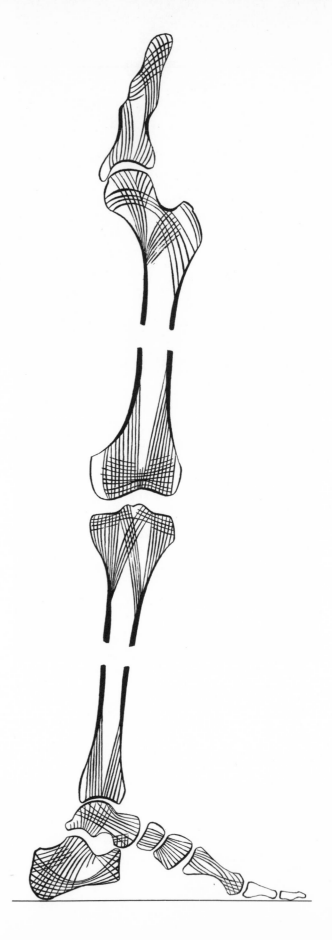

first of fibers and then of girders along the lines of stress. Gradually the fine filigree work of the inner bone builds up. In Saint Peter's and the Taj Mahal, we admire the architecture of man; in living bones we see the architecture of nature.

The Growth of the Bone

The problem of a skeleton that must grow for fifteen or more years without for a moment interrupting the activities of life is one that nature has solved in masterly fashion. If it were suggested to an architect that he build a small house that would from day to day expand and grow to fit the needs of a growing family he would think it an absurdly impossible proposal. But this is a miracle that takes place daily in every human body. The body does the job with an army of special workers consisting of osteoclasts, or bone-breakers, and osteoblasts, or bone-builders. The cells in the marrow of the bones settle around the microscopic arteries of the bone and work as builders. As the child grows, other bone cells form new outer layers of bone structure so that the bones become larger. Imperceptibly, the skeleton becomes larger but without ever interrupting the functions of the body.

Fractures

As we know, bone will crack or break when subjected to a severe blow or considerable pressure. If the bone breaks, the accident is called a fracture. If it cracks but does not break it is a fissure. If the fragments form splinters and pierce the skin, it is a compound fracture. Normally bone heals quickly and perfectly. The area where the broken pieces heal develops a callous which may last for years.

To permit fractured bones to knit together and heal, the broken parts must be brought together and lined up. This is called "reducing" a fracture. Sometimes it may be necessary to use metal plates or even nails to hold the broken parts in position. The fractured limb is then placed in a cast to keep the broken parts aligned. The osteoblasts, the bone-builders, promptly rejoin the broken parts, often so efficiently that the healed fracture is stronger than the original bone.

Inner architecture of bone. Lines of pressure in the bones cause the formation of fibers and then of girder-like structures. Gradually the filigree of the inner bone is built up.

(Left) In its inner structure a bone bears a resemblance to the framework of a bridge.

89

9

The Skeleton

The bones form a framework that keeps the body erect and protects or encases such vulnerable organs as the brain and the spinal cord.

Animals are classified as either invertebrates or vertebrates. Invertebrates are considered fore-runners of the vertebrates, because all of life was for eons restricted to the oceans, and the creatures living in the water were boneless. At first they were all microscopic; later gastraeas, polyps, sponges, corals, worms, and finally snails, developed. All of these primordial creatures were "in-verte-brate," that is, without a vertebral column—a backbone composed of single bones, or vertebrae.

Out of this tremendous variety of invertebrates emerged animals constructed according to a new "mechanical" principle: along the back they developed a supporting member like the roofbeam of a house. First it was a gelatinous rod, called the notochord. One of the most primitive animals still living is the amphioxus, a tiny, snail-like sand-dweller found on the beaches of the North Sea. Amphioxus is not an "ancestor" of ours but probably a degenerated survivor of an extinct species. It has no head, brain or spine but along its back runs a thread like a violin string—the notochord. Even though it does not consist of separated vertebrae, this string is a spinal column.

The human embryo possesses a notochord during the third week of development. This turns into the segmented vertebral column, a process that may resemble the one that took place in some predecessor of the vertebrates.

The Spinal Column

The vertebral column of man is a spine consisting of approximately thirty-three vertebrae. We say approximately, since several of the vertebrae at the lower end are fused into a single segment, the sacrum. From the top down, the sections of spinal column are known as the cervical, dorsal or thoracic, lumbar, sacral and coccygeal; they are made up of seven, twelve, five, five and from three to five vertebrae respectively. The vertebrae are bony rings, through which a string can be drawn as in a necklace.

The vertebral column is not straight, but curves like an interrogation mark, with each vertebra slightly out of line. While providing rigidity, it is also flexible and acts like a shock absorber, absorbing jolts or jerks traveling from heel to head. The

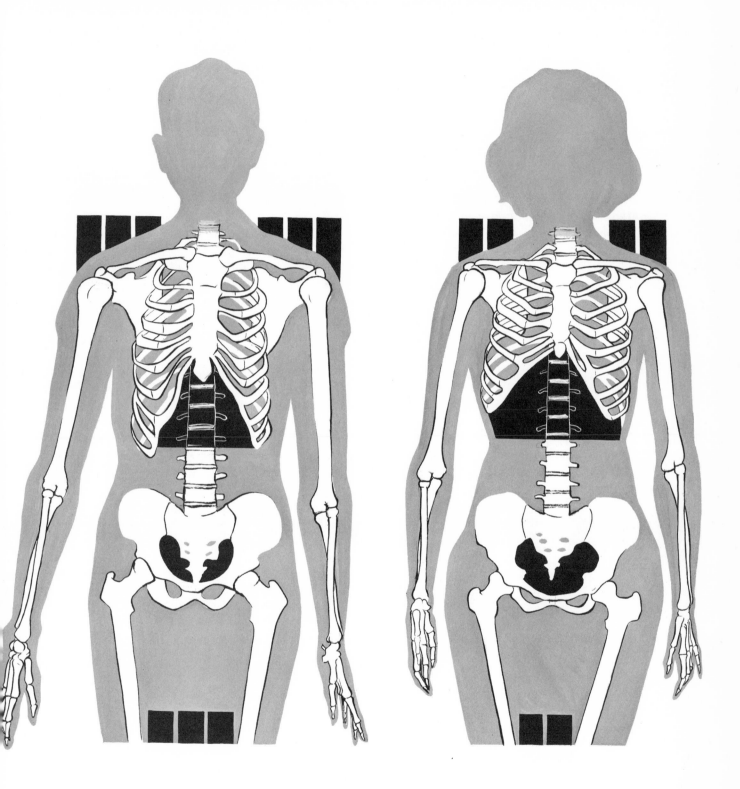

The male and female skeleton. The main differences are broader shoulders in the man but a narrower rib cage. The female pelvis is broader and has a wider opening to facilitate childbirth.

vertebrae are also buffered by the cartilaginous disks we have described in an earlier chapter.

Looked at with the eye of an engineer, the vertebral column, composed of thirty-three units in flowing curves, is an audacious design. It does not run along the middle axis of the body but along the back. All intestinal organs are placed in front of it so that we carry the stomach like a bandsman carrying a big drum. But now comes the most surprising fact: nature has dared to use the narrow, bony and curved column of the spine as the cable for the most sensitive and most vulnerable organ of the body—the spinal cord, which carries the nerves from the brain down through the torso. More than one hundred thousand nerve cells run through this cable and out through the openings between the bony vertebrae to the various parts of the body.

The Neck

The first vertebra at the top of the spine is the only one that does not have a solid, cylindrical body; but the second vertebra not only has such a body but it has a toothlike projection which slips into the ring of the first one like a key into a lock. Because the first vertebra carries the head, just as the mythological demigod Atlas carried the globe, it is called the atlas. The first two vertebrae form a double joint which can operate separately or together. On the top of the first, the atlas, the skull pivots as on a universal joint. When you nod your head in saying "yes," or shake it as you say "no," you demonstrate the two principal movements of the head—in anatomy and in life. Nature must have great faith in her engineering skill, since this nuchal joint, as it is called, is in such a risky location: close behind the pin of the pivot runs a section of the spinal cord that leads to the respiratory center. If this part of the cord were pierced, breathing would be stopped instantaneously. Maintaining the mobility of the neck and the union of skull and spine, and at the same time protecting the spinal cord against the slightest pressure would seem to be contradictory functions. Yet nature masters this problem. The moving parts are kept in position by strong sinews in the muscles of the neck and by ligaments in and around the spine. In former times, when a hanging took place and the condemned man continued to thrash about, the hangman would display his efficiency by leaping from behind onto the shoulders of the hanging man and give him the *coup de grace* by pressing the nape of the man's neck against the spinal cord.

One of the most curious facts of anatomy is that the necks of all mammals, from the towering giraffe to the tiniest mouse, including man, have seven vertebrae.

The Thorax and the Shoulder Girdle

One of the most prominent parts of the human skeleton is the thorax (the Greek word for chest). Below the vertebrae of the neck twelve dorsal vertebrae project laterally around the trunk in the shape of ribs. These ribs form a cage enclosing the heart and lungs. The upper ribs encircle the chest and meet in a breastbone that is partly bone and partly cartilage. The lower ribs do not reach entirely around the body.

Like an old-time horse, man wears a harness, the shoulder girdle. The girdle consists of several parts centered around the articulation of the upper arm. The girdle performs a variety of functions: it connects the arms with the body; it gives the thorax freedom of breath above; and it serves as a scaffold for the numerous muscles that run together at this traffic triangle. A specialized bone, the collarbone, or clavicle, arches from the top of the arm to the breastbone. Because it is in an exposed position and is superficial, the collarbone is a bone that is frequently injured.

The Pelvis

The pelvis is the counterpart of the shoulder girdle. Unlike the shoulder girdle, however, which must be light and loose, the pelvis must hold and protect the heavy mass of the intestines. It is composed of two sides, with the *os sacrum* as the back wall. Each of the sides consists of three bones. Two of the side bones form a pair of rockers on which we swing when we are seated, two serve to close the front of the ring of the cartilaginous symphysis and two attach to the sacrum. The three pairs of bones, firmly grown together, form the pelvis.

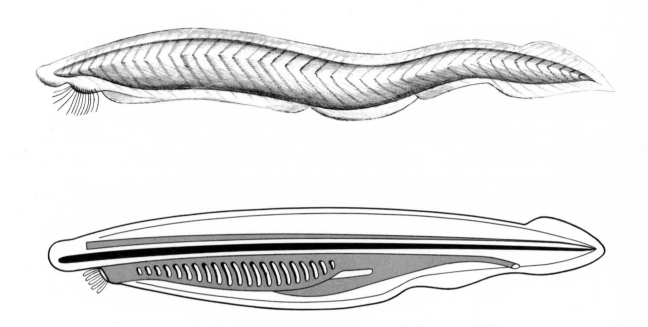

Amphioxus lancellatus, a primitive predecessor of the verte-brates. This snail-like creature found on North Sea beaches has no head, brain or spine, but along its back runs a threadlike notochord, forerunner of the vertebral column.

There are significant differences between the male and female pelvis: the female pelvis is broader, its opening is wider, and its walls are more gracile. The opening is wider because the woman must carry her unborn child inside the pelvis and deliver it through the opening. The delivery is not always easy for a human female since the human child is born with a relatively enormous brain and a large head. A well-developed and wide pelvis is therefore important for a normal delivery. The obstetrician's first step in the examination of a pregnant woman is measuring the pelvis to see whether the expectant mother may deliver a child without excessive labor.

The Limbs

Because they are farthest from the vertebral column, the arms and legs are known as the extremities. Considered segment by segment, arms and legs correspond remarkably in structure. But both have changed very greatly over the ages in the process

93

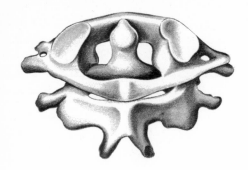

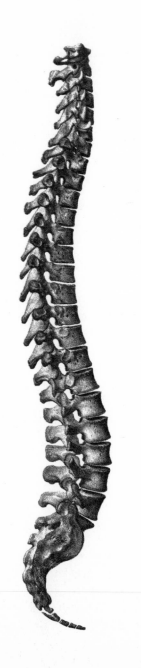

(Left) The spine, composed of vertebrae or bony rings, curves like an interrogation mark. Its flexibility enables it to absorb shocks traveling from heel to head. From the top down, its sections are known as the cervical, dorsal, lumbar, sacral and coccygeal.

The two top vertebrae (left above) form a double joint in which they can operate separately or together. The first vertebra, carrying the head as Atlas carried the globe, is the atlas. The second provides a pin for the atlas and is called the axis. The skull pivots on the atlas, permitting the two main movements of the head—up and down and from side to side.

(Right) The skull. The cranium, which lodges the brain, consists of eight bones joined along so-called suture lines. The skeleton of the face consists of eight bones with immovable joints. The mandible, or lower jaw, is the only freely movable bone of the skull.

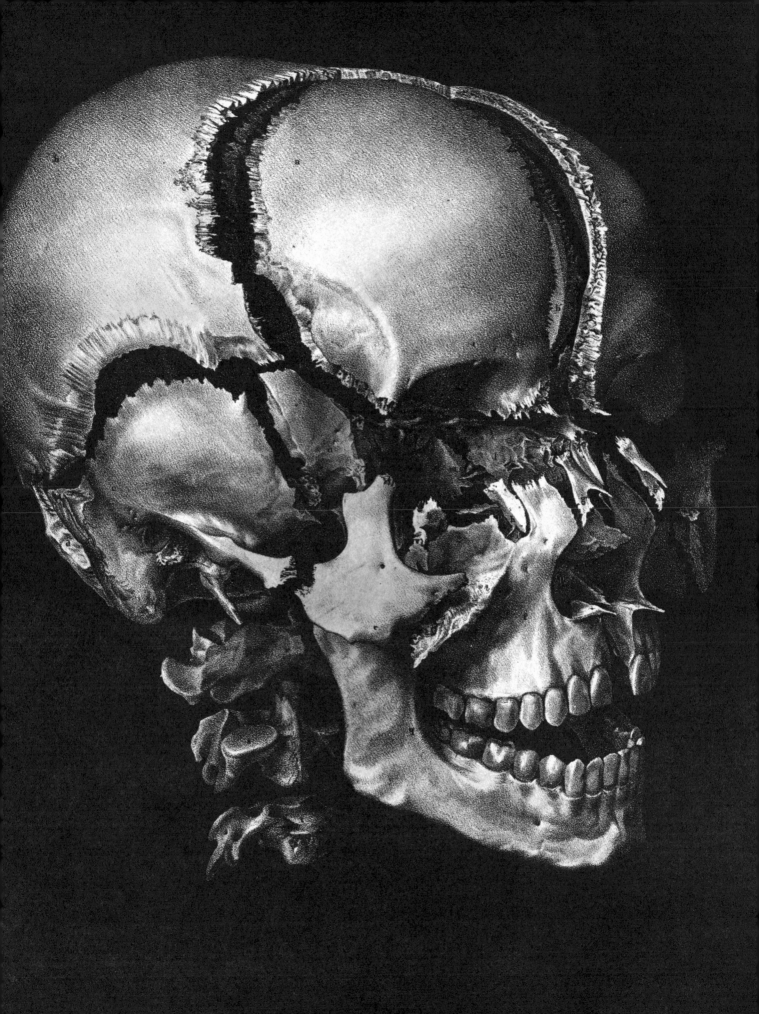

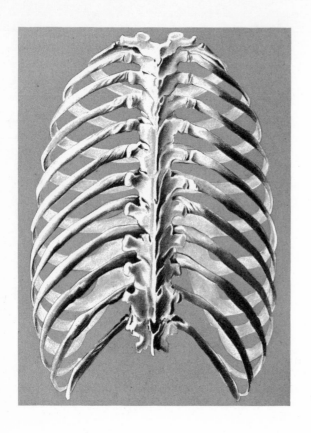

(Left) The thorax or chest. Below the vertebrae of the neck, twelve vertebrae project ribs around the trunk, forming a cage that encloses the heart and lungs.

(Right) The shoulder girdle, which man wears like a harness. It connects the arms with the body, helps give the thorax freedom for breathing, and serves as scaffold for the many muscles that meet in this area. In front are the clavicles, or collarbones, arching from the top of the arm to the breastbone.

The pelvis is the counterpart at hip level of the shoulder girdle. The pelvis protects and supports the weighty mass of the viscera. It is composed of three bones on each side, with the os sacrum as the back wall. Two of the side bones form the rockers we use when we are seated.

of fitting themselves for their quite different tasks. It is now generally assumed that man's ancestors were tree climbers but that when he left the forest for the treeless plains, he became an erect, walking biped. The hind legs developed feet while the forelimbs developed hands.

Both legs and arms are composed of three main sections. The first section, by which the arm or leg is joined to the body, consists of one bone, the second section of two parallel bones. The third section consists of several parts: the wrist, palm and fingers of the hand and the ankle, sole and toes of the foot. The construction of the arm is logical insofar as it is an instrument that is used to reach for, grasp and handle objects. The leg is constructed as a threefold stilt, one balanced on the other in such a way that no acrobat would attempt to walk on it. That is why a human child needs months before it learns to stand, and years before it learns to dance, ride a bicycle or jump from a springboard. Leaving the protection of thickets and trees and rising to an erect position was certainly

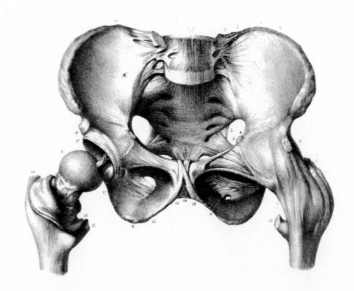

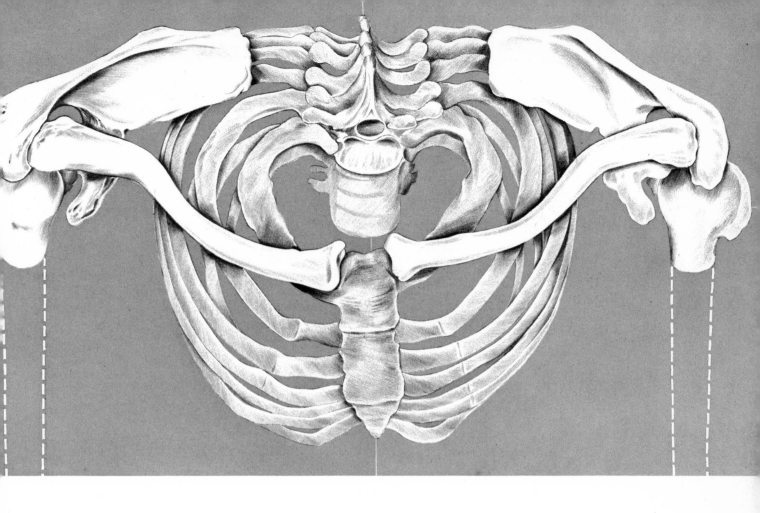

one of the major advances in the history of the human race.

The more one studies man's ability to stand and to walk, the more remarkable these acts seem. We do not really stand on our feet the way a lamp stands on its base; what we do is balance on a collection of small, movable, and loosely connected bones, only three of which touch the ground. At the base is the heel section, consisting of two axle-like bones, one above the other, on which is balanced a pair of column-like bones that reach to the knee; on this combination rests the loose knee joint, and on that in turn rest the thigh bones and the entire body. The knees are known for their unreliability; every storyteller since Homer has used the expression, "his knees grew weak and shook," to indicate the effect of terror.

The human hand is not, as many people think, a late and highly advanced development in man. On the contrary, it is one of the most primitive parts of the human skeleton. After the ancestors of today's land animals had crawled, like alligators,

out of the primordial swamps and became terrestrial vertebrates, they learned in the course of millions of years to stand on their feet—or, rather, on their fins. They probably first moved about on fins that were divided into five parts; from these five-part extremities developed the hands and feet of all land vertebrates.

The arms and legs of the descendants of those early walking-and-climbing creatures were gradually adapted to various special functions. In the birds the fins eventually became thin, backswept forearms that served as wings. In horses, the middle digit became the hoof. The human hand did not change so much from its original form. Physiologically, man continues to have much the same hand as primitive amphibia. The evolution has been psychological or functional rather than organic. It is the use of his hand that distinguishes man from such an animal as an ape. It is not the hand but the brain of man that makes him unique.

A characteristic development of the hand is the thumb. On the human hand it stands out as an

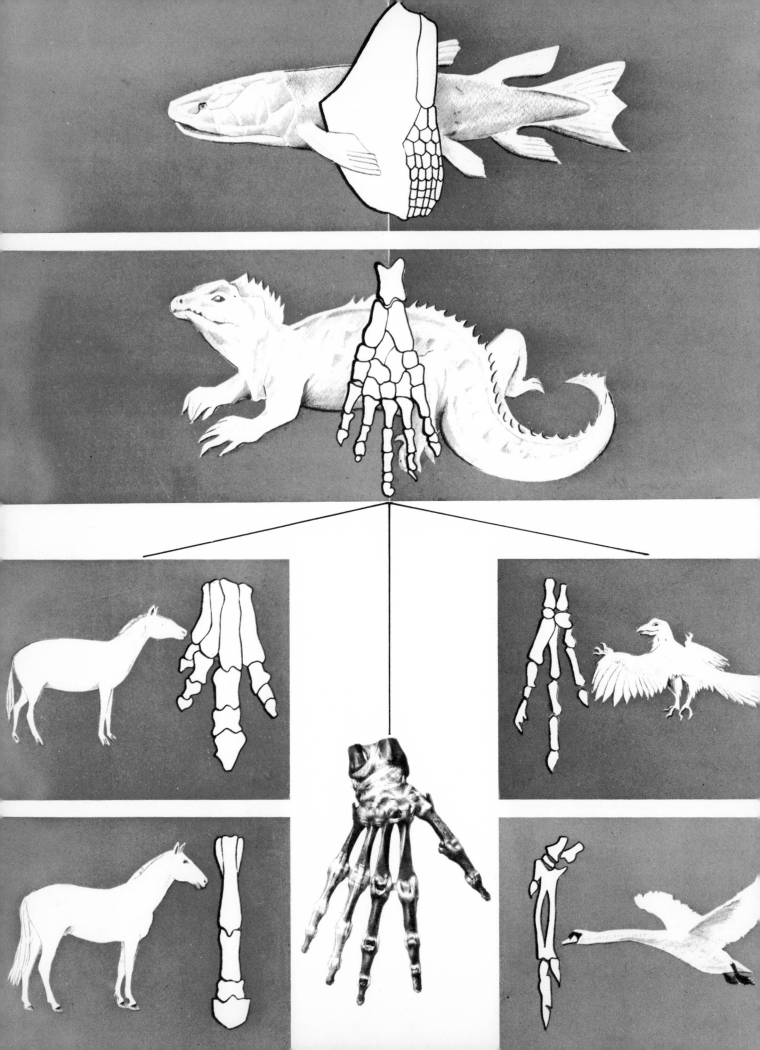

independent finger, whereas in the ape it is a mere stub, so that anatomists used to refer to the ape as *pollulus ridiculus,* "ridiculous little thumb."

The Proportions of the Body

As far as we know, the earliest attempts to analyze the proportions of the human body were made by the Egyptians. They used the hand and the foot as basic units of measurement, and these units have remained in active use for over five thousand years in such words as inches, feet and yards.

Using a hand's breadth, that is, the width of the palm—about four inches—as a basis, the Egyptians worked out the following scale: two hands' breadth—height of face, distance from nipple to navel, and from navel to crotch; three hands' breadth—height of head, and length of foot; four hands' breadth—distance from shoulder to elbow, and from elbow to tip of finger; six hands' breadth—length of leg, length of trunk, distance from the ear to navel, and from navel to knee.

The Greek sculptor Polycleitus suggested the following as the proportions of an ideal human body: the trunk three times as long as the head, the arm three times as long as the hand, the leg three times as long as the foot, the arm plus hand as long as the thigh, the throat equal to the calf in circumference, the distance between the inner angles of the eyes equal to the breadth of the nose and the width of the mouth, and the height of the forehead equal to the height of the nose and the breadth of the lips.

During the Renaissance, Albrecht Dürer, Leonardo da Vinci, and several other great artists pondered the same problem. If, like these Old Masters, we take the height of the head as the standard unit, we get the following proportions: one head from crown to chin, two heads to the nipple, three to the navel, and four to the crotch. From the center line outward we get: one head to the shoulder, two to the elbow, and four to the fingertips. Michelangelo's statues are eight heads high. Bodies of the Gothic period of art stand nine heads tall. El Greco drew his elongated figures ten heads tall.

The body proportions of man change with advancing age. The six-week-old foetus has a head as

(Left) Evolution of the hand. After the ancestors of today's land animals had crawled out of primordial swamps and become terrestrial vertebrates, they learned over millions of years to stand on their feet or fins. At first, they probably moved on fins divided into five parts; from these developed the hands and feet of all land vertebrates. In birds the fins eventually became thin, backswept forearms known as wings. In horses, the middle digit became the hoof. Man continues to have much the same hand as primitive amphibia; it is chiefly the use of the thumb that distinguishes man's hand from an ape's.

(Right) Body proportions change greatly during a lifetime. A line drawn through the midpoint of an embryo would run through the chin; in an infant it would run through the navel; and in an adult, through the pubic symphysis.

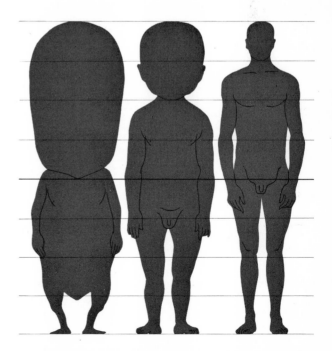

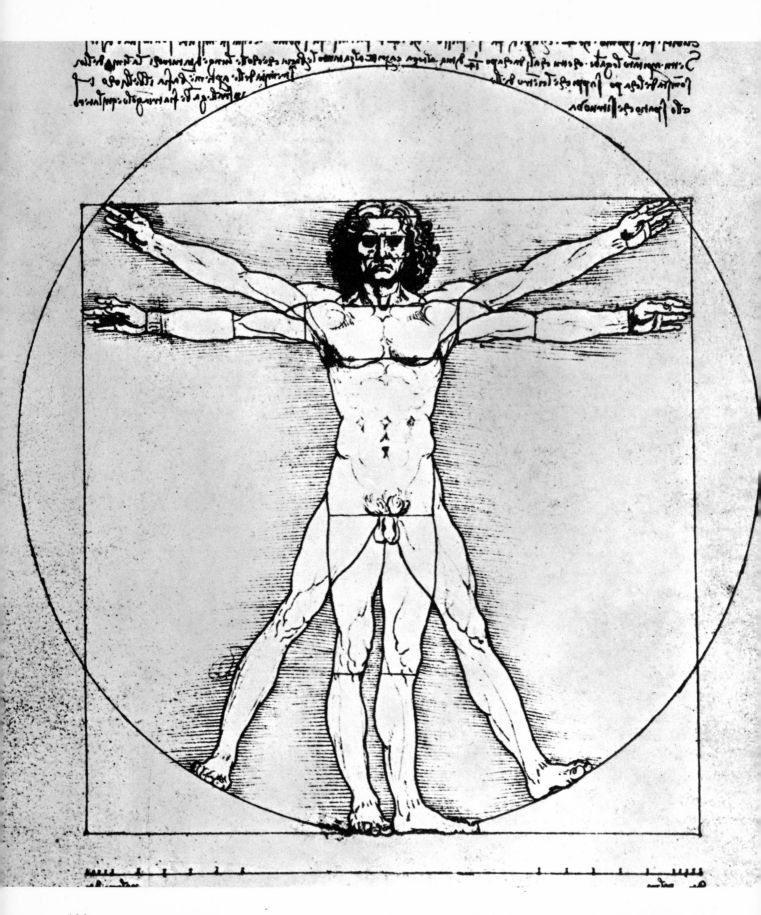

(Left) The study of body proportions dates as far back as the Egyptians and many peoples still use the hand and foot as basic units of measurement. Here Leonardo da Vinci attempts to place a figure in a concentric square and circle. If, as here, the height of the head is taken as the unit, we get the following proportions: one head from crown to chin, two heads to the nipple, three to the navel and four to the crotch. From the center line outward: one head to the shoulder, two to the elbow, and four to the fingertips.

The foot. Unlike the way a lamp stands on its base, we balance on a group of small, movable, and loosely connected bones, with only three supporting points touching the ground. One is at the heel and the other two at the ball of the foot.

long as the body; the horizontal bisecting line of his body runs through the chin. From that time on the head and upper half of the body grow at a relatively faster rate. In the five-month-old embryo the bisecting line runs through the nipple, at birth through the navel, and at puberty through the genitalia.

Sexual Differences in the Skeleton

One of the characteristics of living organisms is variability. Unlike a make of automobile, human beings are not identical. The individual deviates from the type because every human being is a unique combination of millions of genetic traits.

Among the thousands of portraits which artists have painted, no two are identical.

In every individual, male and female traits are mixed. There is thus no male without female traits and no female without male traits. This is evident in our physical characteristics. In theory the ideal man is wider across the shoulders than across the hips, whereas the ideal woman is wider in the hips than in the shoulders. However, a certain percentage of men and women do not run true to type. We regard a person's physical appearance as normal for his sex if the traits of his own sex are dominant and those of the opposite sex recessive. And in general we make our esthetic judgments of the body of man or woman on this basis. The "beauty queen" is expected to be physically a perfect female.

IO

Muscles

The movements of the body and all its parts depend on collections of fibers called muscles, some controlled by the will and some involuntary.

Muscle cells are cells that have specialized in reacting to stimuli by contracting. A muscle cell is principally a cell of motion.

The primordial muscle cell as seen in primitive animals is smooth and not highly organized. This is known as a smooth muscle and consists of a long fiber which appears to be uniform although the electron microscope shows that exceedingly fine threads, the myofibrils, run in parallel lines along its length. In later animals more complex fibers appear. The myofibrils contained in such muscle cells are thicker than those in smooth muscle cells and are crisscrossed by alternate disks and bands. This later and higher form of protoplasmic machinery is called the striped muscle cell. In general, the muscles of the inner parts of our body, the viscera, are smooth, whereas those that move the bones are of the striped kind.

We can assume that for hundreds of millions of years only smooth muscle fiber existed. Then came insects and vertebrates, which developed striped fibers. Although the smooth fibers are simpler in their organization and their contractions are slower, they are not inferior. A worm crawls slowly, and an oyster rarely moves. But the smooth muscle is extremely strong and persevering: an oyster closes its shell with astonishing force and holds it closed for hours or even days without sign of exhaustion.

The striped muscle fiber is highly organized; a fly or bee contracts the muscles of its wings one hundred times a second; in playing tennis a man gives a marvelous exhibition of the movements of striped muscle fibers. However, the two kinds of fibers, smooth and striped, are complementary, not competitive. The striped muscles (color portfolio plates 1–5) are under the control of the will and are called voluntary muscles. The smooth muscles are not under conscious control and are called involuntary muscles.

Muscular Tubes and Sacs

The role of smooth muscle fibers is exceedingly important. The body may be regarded as a machine penetrated by a series of muscular tubes running from head to feet. These pipes serve to transport air, blood, food, urine and excrement. The basic

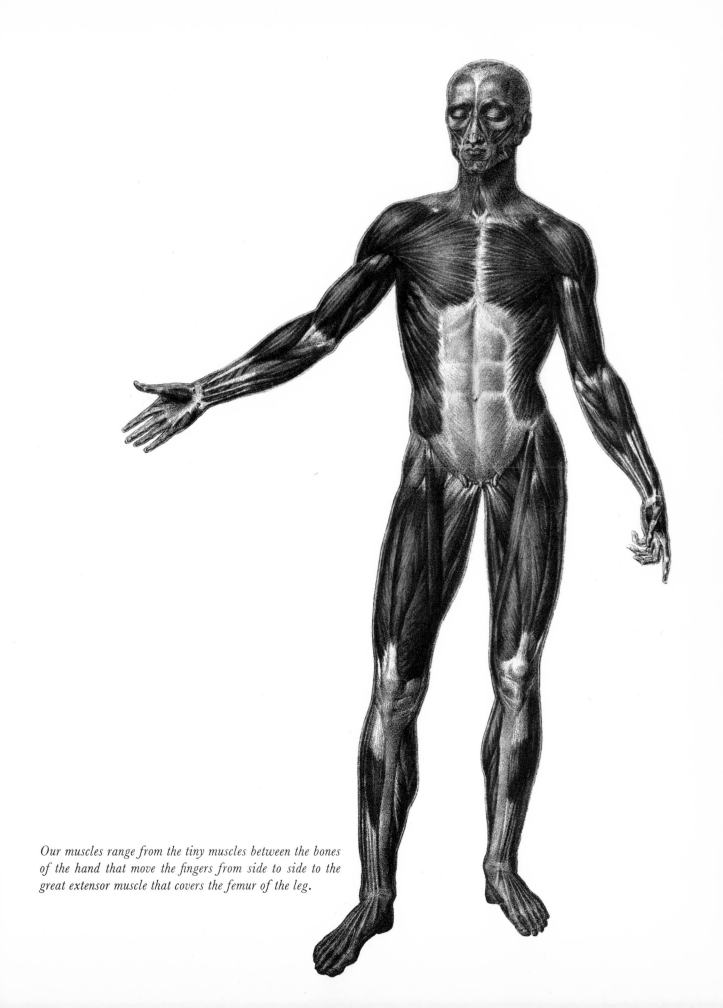

Our muscles range from the tiny muscles between the bones of the hand that move the fingers from side to side to the great extensor muscle that covers the femur of the leg.

The muscular tubes in the body's various systems. From left to right: the respiratory, digestive, circulatory, lymphatic, urinary and reproductive systems. Composed of smooth muscle fiber, the contractions of these muscles are slow and involuntary.

construction of all these tubes is the same. In general they include two or more layers of smooth muscle fibers; an exception is the blood vessels, which have only one layer. The fibers of the inner layer run circularly around the tube; those of the outer layer run lengthwise along the tube. The circular layer serves for contraction, the longitudinal layer for a wavelike movement. The movements are directed by nerve cells that are located along the walls and act like the signals along highways or railroad tracks.

Innumerable smooth muscle fibers are woven through the connective fibers of the skin and other organs. Every hair in our skin carries at its root a little muscle that can make the hair stand up and helps squeeze fat out of a tiny, sebaceous gland for the benefit of the hair and skin. Layers of smooth muscle encircle the digestive canal from the esophagus down to the anal opening. In some areas the muscles are woven into tight rings. At the openings of certain organs the muscle rings, called sphincters, are particularly strong. Like the tops of certain stockings, they are elastic and hold the rim closed

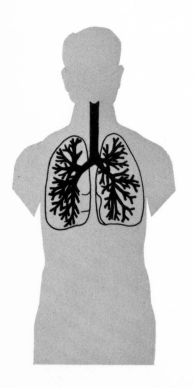 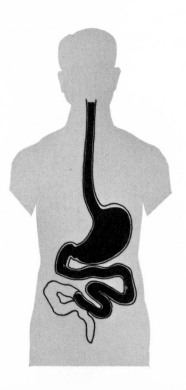 

through their "tonus." They not only open such entrances but also close them. Sphincter muscles are also made up of voluntary muscle fibers. A typical voluntary muscle sphincter holds our bladder closed so that we do not discharge urine involuntarily. A similar muscle ring holds the colon closed; only when we defecate does it open.

At some points the tubes broaden into sacs, such as the stomach in the middle of the alimentary tract, the bladder in the urinary tract, and the uterus in the genital canal of the female.

Striped Muscle Tissue

Just as connective tissue produces fibers out of collagen, so muscle produces fibers out of myosin. The Hungarian biochemist Szent-Györgyi (who was awarded a Nobel Prize for isolating vitamin C) was able to make an "artificial muscle" out of myosin. Just like a natural muscle fiber, Szent-Györgyi's artificial muscle fiber contracted when properly stimulated. In a natural muscle hundreds of fibers

are united into a cigar-shaped form provided with nerves and fed by blood vessels. Just as the electric wires in our homes lead to heaters, electric lamps, or bells, so our motor nerves run to the muscles and end there in "electrodes." With each nerve impulse these electrodes manufacture a chemical compound, acetylcholine, which has a stimulating effect. Not long after the discovery of this "nerve hormone," a substance was discovered that could neutralize its stimulating effect. This substance, which belongs to the family of curare, a poison the Indians of the Amazon basin use on their arrow tips, paralyzes the nerves. Curare is now administered in hospitals to relax the muscles of a patient before certain surgical operations.

Fatigue "Poisons"

If we put a rat on a treadmill and let it work to the point of exhaustion, and its blood is then injected into an alert rat, the alert animal will fall asleep just as though it had been given a narcotic. If the

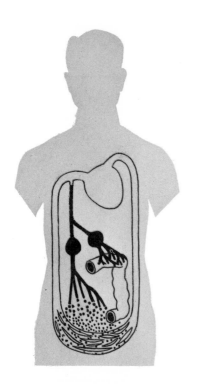

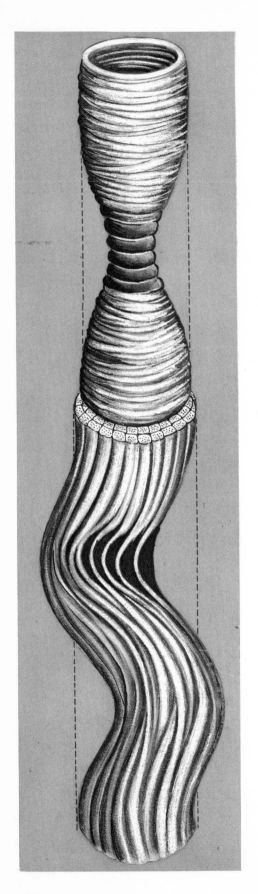

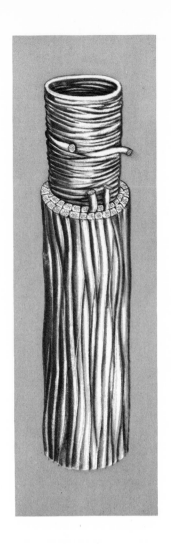

The muscle tubes are in general composed of two or more layers of muscle fiber. The fibers of the inner layer (above) are circular and serve for contraction; those of the outer layer (left) are longitudinal and provide a wavelike movement. The two together produce a motion, peristalsis, resembling that of a worm.

(Facing page) The movement of smooth muscle tubes is directed by nerve cells located along the walls like trackside railway signals. The intestines (left) are organized on much the same principle as the primitive worm (right).

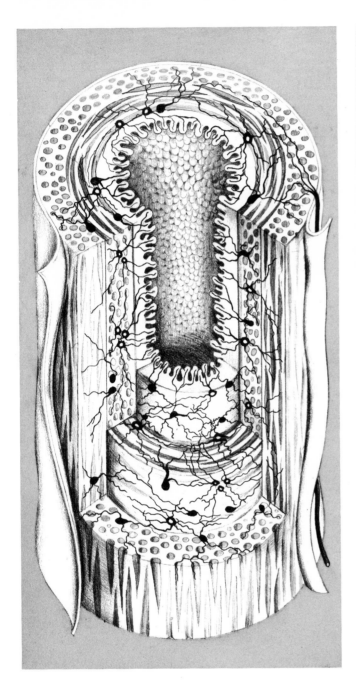

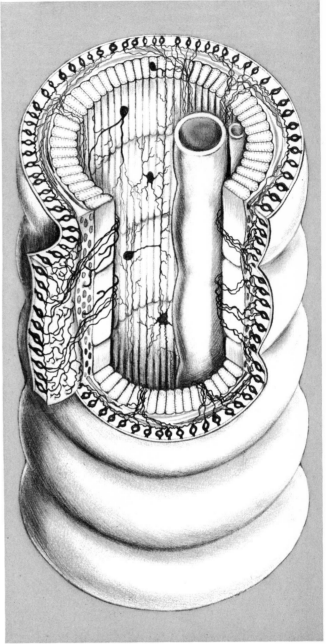

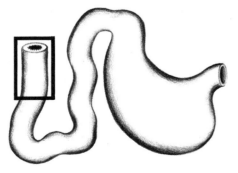

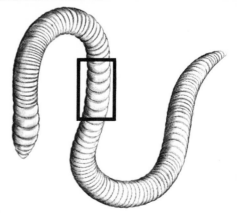

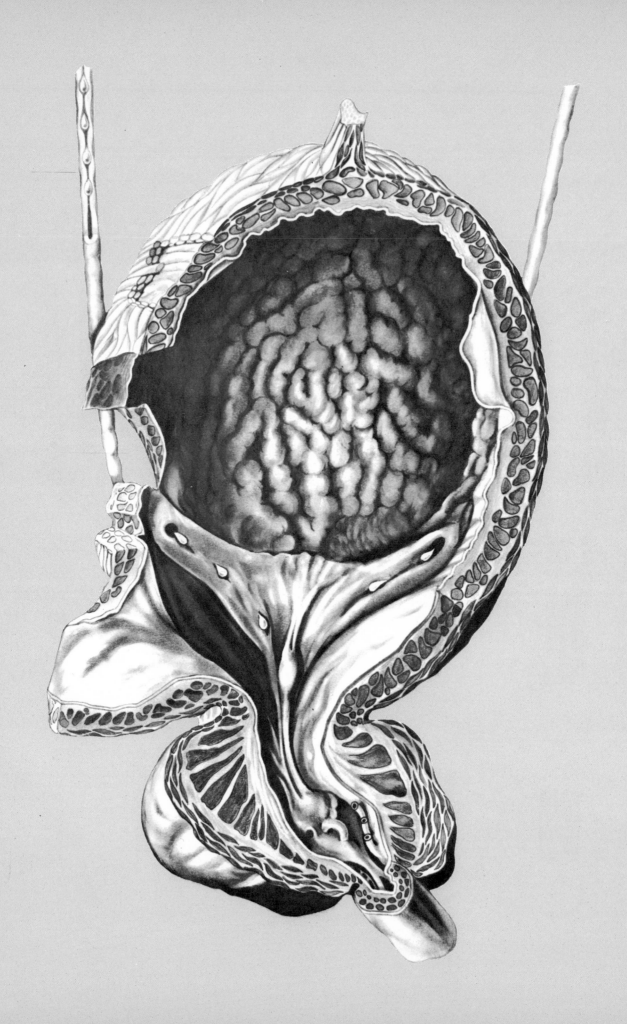

(Left) At certain points the muscle tube broadens out to form a sac such as the bladder of the urinary tract. A tightly woven muscle ring holds the bladder closed so that it does not discharge involuntarily.

(Below) In striped muscle fiber (1), which controls movement, many muscle cells (2) are united. Each cell, consisting of individual fibrils (3) is stimulated to contract through nerves ending in an apparatus like an electrode (4). A rich network of blood vessels (5) feeds the muscle, and special sensory nerves (6, 7, 8) relay messages to the brain concerning the tension and position of each muscle.

blood of the alert rat is injected into the exhausted rat, it will recuperate almost immediately and can be made to run the treadmill again.

One of the "poisons" that produce the symptoms of fatigue is lactic acid, which appears in the blood after incomplete combustion during metabolism. For a time it was thought that fatigue was the result of poisoning from such "fatigue toxins," but this was an oversimplification. In actual fact, during strenuous exercise, the lungs and the circulatory system cannot supply sufficient oxygen for complete metabolism of the lactic acid; but once the body is at rest, it can meet the demand for oxygen.

Muscular Disorders

A muscle is intimately connected with the nerves that direct it. That is why it is difficult and often even impossible to say whether a muscular complaint has its roots in the muscle tissue or in the nerves of the muscle. The most common muscle ailment is a muscular "rheumatism" but doctors

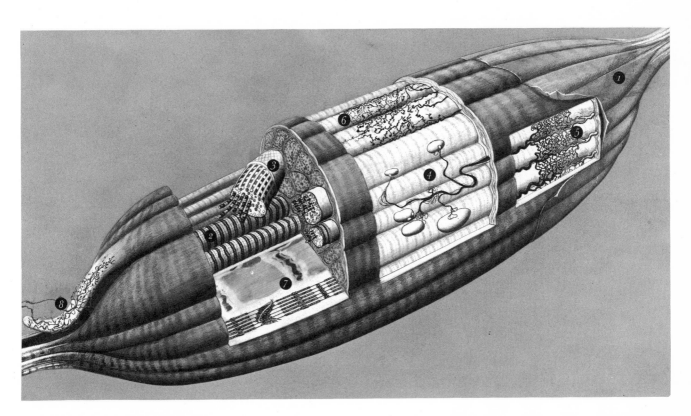

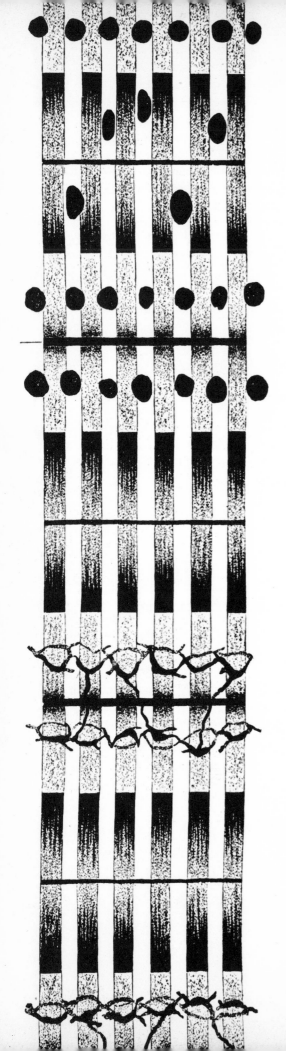

have found it quite difficult to decide what the crux of this complaint is. Many believe that it is an inflammation of the fibrous connective tissue that sheathes the muscles and forms the ligaments and tendons, and they therefore call the disease fibrositis. If the muscles themselves are inflamed, it is called myositis. One of the most common forms of this is lumbago, an acute "rheumatism" of the muscles of the small of the back. The attack does not last long, and after a few hours or days the mobility of the stiffened muscles returns.

Symmetry and Asymmetry of the Body

The human body shows every sign of having been planned as a symmetrical structure. But during the long history of evolution the vertebrate ancestors of man had to adapt to many changes of environment, climate and nutrition, and today the human body is like the Church of San Marco in Venice, which is a mixture of Byzantine, Gothic, Romanesque, Venetian and Baroque styles.

The original design of the body was intended for an aquatic environment. But when the waters receded, continents rose, and swamps dried out, the symmetry of the primordial design dwindled. The pipes of the circulatory system were dislocated, the heart was pushed to the left, the gills "modernized" into lungs, and the liver shifted to the right. Many other asymmetrical details can be listed: the breasts of women are generally not equal in size; the left testicle of the male hangs lower than the right. A pair of shoes does not fit both feet equally well, and a man's shoulders need different padding. We do not walk in a straight line, as is evident when a blindfolded person tries to do so. The explorer Sven Hedin tells of his confusion when he wandered

(Left) Striped muscle fiber. Each fiber is a fusion of threads, disks and bands that change shape as the muscle contracts or relaxes.

(Right) Striped skeletal muscle cell. Electron microscopic view showing changes in the muscle as it relaxes (left) and contracts (right). (Dr. J. A. G. Rhodin, from his Atlas of Ultrastructure, W. B. Saunders Company, 1963)

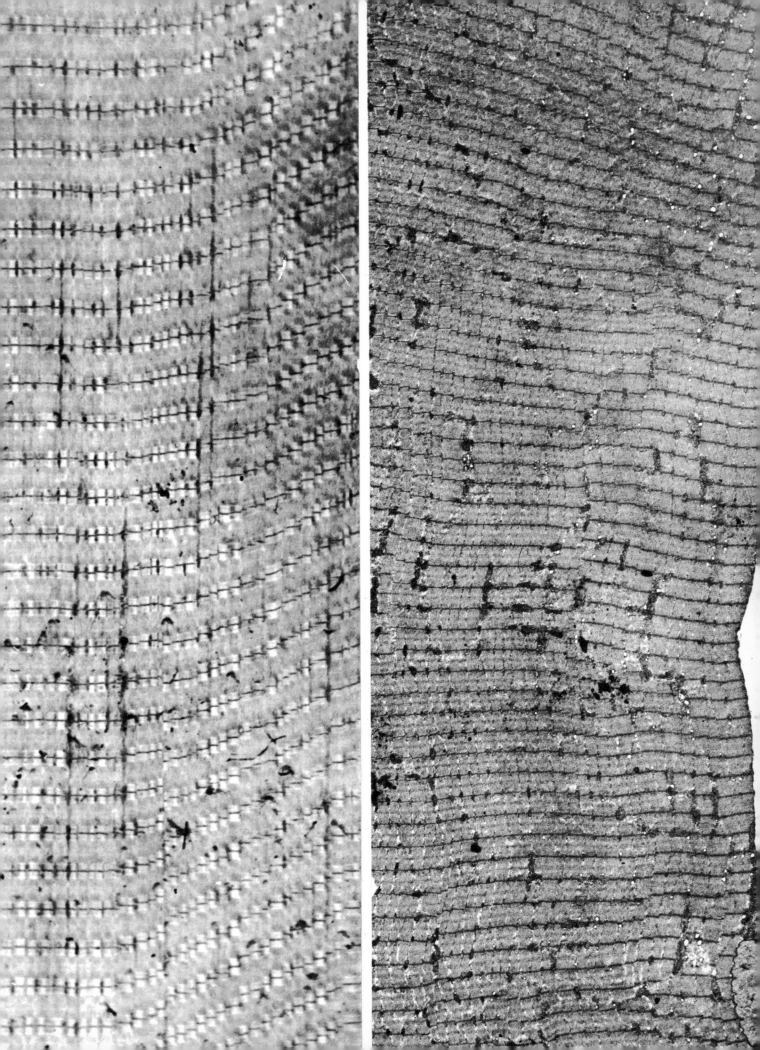

off his course while crossing the Gobi desert and found himself, after weeks of erratic wandering, walking in his own footsteps. He had made a circle. The same is true of a man who rows across a lake in foggy weather. He wanders so far off course that soon he is rowing parallel to the shore, and in the opposite direction; when he finally reaches the shore, he may well find that it is the one he started from.

Right-handedness

The majority of nerves descending from the brain to the spinal cord cross at the neck and thence run down the opposite side of the body. The nerves serving the muscles of the right arm come from the the left hemisphere of the brain. Thus a man who suffers a hemorrhage in the left side of the brain is paralyzed on the right side of his body. When we write, paint, hammer, or do other work with the right hand, we use the nerve centers in the left brain. There is a speech center in the right hemisphere of the brain but we use only the speech center in the left brain. If a man suffers a hemor-

rhage in the left hemisphere, he loses the power of speech. But not hopelessly; after a while he may learn to use the speech center of the other half of the brain.

The fact that we speak, write, and work with the muscles of the right side of the body is called right-handedness. All our instruments and buildings—auto gearshifts, doors, stairway handrails, books, violins, armchair desks—are designed for persons who are right-handed. Four per cent of all people are left-handed. Although left-handed individuals are handicapped, it is an unimportant handicap and some of the greatest artists and thinkers have been left-handed: Leonardo da Vinci, Michelangelo, Holbein. The Bible tells us that the tribe of Benjamin contributed to the army seven hundred élite soldiers who were left-handed; and Hector, who was defeated by the great Achilles, was left-handed.

We do not know why one person in every twenty-five is left-handed but we do know that there is no reason to go to any real lengths to make a child use his right hand instead of his left. In fact, the attempt to make a left-handed child prefer his right hand sometimes seems to lead to stammering, as if the effort has confused the child's speech center.

The discus thrower. Cross section of a famous classical sculpture, showing some of the many muscles involved in a single action.
1. *The sternomastoid muscle rotates the head.*
2. *The trapezius draws the shoulder-blade to the spine and rotates it.*
3. *The deltoid moves the arm away from the body.*
4. *The biceps flexes the forearm.*
5. *The pectoral or breast muscle draws the arm toward the body.*
6. *The serratus anterior rotates and moves the shoulder blade.*
7. *Abdominal muscles compress the abdominal cavity.*
8. *The gluteus muscles return the body to an erect position.*
9. *The iliotibial band, a broad tendon, helps straighten the leg and trunk.*
10. *The gastrocnemius of the calf bends the leg and points the toe.*
11. *Achilles' tendon joins the calf muscle to the heel bone.*
12. *Various tendons bend the foot and ankle.*

II

The Blood Vessels

An incredibly intricate network of arteries, veins and capillaries carries blood to and from every cell in the body.

(Facing page) The blood vessels. The circulatory system consists of a network of vessels, with the heart, a muscular pump, in the center. The arteries leading from the heart grow finer as they spread through the body until they lead into capillaries with single-cell walls. After these come the smallest veins, which lead to progressively larger veins as they return to the heart.

When the chick embryo develops from the hen's egg, the first organs that become visible are blood vessels spreading out over the globule of yolk. At first they are solid shoots; then the core of these shoots dissolves, the shoots become tubes, and the liberated cells of the core float as "blood cells" through the tubes. The tubes continue to spread out, growing finer and finer until they form the network of vessels that make up the circulatory system. The circulatory system (color portfolio plates 6–12) consists of two components: the vessels, and the cells which flow through the vessels as blood. At the center of the system, the main vessel thickens into a sac of specialized muscle fibers—the heart. By means of rhythmic contractions occurring about once a second, the heart drives the blood out through the vessels and then back again to the heart. This flowing out and back is called the circulation of the blood.

The vessels through which the blood flows away from the heart are called arteries, which is a misnomer, since "artery" means "air pipe." In a corpse the vessels radiating from the heart are found to be empty, which led the early anatomists to believe they were air conduits. Eventually, the British physician William Harvey became convinced that arteries conduct blood. Yet his contemporaries continued to support the old concept, asserting: "I prefer to err with Galen than to accept Harvey." The polemic became so passionate that Harvey had to flee from the howling of the professional anatomists. In his comedies, Molière, who lived at the time of this scientific revolution, immortalized the fury of the professionals against the "circulators."

The vessels that bring the blood from the tissues back to the heart are called veins. Arteries and veins usually run side by side through the body, the arterial blood bright red and the venous blood "bluish."

A blood vessel is not a simple tube but a complex structure. An artery wall is made up of several layers, giving the tube the strength and flexibility to enable it to expand and contract alternately. As they branch off from the main vessels, the arteries become narrower until finally they branch off into vessels finer than a hair. These are called capillaries (from *capilla*, hair), and form the connections between arteries and veins.

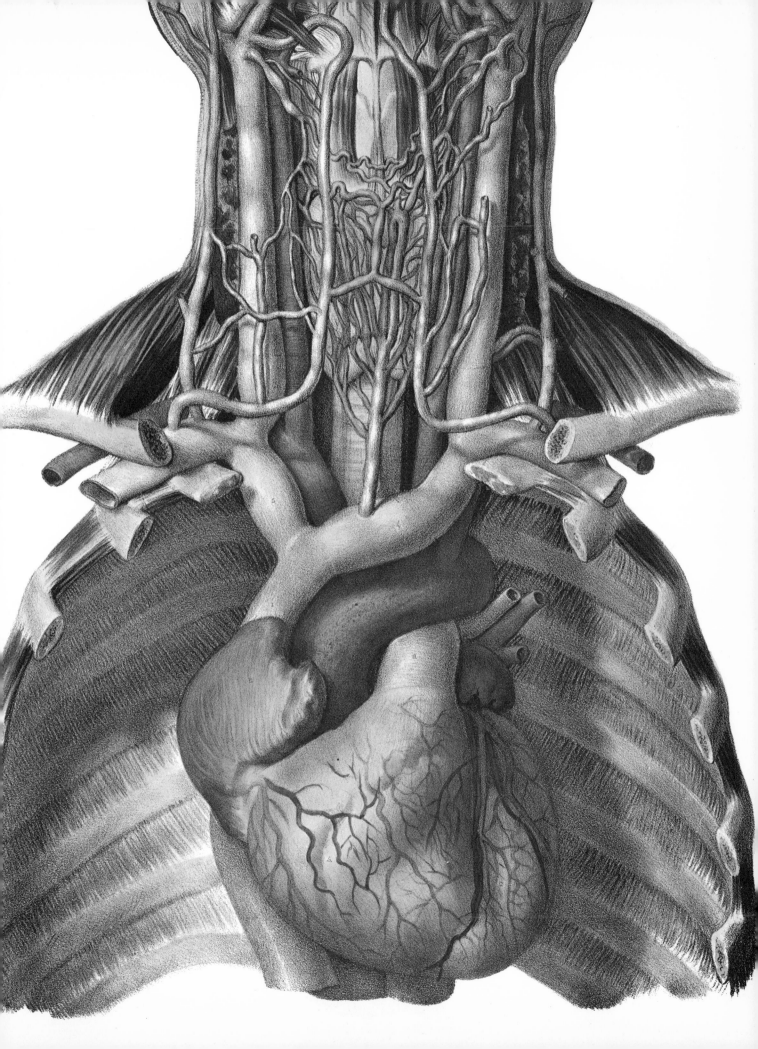

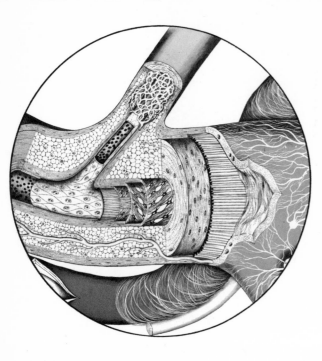

Arteries. Since arteries must withstand the pressure of blood pumped by the heart, they are made up of several layers, including a few of muscle fiber.

(Right) Veins are not subjected to much pressure as they carry blood back to the heart and therefore have thinner walls than arteries. Veins near the surface of the body show through the skin as bluish lines.

(Facing page) Distribution of blood vessels in approximately one square inch of intestinal wall. As the arteries branch out, they form the hair-thin capillaries that bring the blood into contact with tissue.

116

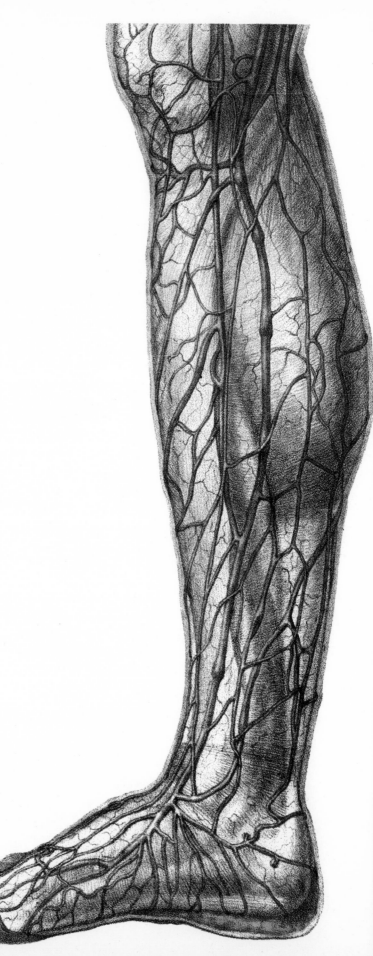

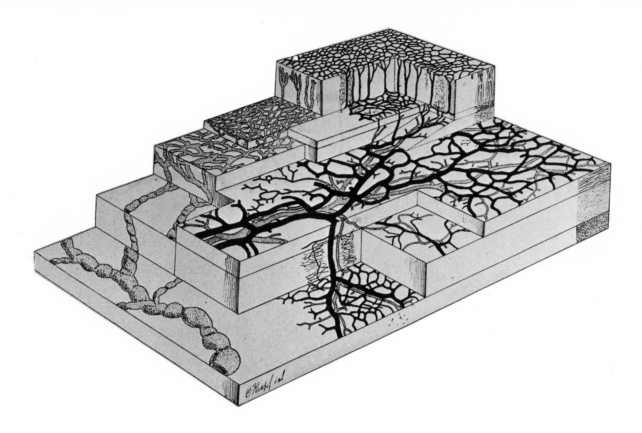

Capillaries and Veins

The capillaries are small and short, as a rule no longer than a tenth of a millimeter, but they are innumerable. They are a vital part of the blood system because they are the only vessels that bring the blood into practical contact with the tissues. At that point the tubes of the circulatory system are so fine that they consist of only a single layer of cells; these interlock like the logs at the corner of a log cabin. On the outer walls of the capillaries, cells called pericytes hang like starfishes, and migratory lymph cells penetrate the wall from the blood into the tissue and vice versa.

With each branching off into smaller vessels the resistance in the vessels becomes greater, the blood stream slowing down until in the region of the capillaries it comes almost to a standstill. Then a fresh impulse, from the next heartbeat, thrusts the blood through the capillaries into the veins and back toward the heart. If the blood is returning from the head to the heart, that is, moving downward, it faces no mechanical problems in its move-

ment, but if it comes from the lower half of the body the stream must rise vertically. To assist this upward movement the veins form valves in their walls. As the veins approach the heart, their walls become thicker but never so firm as those of the arteries. Generally, the veins are greater in number. Fairly large-sized veins wind their way near the surface of the body and in many places their bluish outline can be seen through the skin. It is into these veins that run close to the surface that drugs or transfusions are injected.

The total number of blood vessels is unimaginable. During the Renaissance a technique for draining the blood vessels in a dead body and injecting a colored plaster into them was developed; when the plaster hardened the anatomists were the first to see the smaller branches of arteries and veins. This led the Dutch anatomist van Hoorne to conclude that the body was made up of blood vessels.

Since the walls of the veins are not so resistant and resilient as those of the arteries, they tend to stretch and to lose their firmness, particularly in the legs. They become knotty and protrude, and they are then known as varicose veins. Varicose veins cause itching and sometimes inflammation of the skin and are the bane of elderly people. The treatment of them includes injection with substances that close them off, or tying them off and then removing them by excision.

The Vasomotor Nerves

All blood vessels, and particularly the arteries, are supplied with nerves of which the most important are the vasomotor nerves because they regulate the expansion of the arteries and thereby the amount of blood that passes through the vessels and reaches every organ. When we exercise, our voluntary muscles immediately require and are fed an additional supply of blood. If we take food, the blood vessels of the digestive system open wide. In this way the flow of blood is constantly adapted to the activities and needs of the various parts of the body.

The vasomotor nerves are governed by special centers in the brain—a part of the autonomic nervous system that is not under conscious control.

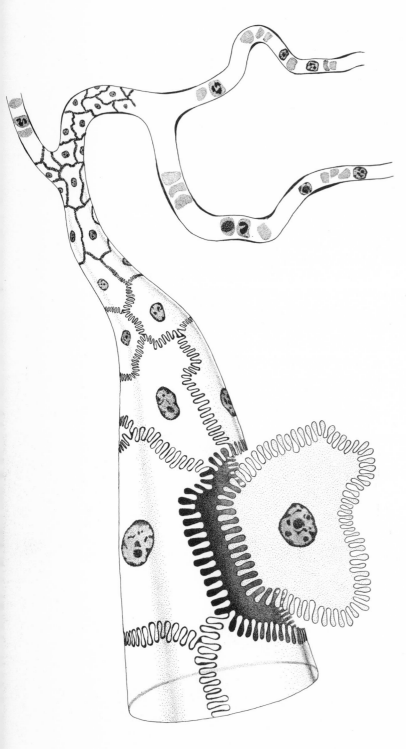

(Left) Capillaries. The final branches of the circulatory system, capillaries, consist of only a single layer of cells. Blood lymph passes through these cells into the tissues and lymph returns through these cells into the blood stream.

(Right) Blood vessels. A tiny portion of stomach wall shows how numerous blood vessels are and how they become smaller as they approach the surface.

118

The function of these centers often is revealed in behavior based on psychological reactions. The sensitivity of the vasomotor centers affects what we might call the sensitivity of the personality. We say of one girl that she is "sensitive" because she reacts vividly, the color in her face changing quickly, whereas another is considered phlegmatic because she does not blush readily. Their vasomotor centers respond differently.

The vasomotor nerves also send a continuous "low-voltage current" to the arteries so that they are never without tension or "tonus." We call this tension "blood pressure."

Blood Pressure

At the end of the 19th century an Italian physician, Riva Rocci, introduced a device for measuring blood pressure that was to become one of the most commonly used medical instruments. The physician puts a cuff containing a flattened rubber hose around the upper arms, and inflates it, thereby compressing the main artery of the arm. The manometer is connected with the rubber hose and shows how much pressure is necessary to stop the flow of blood through the arteries. When the pressure is released, the blood, as it begins to flow through the artery, makes a sound that can be heard through a stethoscope applied to the artery. This is called the systolic pressure. When the pressure is sufficiently released so that no sound is heard through the stethoscope, the manometer reading is called the diastolic pressure. Normally, the blood pressure in adults should not be above one hundred and forty millimeters for the systolic pressure on the mercury manometer, nor above ninety millimeters for the diastolic. Blood pressure readings above these figures are called hypertension. In some persons the pressure stays low; but usually it increases between five and ten millimeters every ten years.

If the systolic blood pressure gives a high reading when the patient is at rest, the most common cause is hardening of the walls of the arteries, particularly of the largest artery, the aorta. This condition is called arteriosclerosis; its cause is still unknown.

Much more serious is hypertension of both the systolic and diastolic blood pressures. Occasionally

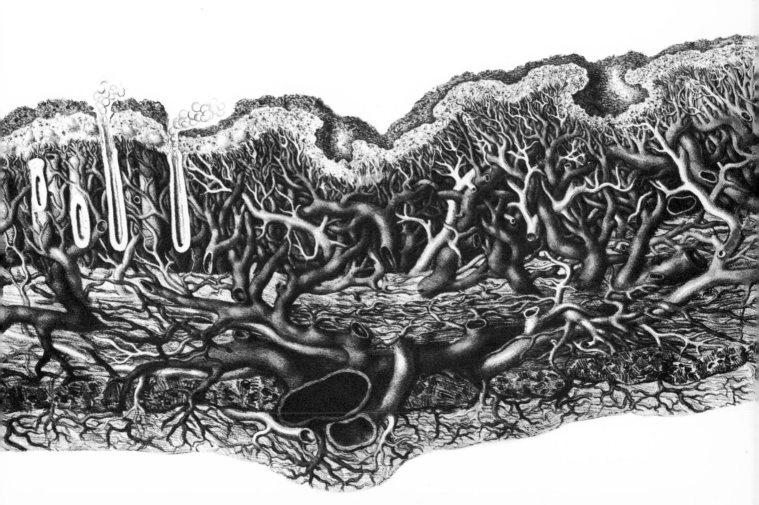

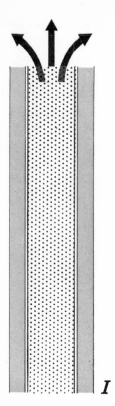 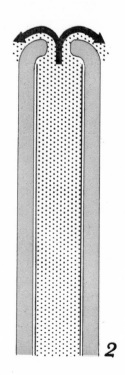 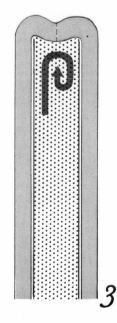 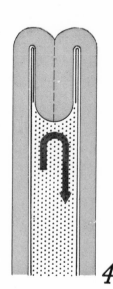

this is due to a detectible cause, such as an anatomic abnormality of the arteries to the kidneys. Generally the cause is unknown, and the hypertension is then called essential hypertension.

The higher the blood pressure, the greater the possibility that an artery will burst. Therefore, a physician tries to bring the pressure down when it seems too high. All kinds of drugs have been tried. One of these, a decoction of the Indian plant Ranwolfia, was being used in India as a tranquilizer. An extract made from it proved to be very effective in lowering blood pressure. Today a whole array of drugs that lower blood pressure is available.

Arteriosclerosis and Cholesterol

After about fifty years of faithful service, the vessels of the circulatory system, just like our teeth, eyes and hair, show signs of aging. The body ultimately reacts by plastering the walls of the vessels with lime; this makes them hard, or sclerotic, and the process is therefore called arteriosclerosis. But an earlier sign of this process is not the appearance of the lime, but of patches of a yellow, fatlike substance. It is no ordinary fat but a fatty chemical structure, cholesterol, so called because it was discovered in the bile, as well as in the stones of the gall bladder.

A hundred years after it was first described, two German chemists, Windaus and Wieland, discovered that cholesterol was the ancestor of a whole family of substances that play an important role in the chemistry of the body. The best-known members of the family, besides cholesterol, are ergosterol, the mother of the vitamin D that the skin produces under the influence of sunlight, and the sex hormones, testosterone for the male and estrogen for the female—the latter being the mother of medicines designed to control the menstrual cycle and pregnancy.

Early in the 1950's it became fashionable to assign to cholesterol the part of villain in the aging of the arteries. During the 19th century, when

(Facing page) Torn blood vessels. When torn, the elastic walls of small arteries can automatically seal themselves. In (1) and (2) blood is escaping but the cut or torn end is beginning to close. In (3) and (4) the closure is complete and blood loss has been stopped.

(Below) Injured artery. At the point of injury blood coagulates in a thrombus, or clot, inside and outside the vessel. The clot contains red and white blood cells and platelets and is interwoven with fibrin fibers.

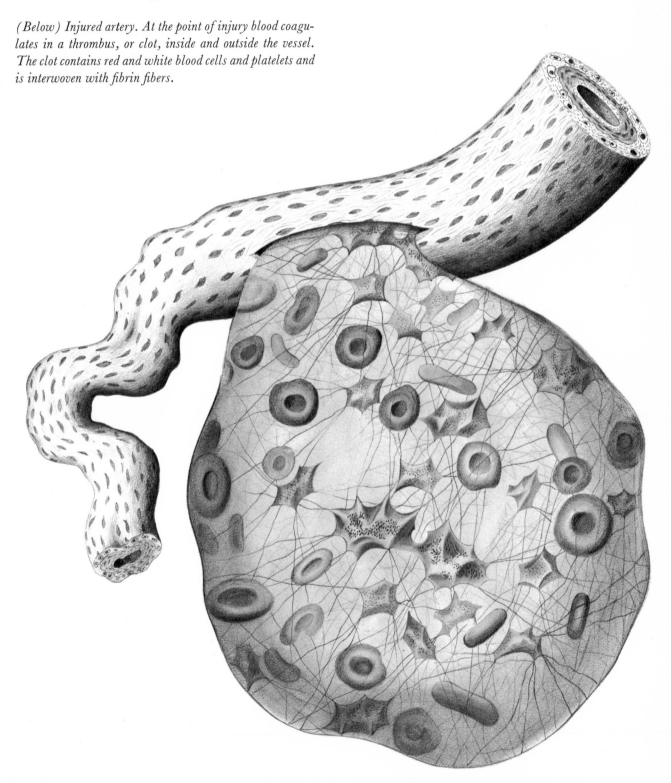

arteriosclerosis was first recognized as containing chalk, or calcium, deposited in the walls of the arteries, physicians warned their patients to avoid milk, strawberries, spinach, and other foods rich in calcium. The advice was pointless because the lime on the walls of the blood vessels comes not from milk or other foods, but from the calcium normally and necessarily present in our blood and tissues. It is therefore fair to say: Milk or no milk, aging arteries harden.

Now a new Medical Enemy No. 1 was detected. When it was found that the level of cholesterol in the blood stream rose as people entered their fifties and sixties, the cholesterol panic of the 1950's started. The public was warned against foods rich in "fats." As a result of more thorough investigation, it was found that there are saturated and unsaturated fats. The suspected fats are the saturated ones, prominent in animal fats: milk, cream, cheese, butter, bacon and the fat of lamb and pork, while the unsaturated fats, coming from vegetable sources—soya beans, corn, margarine—and from fish were regarded as harmless.

The whole question of what foods contain saturated or unsaturated fats is now complicated by the fact that food processors may convert an unsaturated fat into a saturated fat or the other way around.

It is possible that the kind of fat we eat does have some bearing on the development of arteriosclerosis but this is unquestionably not the entire story. Complex physiological problems rarely can be solved by such simple solutions as avoiding calcium or fat. Such problems are as complex as life itself. A little thought suggests that arteries in aging persons tend to degenerate regardless of the intake of cholesterol or any other single kind of food.

Sclerosis of the arteries. As arteries age, the body reacts by depositing cholesterol in the artery walls and plastering them with lime. The walls become hard, or sclerotic, and less flexible, forcing the heart to work harder in pumping blood through the body.

12

The Heart

At the center of the circulatory system is a marvelous organ which collects the blood and pumps it throughout the body.

The main artery of the circulatory system, which travels from the heart down along the spinal column to the pelvis, is called the aorta. It is a thick tube, about two inches in diameter; its rupture ordinarily means instant death. The aorta forms a curve like a bishop's staff, and from its upper end issue three arteries: the innominate artery, the left common carotid and the left subclavian. The innominate divides into the right common carotid and the right subclavian. The carotid arteries conduct blood to the head and brain; the subclavian to the arms (color portfolio plates 6 and 7). At the other end, inside the pelvis, the aorta branches out finally into the two arteries of the legs, the femorals.

Embryologically, the blood vessel that formed the aorta also formed the heart. The vessel thickened and twisted into a knot similar to that of a man's tie. The heart, like the brain, is a complex organ and the best way to study it is to buy an animal heart in a butcher shop and dissect it.

The modern science of the study of the heart started at the end of the 18th century with the development of two examining procedures, percussion and auscultation. In percussion the investigator puts the middle finger of the left hand against the thorax and taps it with the middle finger of the right hand. If the finger is resting over the lung, the sound of a normal, air-filled lung has a resonance like a violoncello. If the finger is over the heart, the sound is short and dull. After years of training, an expert can determine the outline of the heart and detect whether it is normal, small or enlarged.

The second procedure, auscultation, is generally performed with a stethoscope by listening to the flow of the blood through the different chambers and valves of the heart. The beginner hears only confusing noises, but the experts have developed a whole vocabulary of vivid expressions to describe what they hear. The four valves of the heart have a characteristic sound in closing and the expert can tell whether they are closing and opening properly, whether the heart is strong or weak, and whether it is pumping regularly or spasmodically.

The Heart Valves

The heart (color portfolio plate 10) is composed of two halves (called the right and the left heart) and

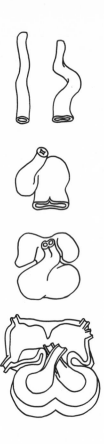

(Left) Formation of the heart. The heart develops out of a blood vessel that also forms the aorta, main artery of the circulatory system. The vessel bends first into a U-shaped loop, then into an S shape and finally into the heart shape. On each side of the double pump of the heart there is an atrium on top and a ventricle below.

The blood flows through the right pump of the heart in four stages. (From left to right) It arrives through the vena cava and fills the atrium. It passes through the atrio-ventricular valve into the ventricle. The ventricle contracts and closes the atrio-ventricular valve while the blood pushes through the semilunar valve into the artery leading to the lung. Blood does not flow back from the artery into the ventricle when the ventricle relaxes because the weight of the blood closes the semilunar valve.

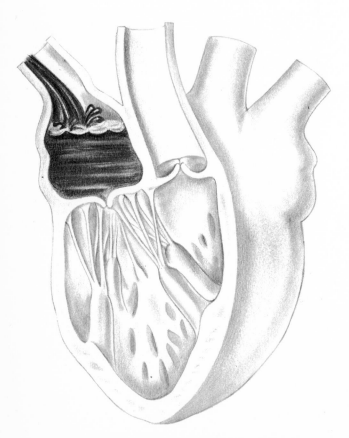

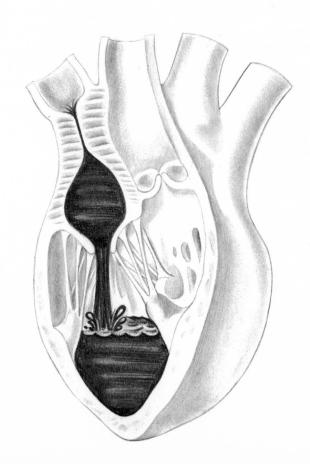

each half consists of a small upper room, the atrium, and a large lower room, the ventricle. The incoming blood fills the atrium, and then the atrium contracts. This contraction helps open the valve into the ventricle and allows the blood to pass down into the ventricle. When the ventricle is filled, this main part of the heart contracts and causes the valve leading to the atrium to close so that the blood cannot flow back. At the same time, in the left heart, the valve that opens into the main artery, the aorta, is pushed open and the blood is pumped into it by the contraction. In the right heart, the valve leading to the pulmonary artery opens and blood flows to supply the lungs. When the contraction of the ventricles ends, the aortic and pulmonic valves close and the blood cannot flow backward into the heart. The whole process is repeated with each heart beat and this creates the rhythm of the pulse.

Heart Disorders

In a disease such as rheumatic fever, the valves of the heart become inflamed, and after the healing, scars may remain. This is called rheumatic heart disease. The valves become either too tight or too slack, and the heart must work harder in order to drive a normal amount of blood through the impaired system. After inflammation, the valves may break down entirely or the scars may narrow the passage seriously. After years of practice a heart specialist can give an astonishingly detailed description of the condition of disturbed valves.

The Heart Nerves

The heart is supplied with nerves from the autonomic nervous system, a part of the nervous system

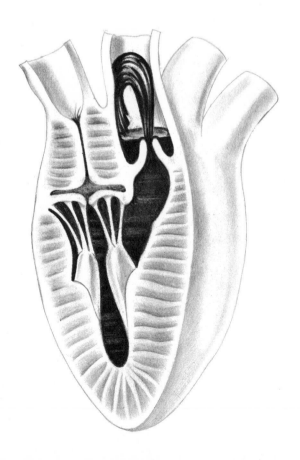
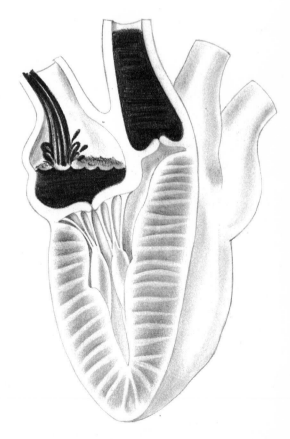

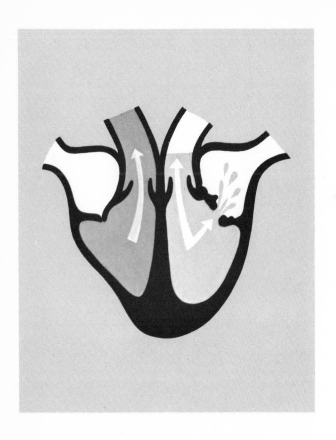 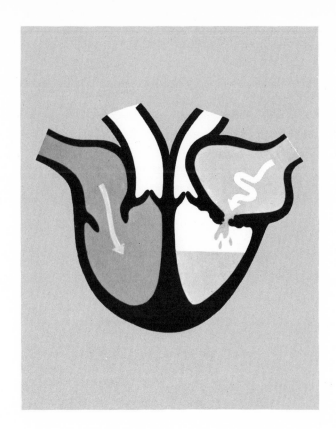

that is not voluntarily controlled. The vagal nerve slows the heart rate while the sympathetic nerves speed it up. But the heart muscle has a basic rate of automatic contraction. Thus when a turtle's heart is cut free from its body and placed in a salt solution, the heart will continue to contract on its own.

The heart muscle is a striped muscle but unlike a voluntary striped muscle, in which the fibers are separate from one another, the heart muscle fibers form a continuous network. The contraction of the heart muscle sets up a relatively large electric current in the body and it is this electric current that is measured and recorded by means of an electro-cardiograph.

More than any other organ the heart is, as we all know, influenced by nervous irritants. That is why the heart is—erroneously—regarded in all religions and literatures as the center of feeling. If a heart is irregular in its rhythms and thus the source of disturbing sensations, we call it a "nervous heart." In at least half of all cases, the root of complaints

Heart valve defects. When heart valves become inflamed and develop scars they may be unable to open or close completely. At the left, the atrio-ventricular valve on the left side of the heart (the mitral valve) cannot close completely, so that when the left ventricle contracts, blood is ejected into the aorta but some blood leaks back through the mitral valve into the left atrium. At the right, scarring of the mitral valve prevents it from opening fully, so that the atrium is not completely emptied and the ventricle not completely filled.

(Facing page) Examining the heart. In percussion (above) the doctor places the middle finger of one hand against the chest and taps it with the middle finger of the other hand. The sound thus evoked can tell him, for example, whether the heart is enlarged. In auscultation (below) the doctor listens with a stethoscope to the sound of the valves to determine whether they are opening and closing properly.

about the heart are emotional, psychological or psychosomatic and it is the task of a competent doctor to distinguish between the organic and the nervous or psychic disorders.

The New Heart Therapy

The right and left heart, each containing an atrium and a ventricle, are separated by a wall. The right heart receives the blood from the veins of the body and since this blood has given up its oxygen to the tissues, it is unoxygenated or "blue" blood. The right ventricle pumps this blood to the arteries and capillaries of the lungs where the blood becomes oxygenated and is returned through veins to the atrium of the left heart. The left ventricle then pumps this oxygenated blood into the aorta which, through branches, supplies the blood to the entire body with the exception of the lungs.

If there is a hole in the wall separating the left heart from the right heart, whether in the wall of the atrium or of the ventricle, unoxygenated and oxygenated blood may become mixed in the left ventricle. Or the large vessels leading to and from the heart, the arteries and veins, can become transposed. If both of these irregularities of development occur in the fetus, a "blue" baby can be born. Heart surgeons today can repair a hole in the wall of the heart, relieve the effects of the transposition of the blood vessels, and thus save lives.

Heart surgeons can also correct valvular abnormalities. Indeed, artificial valves made up of synthetic materials like Teflon can be sewn into place after removal of defective valves. Much of this has been made possible by modern anesthesia and the use of heart-lung machines.

The Pulse

With every contraction the heart sends, say, a cupful of blood into the aorta. This wave of blood is palpable as a pulsation traveling along the arteries away from the heart and becoming weaker as it moves along. If we take the pulse first at a point on the throat next to the larynx, which is near the heart, we can easily feel the big carotid arteries pulsing strongly. Normally the pulse is taken on

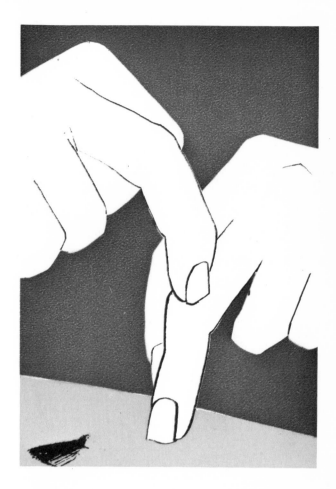

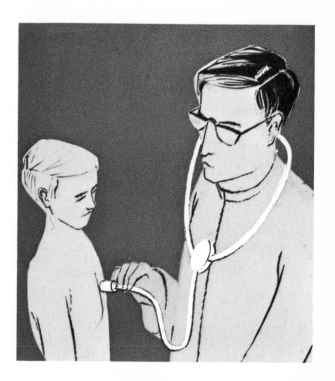

127

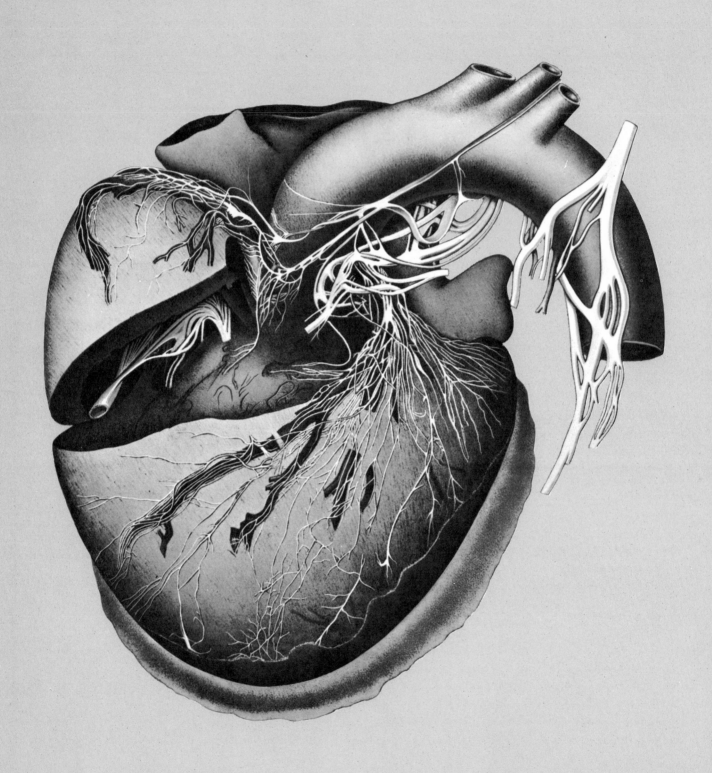

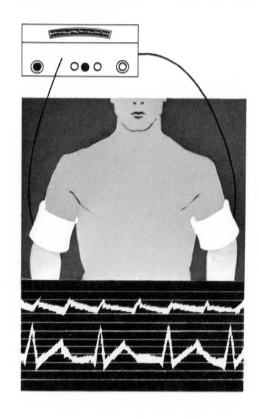

(Left) The nerves of the heart are part of the autonomic nervous system, which operates involuntarily. The heart rate is accelerated by the sympathetic nerves and slowed down by the vagal nerve.

(Right) Measuring the heart beat. Every heart beat sends out electric impulses that can be registered by an electro-cardiograph. An electrocardiogram reveals abnormalities in the heart beat that can help in detecting, for example, an injured heart muscle as in a coronary occlusion.

The heart-lung apparatus permits the heart and lungs to cease functioning while the machine oxygenates the blood and pumps it through the body. It makes possible such operations as closing a hole in the heart wall or the replacement of a valve.

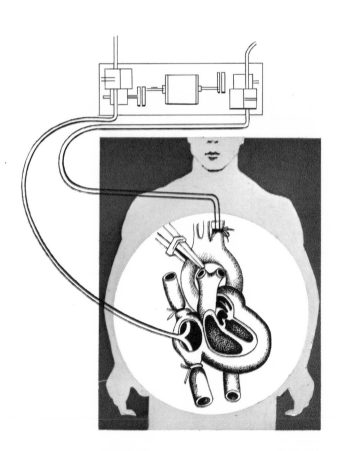

the thumb side of the wrist, where the radial artery of the forearm is easily accessible. A physician who takes the pulse of many patients daily becomes adept at detecting the slightest irregularities in the heart beat. To see how the heart reacts to strain he may also check the pulse after the patient has done some physical exercise.

The number of pulsations per minute depends on many factors. Small animals such as sparrows have a pulse of two hundred a minute. The heart of a newborn child beats one hundred and fifty times a minute but the rhythm of the normal adult pulse at rest is between sixty and eighty beats per minute. The heart beats more rapidly by day than by night. After meals it works harder to provide blood for the gastrointestinal tract. In heart disease it may be necessary to rest in bed with light meals taken at relatively short intervals. Also important is an atmosphere free of tension or excitement.

13

Blood

Passing constantly through the body, the blood feeds all cells, helps defend them and carries off waste.

It is an astonishing fact that seventy per cent of the human body is made up of fluids. Five per cent of our body weight consists of the fluid in the blood—the blood plasma. Fifteen per cent consists of the fluid present around the cells in all our organs—the interstitial fluid. And fifty per cent consists of the fluid present within the cells themselves. We go through life as if we were aquaria and our cells tiny water animals. Millions of millions of blood cells and hundreds of millions of white cells live in the blood. All the other cells—of muscle, nerve, liver, intestinal tract, glands and so forth—live in the fluids outside the blood vessels.

The blood cells remain in the blood vessels, but the fluid wherein they swim seeps through the walls of fine capillaries in the form of a yellowish water, lymph or plasma. It is lymph that seeps out of wounds and blisters, and out of the nose on cold days; it is the general body fluid.

The Electrolytes of the Body Fluid

The body fluid or lymph contains the same four salts as the sea—sodium, calcium, potassium, and magnesium—and in strikingly similar proportions. It differs from sea water particularly in the amount of magnesium it contains. There is something romantic in the idea of sea water flowing through our veins; it is small wonder, then, that the theory of man's descent from marine creatures has been propounded repeatedly. It may perhaps be said that fish were our ancestors, but it must not be thought that these aquatic ancestors were like present-day fish. They were, if anything, primitive creatures of long extinct types. It is also doubtful whether they lived in the oceans. Saltwater fish of today seem to have descended not from primordial saltwater species but from freshwater fish; in their embryonic stage they begin life with the kidneys of freshwater organisms, as if their ancestors had been inhabitants of fresh water.

Fluids containing salts are called electrolytes because they are good conductors of electricity. Our body fluids are electrolytes, and therefore all biological processes are accompanied by electric currents. The heart emits with every beat an electrical impulse that can be recorded as an electrocardiogram. The brain also produces currents that can

Blood crystals. Plasma holds all the constituents of blood (except for the red and white blood cells) in solution. If a drop of plasma is dried out, a host of crystals remain from the various substances in solution.

be registered as an encephalogram; and if we used sufficiently sensitive instruments we could record electrical currents from all our organs. The registering of these currents have become important in identifying disorders.

The Lymph System

While the red blood cells normally do not leave their vessels, the lymph seeps through the capillaries and thence through the tissues. It then collects in small vessels, called lymph vessels (color portfolio plates 13, 14 and 23), and returns through special tubes back into the blood stream. Although color plate 14, for example, may seem astonishingly detailed, there are in reality thirty times as many lymph vessels as are shown in the drawing.

A part of the fluid of the body surrounds the central nervous system, which is suspended in it as in a water bed. It represents one of the strangest formations in the human body and is similar to lymph. Tiny knots of veins called the choroid

131

plexus hang from the roof of part of the brain and filter fluid into cavities called the brain ventricles. The fluid drips from the ceiling of the ventricle like water from the roof of a mountain cave and trickles down as the cerebro-spinal lymph that protects the brain and spinal cord from concussions and mechanical injury.

The Lymph Glands

Compared to the blood the lymph is not rich in cells, but neither is it a characterless fluid. It slowly carries the lymph cells (identical with the cells known as phagocytes) to the lymph glands. These glands, or nodes, consist of aggregations of proliferating young lymph cells. As they ripen, some of them migrate, like young birds or fish leaving the nest, and go off with the lymph stream. The lymph nodes are as numerous as drinking places in big cities; at every turn there is a node. If a man becomes ill from an infection, the lymph nodes, normally unobtrusive, swell and are therefore called lymph glands. Most lymph glands are tiny; but some, such as our tonsils, are quite large. The wall of the intestines is particularly rich in lymph nodes.

The Spleen

The largest lymphatic organ—about the size of a fist—is the spleen. Unlike other glands, the spleen has no secretory duct but discharges directly into the blood stream. Inside the spleen are sacs encircled by lymph tissue; lymph cells issue from this tissue and float away in the blood stream. The blood is sixty times richer in lymph cells when it leaves the spleen than when it enters it.

The true functions of the spleen and the lymph organs are not completely known. An anecdote attributed to the great anatomist Rudolph Virchow tells of a medical student who, upon being questioned about the function of the spleen, stammered: "I knew it quite well a few days ago, but I'm afraid I've forgotten it." Whereupon the professor exclaimed: "What a pity! Here at last was a fellow who knew why we have a spleen—and now he has forgotten it!" We do know that the spleen, besides providing lymph cells, helps regulate the blood

stream. When we run, the spleen fills with blood and may blow up. It is said that when the man who ran the twenty-five miles from the battlefield of Marathon to Athens to announce the Greek victory over the Persians had delivered his message, he clutched at his side in the area of the swollen spleen and collapsed.

As a rule, certain infections cause the spleen to "mobilize" the army of lymph cells and to enlarge. Therefore, the doctor who suspects his patient of having an infection, will almost automatically check whether the spleen is swollen. Such chronic infections as malaria, syphilis, or various tropical diseases usually cause a considerable enlargement of the spleen. The illustration on page 140 shows a tropical parasite, that of sleeping sickness, under a microscope, wriggling among the cells of human blood; the young lady from whom it came crept around with an enlarged spleen as if she had a huge child in her womb. After years of being overworked, a diseased spleen is sometimes found to be as much as twenty times as large as normal.

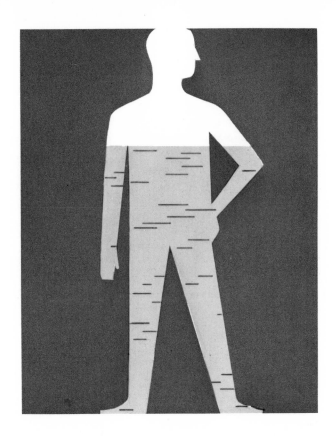

Body fluid and sea water. The blood plasma and the lymph outside the circulatory system are strikingly similar to sea water. They contain four salts, sodium, calcium, potassium and magnesium, in much the same concentrations as in the primordial seas in which life originated. Seventy per cent of our body weight consists of this saline fluid.

The Body and its Antibodies

Every creature tends to defend itself against the hostile outer world. If a foreign protein is introduced into the body, the body manufactures antibodies against it. Bacteria or viruses, for example, contain protein substances and when the body is infected, antibodies against the bacteria or viruses are manufactured by the lymphocytes in the lymph nodes. The spleen also plays a part in this defense mechanism.

Doctors can now help to create defenses against disease by deliberately injecting a weakened virus or bacteria into the body. The cells in the body's lymph nodes then manufacture antibodies against the disease agent; when enough antibodies have been manufactured we are immune to the disease.

The body's tendency to resist a foreign intruder poses a special problem to surgeons attempting to replace a diseased organ, such as a kidney, with an organ from a healthy donor. Unless the donor is an identical twin to the recipient, the latter's body begins manufacturing antibodies to the alien organ and, after a while rejects it. For this reason, when organ transplants are made, the patient is now given drugs to suppress his immunizing mechanism and prevent the lymphocytes from producing antibodies against the foreign organ.

Lymphocytes and Leucocytes

Now and then lymph cells float into the blood stream, sprout microscopic feet and arms and wander around like amoebae. The discovery of this movement of cells was made by the Russian biologist Metchnikoff, and won for him the first Nobel Prize in biology. He called the migrating lymph cells phagocytes, which means devouring cells. (When they float through the blood stream they are called leucocytes, or white blood cells, in contrast to the erythrocytes, the red blood cells.) These phagocytes pass through all the avenues of the tissues and lead a fantastic life. They act as the civil defense force of the cell community against all aggressors, and, wherever they are needed, as the street cleaners and the police. After every meal several million phagocytes leave the lymph nodes on the walls of the digestive tube to enter the intestinal tract to help, so to speak, unload the ship of food. Or when a splinter enters the skin, the phagocytes come in such hordes to combat the bacilli and to gather around the wound that the area swells. The phagocytes consume the bacilli and, filled with them, die. Pus, which is the aggregation of these dead phagocytes, flows out of the wound. Just as after a battle, the battlefield is devastated; then fresh phagocytes arrive to clean up the site and rebuild the tissues. Connective tissue cells manufacture collagen fibers, and if the wound is deep, special scar tissue closes the gap.

There is no tissue in the body which is so tightly woven that phagocytes cannot squeeze through it. They trickle with the urine from the kidneys into the bladder. They are secreted with male sperm and are found in the vaginal mucus and the menstrual discharges of women. They are discharged from the nostrils whenever someone blows his nose. Even after we are dead, a few phagocytes continue for hours to wander down the lifeless alleyways of the crumbling mansion of the body. The last to die is not the heart, but these wandering cells.

Bone Marrow

The birthplace of blood cells is the bone marrow, which is a gelatinous paste that fills the interior of the bones. If we collected all the bone marrow in the body we would have an organ as large as the liver and it would weigh about six and one half pounds; although we are not conscious of its work, it is an active agent in the body.

The cells of the bone marrow remain embryonic, that is, not specialized or differentiated. In the process of development they transform into red or white corpuscles. Some of them form blood platelets, others become osteoblasts, or builders of bone, and still others grow into giant cells that devour the worn-out blood corpuscles and utilize their material in the formation of new blood elements.

At the beginning of this century public attention was directed to the bone marrow by a startling increase in a malignant disease called leukemia, which is a form of cancer. In this disease, the affected marrow ceases to produce normal mature blood cells. Instead, abnormal leucocytes form; in the acute disease these multiply wildly and crowd out

the formation of red blood cells so that anemia develops. The abnormal leucocytes are spread by the blood stream to the lymph nodes, the liver and the spleen. The patient loses the ability to resist infection and develops bleeding tendencies. In acute leukemia, treatment is only temporarily successful, but in chronic leukemia the patient may live a long time.

The Red Blood Corpuscles

Just as the phagocyte is the characteristic cell of the lymph system, so the red corpuscle is the characteristic cell of the blood. The red blood cell possesses a nucleus only during its youth while it is still in the bone marrow. Afterward, this nucleus disappears and the blood cell loses its ability to act as a normal cell. It swims in the blood only for about 120 days and then must be replaced. The fertility of the bone marrow is incredible and the number of blood corpuscles is almost inconceivable: about twenty-five trillion of them float in the blood of the human body. To replace them over two million new blood corpuscles must be sent from the bone marrow—not every day or every minute, but every second! Bone marrow is undoubtedly the most productive tissue in the human body.

The red blood corpuscles are not only the most numerous cells in the body, but also among the smallest. Their smallness and elasticity permit them to pass through the capillaries. The most important function of these corpuscles is to bind oxygen from air inhaled into the lungs, convey it through the blood stream to the region of the capillaries, and release it there. Such creatures as the olm, a salamander living in underground caverns and leading a relatively inactive existence, have little need for oxygen. Their blood carries fairly large cells but there are something less than fifty thousand per cubic millimeter of them. The higher above sea level men live, the more numerous their blood corpuscles because they need more oxygen. Those who live at sea level have five million red corpuscles per cubic millimeter of blood, whereas the Incas or Tibetans, who dwell on very high mountains, have from seven to nine million per cubic millimeter. Small, very active mammals living at high altitudes, such as musk deer, have the largest number of blood cells and the smallest in size.

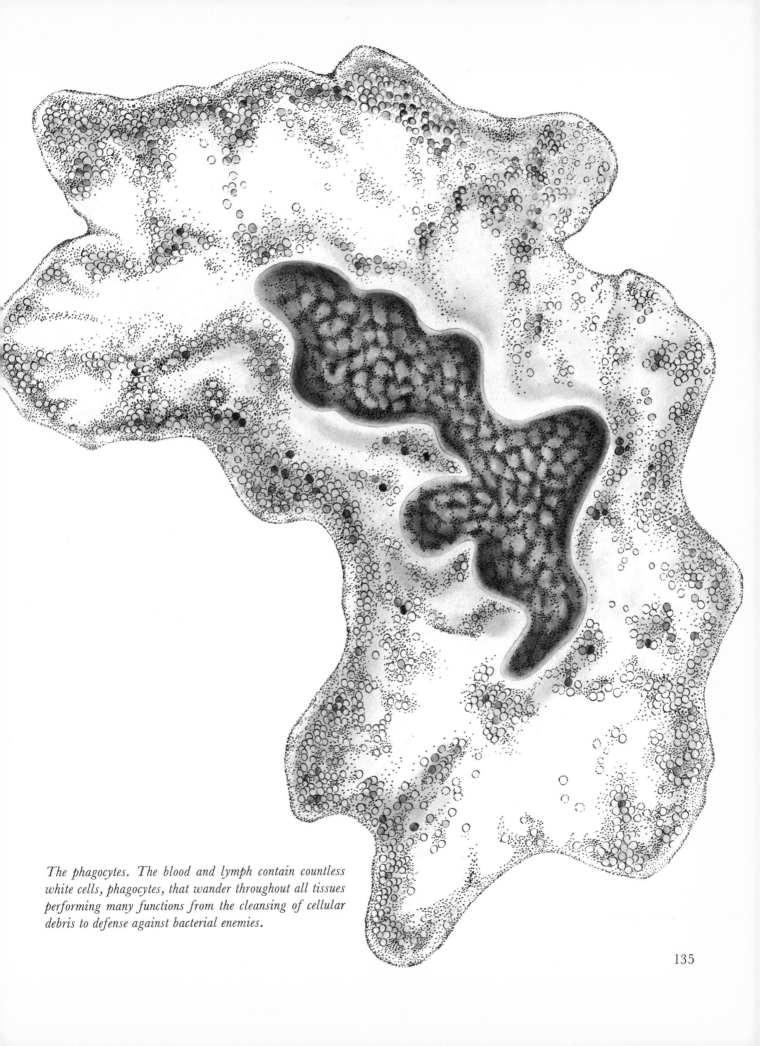

The phagocytes. The blood and lymph contain countless white cells, phagocytes, that wander throughout all tissues performing many functions from the cleansing of cellular debris to defense against bacterial enemies.

135

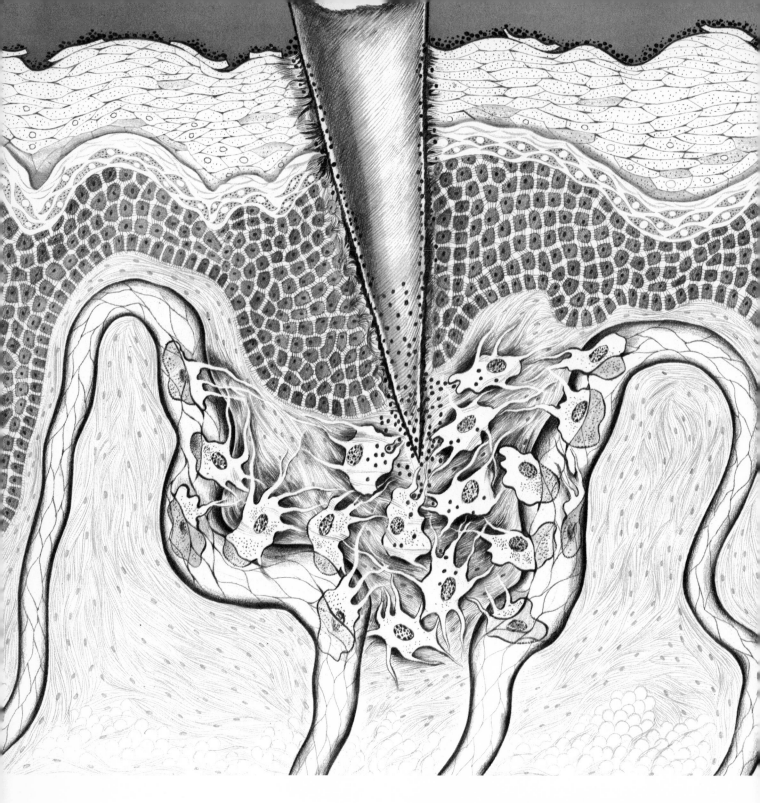

Phagocytes vs. bacteria. When a skin wound is invaded by bacteria the blood rushes phagocytes to fight the invaders. The influx of blood causes swelling and inflammation (*1*). Once the phagocytes consume the bacteria, they die and are forced from the wound as pus. Fresh phagocytes clean the area and begin repair work (*2*). If the wound is deep, collagen and other fibers supplied by connective tissue cells close the wound with scar tissue (*3*).

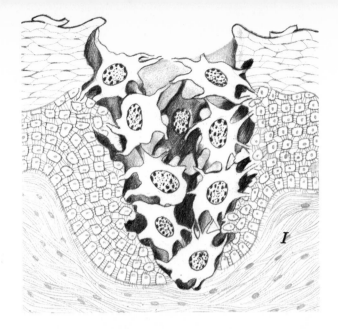

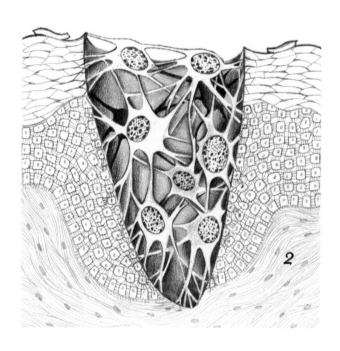

Hemoglobin, the Blood Coloring Matter

A blood corpuscle is a tiny balloon filled with a colored protein; it is called hemoglobin, meaning blood protein. The distinctive feature of the globin is its central iron atom, which is present amidst hundreds of amino acids and other complexes. According to modern theories the iron atom functions by means of electromagnetic forces. It oscillates millions of times a second, and is alternately magnetized and demagnetized in the course of these millions of oscillations. In tune with these oscillations, the hemoglobin constantly acquires and loses an ionic charge. Twenty-two trillion blood cells, each containing several million hemoglobin molecules, each of which contains an oscillating iron atom, charge and discharge ten million times a second—this is what we call "respiration."

Healthy blood with a normal content of iron has a cherry-red color. If iron is lacking, blood becomes pale. In such cases it helps to eat such iron-rich foods as egg yolks and meat, and vegetables, such as salads, are also helpful as blood-building material.

Air is a mixture of about eighty per cent nitrogen and twenty per cent oxygen. Hemoglobin is an ideal oxygen carrier, conveying fifty times as much oxygen as can be carried in an equal amount of sea water. In the two seconds during which the blood traverses the capillary region, the oxygen escapes from the blood cells and into the tissues. With the departure of the oxygen, the hemoglobin loses its bright red color and takes on the bluish color of venous blood as the red cell picks up carbon dioxide. While flowing through the lungs, venous blood gives up its carbon dioxide and absorbs new oxygen from freshly inhaled air. This happens for one hundred and twenty days—the life span of a blood cell, during which it travels about one hundred miles in the circulatory system.

Blood Clotting

In addition to the red and white corpuscles, the blood contains a third group of extremely small, polygonal bodies called platelets, a fifteenth the size of the red corpuscles. These are borne by "giant cells" of the bone marrow, the megakaryocytes,

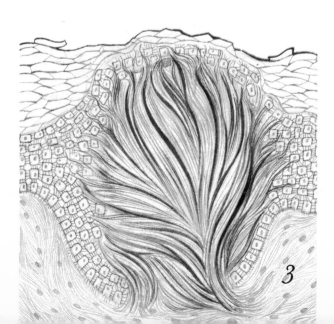

137

which scatter them like a flower does its pollen. The mission of the platelets is to help clot the blood in case of need; but the clotting must take place only in case of need, and therefore a complex series of safeguards is set up against unwanted clotting. First of all when a vessel is injured, platelets stick to one another and to the edge of the injury, forming a platelet plug and sealing the gap.

The platelets are like matches; they do not act until we rub them against a rough surface. The moment it is stimulated, a platelet produces an enzyme, or enzymes, and releases it into the surrounding blood plasma. One of these is probably a thromboplastic enzyme that helps transform a substance floating in the blood, prothrombin, into thrombin. But thrombin is still not the substance that encourages clotting; what is needed is a material resembling cotton fibers and called fibrin. Since it would hinder the free flow of blood, this fibrin does not appear as such in the blood stream. It remains

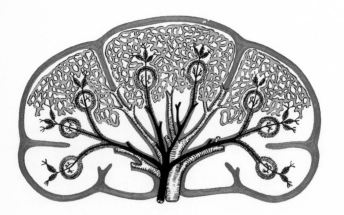

(Above) Following a 16th-century practice, the artist Dürer sent this drawing to show that his ailment was located in the spleen.

(Left) The spleen, largest organ of the lymph system, supplies the blood with lymph cells. It also serves for defense in a generalized infection, as a storage place for red blood cells, and as the source of iron for new red blood cells formed in the bone marrow.

(Right) Arterial blood (1) entering the spleen; (2 and 3) being distributed through it; (4) returning to the veins.

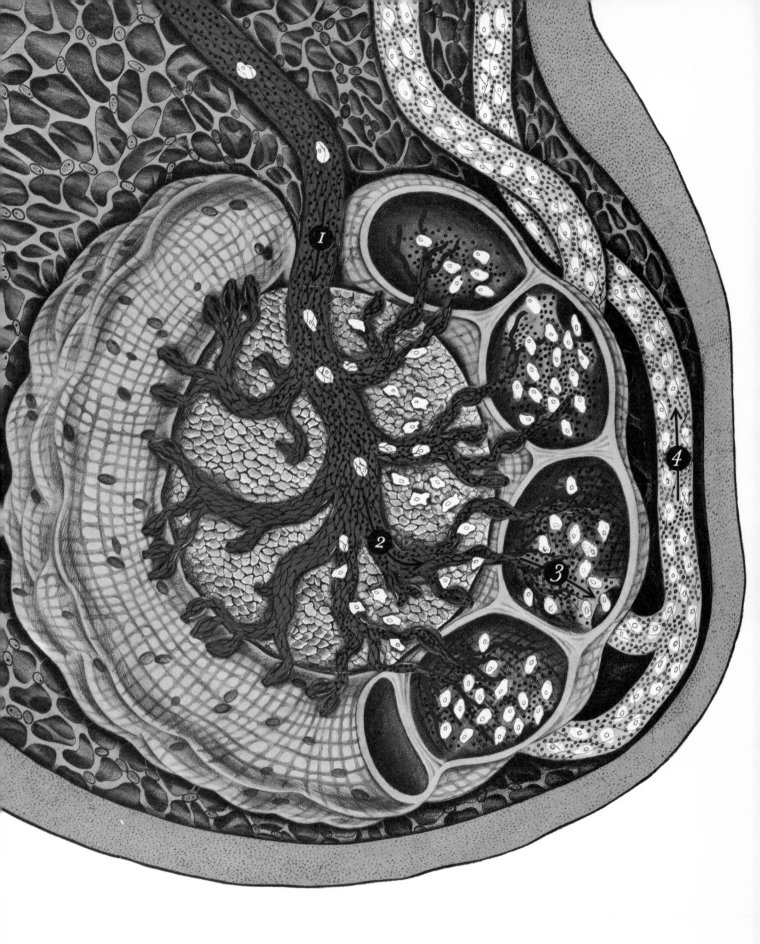

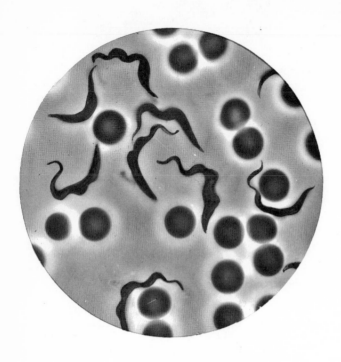

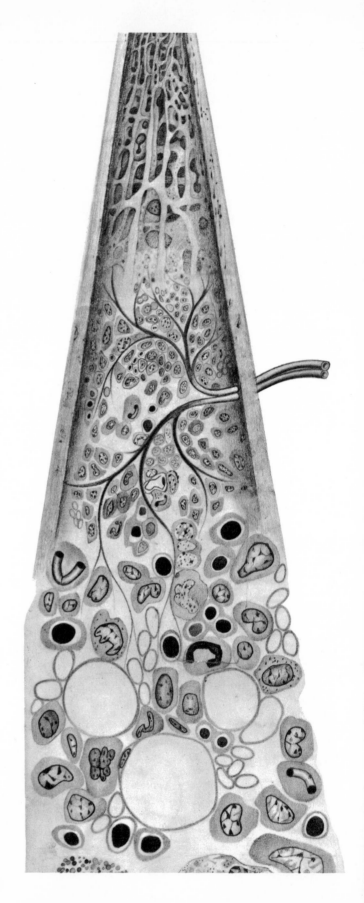

The parasites in the blood that cause sleeping sickness are spindle-shaped organisms transmitted by the bite of an insect such as the tsetse fly.

(Right) Bone marrow contains parent cells that have an amazing capacity to replace millions of blood cells—such as leucocytes, lymphocytes and white blood cells—at every instant.

(Facing page) The approximately twenty-five trillion corpuscles floating in the blood far outnumber any other cells in the human body.

140

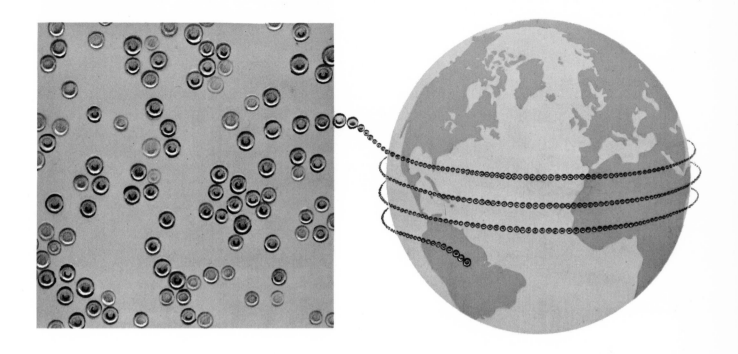

in an invisible soluble form called fibrinogen until the platelet-prothrombin-thrombin sequence has been completed. It sounds complicated but is no more so, in its way, than the procedure of lighting a cigarette.

Thrombosis and Embolism

The blood clot that closes the crack in the wall of a blood vessel or sometimes shuts off the whole vessel is called a thrombus; the occurrence itself is a thrombosis. If the thrombus or a part of it is then carried away by the blood stream and comes to a narrow place in the vessel, it may clog the vessel and stop the blood stream. The area beyond the stoppage is like a city district when the water main has been shut off. The movement of a thrombus and the stoppage in a vessel is called an embolism.

A thrombosis usually strikes elderly people because the blood no longer streams with the vigor of youth. Furthermore, the artery walls have been roughened by arteriosclerosis so that the platelets

adhere and may start the clotting sequence that will culminate in a thrombosis. A thrombus in a coronary artery supplying blood to heart muscle is the main cause of heart attacks. Brain attacks known as apoplexy, or a stroke, are due to a thrombus in a blood vessel supplying the brain.

Blood Groups

Among the many discoveries in the year 1900 was the identification of various "blood groups." The Viennese pathologist Landsteiner found that there are four types of red blood cells in human beings, and he labeled them type A, type B, type AB and type 0. A little over forty per cent of all human beings carry the substance A in their red blood cells, ten per cent the substance B, and three per cent the substances A and B; about forty-five per cent carry neither A nor B and are therefore labeled 0. It was also found that the blood plasma may contain antibodies to substances A and B which cause the red blood cells containing substance A or B to clump

together. Invariably type A blood contains anti-B but no anti-A, or else the individual's own red blood cells would clump together. Type B blood contains anti-A but no anti-B. Type AB blood contains neither anti-A nor anti-B while type 0 blood contains both anti-A and anti-B.

The ideal donor for a transfusion should be in the same blood group as the person receiving the blood. If a type A patient received a transfusion from a type B donor, all the donated red blood cells would be clumped by the anti-B antibodies in the patient's plasma and a severe reaction or even death could follow. A patient whose blood is of group AB can receive a transfusion from donors of group A, group B and group AB since the patient has no antibodies to clump the red blood cells from any of these donors.

Individuals of group 0 blood can be universal donors since their red blood cells do not contain either substance A or substance B. But it is best that the donor have exactly the same blood group as the recipient.

The Rhesus Factor

When Landsteiner extended his research to monkeys he found that human red blood cells contain still another substance, which he called the Rhesus factor because he first discovered it in the blood of a small Rhesus monkey. It is found in the blood of all Indians and Mongols, but in only ninety-two per cent of American Negroes and eighty-five per cent of Caucasians. Blood containing the factor is called Rh-positive; if the factor is absent, the blood is Rh-negative.

It is dangerous to give repeated transfusions from Rh-positive donors to an Rh-negative recipient. The Rh-negative recipient begins to manufacture antibodies to the Rhesus factor and soon there are enough anti-Rh antibodies to clump the donated red blood cells and cause a reaction.

If an Rh-negative woman is married to an Rh-positive man, she may have an Rh-positive baby. If some of the red blood cells of the fetus leak through the placenta into the mother's circulation, the mother will develop anti-Rh antibodies. This is usually not serious in the first pregnancy in which it occurs. But after several such pregnancies, the

Since the red blood corpuscles extract oxygen from inhaled air for use in the body tissues, their number varies in relation to altitude, increasing as the air becomes rarefied. The olm, living in caverns and having little need for oxygen, has large but few blood cells—less than fifty thousand per cubic millimeter. Men at sea level have five million corpuscles per cubic millimeter, while dwellers on high mountains have from seven to nine million. Small, active mammals living at high altitudes have the most and the smallest blood cells.

mother may have developed enough anti-Rh antibodies to endanger the fetus. If the baby's life is endangered at birth it is possible to drain the baby's blood and replace it with healthy blood.

The Rhesus factor is also very helpful in determining the paternity of a child. When a mother is Rh-negative while the child is Rh-positive, the father must have been Rh-positive. Charlie Chaplin once associated with a young woman who became pregnant and sued him, charging he was the father of her child. The child could not have been his because blood tests showed that its blood was Rh-positive, whereas Chaplin's blood as well as the mother's was Rh-negative.

Hemophilia, or Bleeders' Disease

We know that certain deficiencies and diseases are hereditary, but we do not really know which of the forty-six chromosomes carries the pathological factor. Apparently some hereditary traits are, moreover, distributed over several chromosomes.

We also know something about the smallest pair of chromosomes, the X and Y chromosomes, because they transmit the factors that determine the sex of a child. In rare cases, one of the X chromosomes of the mother transmits a defect in the blood-clotting mechanism called hemophilia. But the defect usually becomes evident only in boys, because girls get two X chromosomes, one from the mother and one from the father, and the father's healthy X chromosome is always dominant over the mother's defective one. The boy, however, has only one X chromosome and one Y. In his case the single hemophiliac X chromosomes causes trouble. A hemophiliac boy may die young, bleeding to death even from as minor a cause as bleeding gums.

It is extremely unlikely that hemophilia will appear as a mutation in a hitherto healthy family. However, such a mutation possibly did occur in the British royal family in the 19th century. No case of bleeding had been known in the family before Queen Victoria's time but two of her daughters, who became the wives of European monarchs, each had a son who was a bleeder. This pathetic situation became the sensation of the time, because one boy was heir to the throne of Russia and the other to that of Spain. The most famous specialists were summoned to the royal palaces in Moscow and Madrid to attend the little princes and although both boys came safely through their school years, neither of them lived to ascend the throne—one dying of the disease and the other desperately ill when assassinated during the Russian Revolution.

Today it is known that hemophiliacs lack a substance in the blood called antihemophiliac factor and that this deficiency is responsible for the bleeding tendency. Transfusions of fresh blood or plasma from normal donors will stop the bleeding, or the factor itself may be injected into a vein of the bleeding hemophiliac.

14

Respiration

The nose, windpipe and lungs not only combine to supply the body with oxygen but help to produce the human voice.

The respiratory apparatus is specialized to the intake of air. Fish simply pass water through gills where the red blood cells in fine blood vessels pick up the oxygen. The terrestrial vertebrates developed a special air filter, the nose, while the old gills, no longer used, became hormonal organs such as the thyroid, the thymus, and the pituitary gland.

In the human body, the upper part of the embryonic digestive tube divides into two parallel pipes, one for air, the windpipe, and the other for food, the esophagus or gullet (color portfolio plate 5). The respiratory apparatus itself consists of three main parts: an upper part, the nose, which serves to condition the air as it is taken in, a middle part, the larynx, which is used to produce sounds, and a lower part, the lungs, which regulates the exchange of the incoming oxygen with the outgoing carbon dioxide.

The Nose

The nose is far more elaborate than is evident from without. It is like the palazzi of Italy; on the outside they appear to be modest but when the traveler enters them, he finds them filled with striking and admirable features. The nose is a deep cavity with labyrinthine passages and many side caves. In passing through this passage and its caves the air is subjected to a sevenfold control and conditioning.

1. *Dust filtering*. First the air passes a screen of thick hairs inside the entrance to the nose.

2. *Wet cleaning*. After the dry cleaning the air passes the labyrinth of the conchae, or turbinates, that divide the sides of the nose into groovelike passages. The inner walls of the nose are wet and are covered with cells that produce an adhesive mucus. Dust particles in the inhaled air are caught by the mucus, sticking to it like flies to flypaper.

3. *Air heating*. The walls of the long passageways inside the nose are rich in blood vessels and are as warm as the walls of a steam bath. By the time the air reaches the lungs its temperature is equal to that of the body.

4. *Humidification*. The wet walls humidify the passing air.

The respiratory apparatus:
1. frontal sinus
2. nasal cavity and conchae
3. base of tongue
4. pharynx
5. larynx or voice box
6. trachea
7. bronchial tubes
8. chest wall
9. bronchioles, ending in
   the alveoli, where
   air exchange takes place.

5. *Purification*. The nose helps purify the air before it reaches the lungs by trapping bacteria in the sticky mucus. Breathing through the nose is therefore a moderate protection against infection.

6. *Odor detection*. Another function of the nose is odor detection. Located below the roof of the nasal cavity are the fine fibers and receptors of the olfactory nerve, which transmit odor sensations to the brain.

7. *Sound resonating*. The nose also serves as a resonating structure in the production of sound.

Colds, Sinusitis and Catarrh

When the mucous lining of the nose cavity becomes infected we call the condition a cold, scientifically termed rhinitis. The cause may be a bacillus or a virus—not one specific virus but a host of viruses, including at least thirty different types. The cold is generally a mild infection, with symptoms well known to us all: it starts with an inflammation of the mucous membrane, a clogging of the air passage, and a swelling of the entrances to the sinus cavities.

The cavern of the nose is surrounded by side cavities, the sinuses, which have openings into the grooves formed by the conchae.

The entrances to these sinuses are normally open; if they close and the air cannot pass freely we have a feeling of being plugged or stoppered. The ability to hear, smell and consequently taste is impaired. The swollen sinuses feel "heavy" and painful and may cause sinus headaches. Sometimes the infection may reach the ear and, especially in children, cause an inflammation. Sometimes, too, the infected glands of the mucous membrane will produce a purulent secretion that collects inside the sinus or in the cavity of the middle ear and it becomes necessary to tap the sinuses or an ear. Although the physician today has a whole arsenal of medicines at his disposal, from aspirin and the antibiotics to cortisone and the antihistamines, the control of colds and sinusitis is not a simple one. The enemy is not one single parasite but a whole Maffia of viruses. These may also be supported by various "guerillas." And as soon as certain aggressors are checked others may become active.

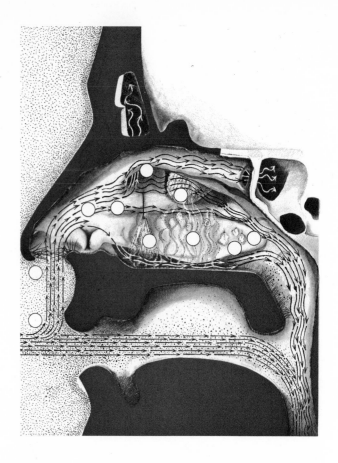

The nose. In passing through the nose, air is filtered by the hairs inside the entrance, cleansed of particles by the mucus, warmed by the blood vessels and humidified by the wet walls of the passageway.

(Right) The ciliated epithelium. The inside of the trachea is lined with epithelium whose hairlike cilia move particles of dust or other material out of the tube and back into the nose and mouth. (Dr. J. A. G. Rhodin, from his Atlas of Ultrastructure, W. B. Saunders Company, 1963)

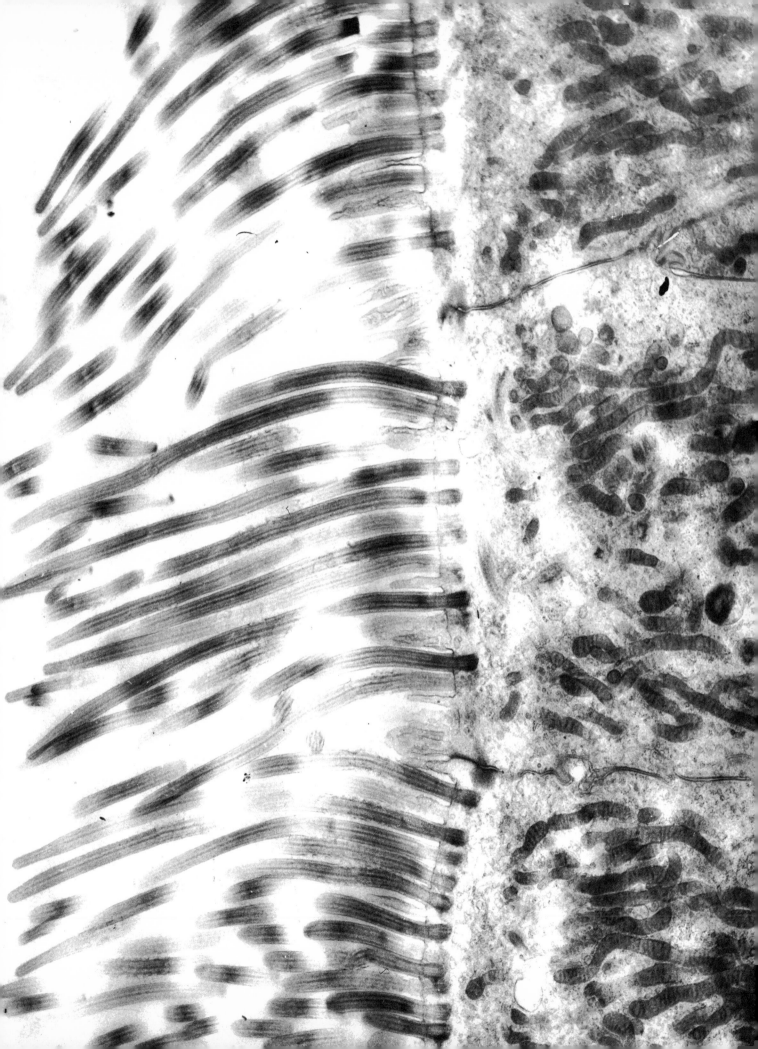

The Ciliated Epithelium

The inside of the respiratory tube is covered with a lining of so-called ciliated epithelium. This consists of cylindrical cells covered with hairs, or cilia. The hairs wave rhythmically like ears of corn in the wind, their motion brushing microscopic particles of dust upward out of the respiratory tube and back up into the nose. The ciliated epithelium is a carpet sweeper that works day and night without a pause. In microscopic organisms that live in water ciliated tissue serves for locomotion. In the higher animals this tissue is replaced by muscle fiber; in the human body it survives in the respiratory tract and the tubes of the female sex apparatus, where it moves the egg cell along the oviduct.

Seen through a microscope, the waving motion of ciliated epithelium is an impressive sight. If we place a piece of lining from the throat or windpipe of a freshly-killed frog under the microscope we can see the cornfield of the ciliated epithelium in motion. We have only to take care that the epithelium does not lose its humidity and warmth. If we blow a few grains of coal dust or any other light matter on it we can watch them being transported. They will seem to creep along and will eventually move out of sight.

The Larynx

The larynx is a musical instrument hanging in the frame of the windpipe. It can be seen and felt on the outside of the throat of the male but generally not on the female; it is called the Adam's apple because it is said to have appeared when Adam tried to swallow the apple Eve offered him. The larynx is the largest piece of cartilage in the human body.

The opening to the larynx is just behind the tongue and is called the glottis. A flap of cartilage is attached to the root of the tongue just above the glottis; it is called the epiglottis. This is a most necessary device because the food tube lies directly behind the respiratory tube and when we swallow food there is the ever-present danger that it may slip into the respiratory tube and choke us. But nature has taken measures to prevent that. When we swallow food or drink the epiglottis closes tightly over the glottis and food can then enter only the

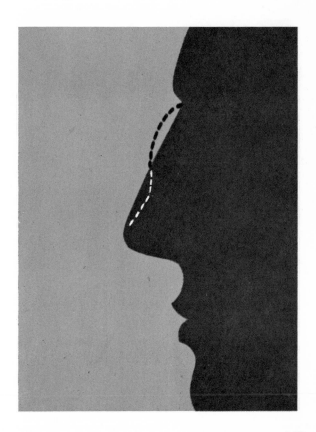

(Left) Inside the nose. Hairs inside the nose screen incoming air. Ciliated cells line the cavities, and simple goblet-shaped cells secrete mucus. In the foreground is a more complicated mucus-secreting gland.

Plastic surgery cosmetically realigns a nose by removing the bony hump and reshaping cartilage. A deviated septum, which may obstruct nasal breathing, is usually straightened during such an operation.

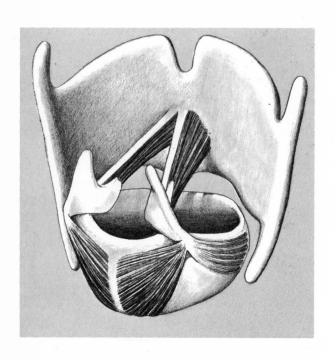

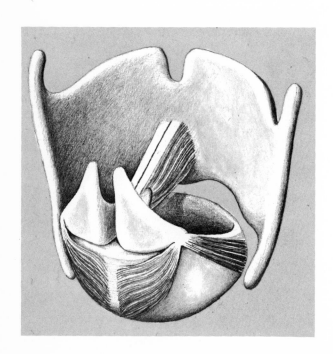

(Left) The larynx. The two vocal cords of the larynx, the most elaborate cartilaginous organ of the body, are slack in quiet breathing (above) so that air is inhaled and exhaled without sound. In speech the cords tighten (below), and as air passes through, the cords vibrate and sound is produced.

(Right) When we breathe in, the diaphragm expands downward and the ribs move out so that the chest cavity increases in capacity and the lungs fill with air. When we breathe out, the diaphragm rises and the ribs close in, reducing the chest cavity. The lungs, becoming compressed, expel air.

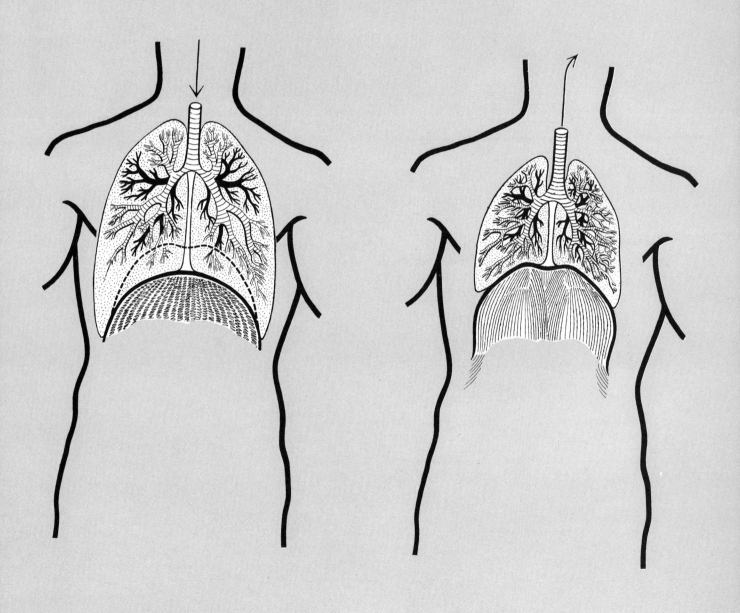

oo

oh

ah

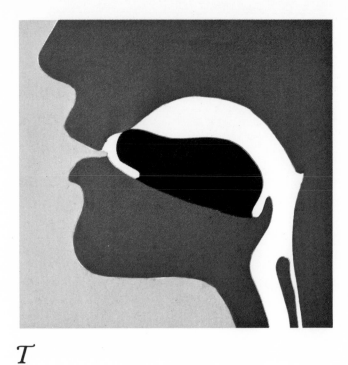

T

The voice. Shown above is the role of the tongue in producing the consonants "t," "l" and hard "g."

(Left) Sounds are produced by vibration of the vocal cords, but the special sounds of speech result from the concerted action of lips, tongue, nose and teeth. In forming vowels the lips are almost closed for the "oo" sound, are rounded for the "oh," and are open wide for the "ah."

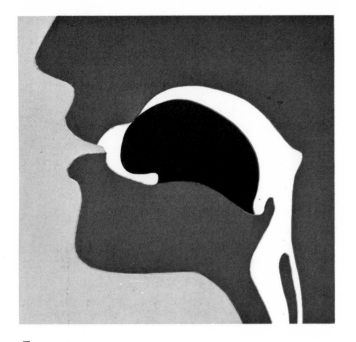

L

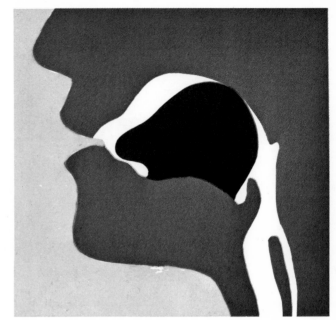

G

esophagus. We all know the coughing and choking we experience when food or drink goes down the wrong pipe and how we are relieved only when we have coughed up the errant mass.

Two folds of tissue called the vocal cords lie across the glottis. When air is drawn through the windpipe and these vibrate, they do so like the tongues of a trumpet. The movement is regulated by two pyramids of cartilage which, under the control of small muscles, turn on an axis like the steering wheel of an automobile. When the cartilages bring the vocal cords close together, the air passage becomes so narrow that the air current sets the cords vibrating. The larynx does not produce song or speech; it is only a trumpet. Song and speech are the result of the use of the trumpet together with a whole orchestra of other instruments—lips and tongue, diaphragm and nose—and the control exercised by our hearing and brain.

The Lungs

The heart and lungs fill the thoracic cavity. Descending from the top is the trachea, popularly called the windpipe, encased in strong cartilaginous rings so that it will neither collapse nor be strained by hard breathing. As the windpipe descends, it branches out like the trunk of a tree and the inhaled air is distributed through two hundred million tiny tubes that bulge at the tips like minute balloons on their stems. Each "balloon" is covered by a network of capillaries; gases pass through its incredibly thin walls by diffusion. From the blood the carbon dioxide, the residue of metabolism, seeps out into the air pipes of the lungs, and at the same time the oxygen of the inhaled air diffuses into the blood. This exchange of gases is a relatively simple one but it is essential to breathing.

In inhaling, the diaphragm is drawn downward and the ribs outward, allowing the lungs to expand like a bellows and suck in air. In exhaling, the diaphragm relaxes and moves upward, the walls of the thorax press inward on the lungs, and air is expelled.

The relation of the air spaces in the body to the heavier parts is interestingly demonstrated when we float in water. The specific gravity of the arms and legs is greater than that of the water and therefore these parts tend to sink, while the air-filled lungs and the gas-filled intestines keep the trunk above water. The head is kept from sinking more than half way by the air-filled nasal cavities and the sinuses.

15

Digestion

The vital process of reducing foodstuffs to chemical units that can be absorbed by the body is performed by a system consisting of mouth, stomach and intestines.

The digestive system (color portfolio plates 15–21) performs the essential task of breaking up food into its chemical building units, otherwise food cannot be absorbed through the intestinal wall and pass into the blood and lymph of the body. Foodstuffs must first be broken down into their basic molecular units—the "bricks"—and from these bricks the body must build up its tissues.

Nutrition is the importing of material that is suitable for growth and development during infancy and childhood as well as for energy and for replacing the tissue we use up in the daily life processes.

Digestion is the chemical separation of the complex molecules of food into the simple ones that can be absorbed. Next comes assimilation, in which these simple molecules are recombined into new and more complex molecules—molecules that can form the body of an athlete who can run a mile in less than four minutes, or the brain of a Shakespeare capable of fashioning an immortal Hamlet. The proteins of the hen's embryo, which we call an egg, digested and then assimilated, are transformed into the cells of a brain capable of human feeling and thought. Yesterday a plant in the field, today food on the table, tomorrow human energy—this is digestion!

The Three Basic Foodstuffs

Carbohydrates. This is the chemical term for the bulk of our food: bread, flour, cake, cereals, rice, potatoes, sugar. Its molecule is composed of carbon (C), hydrogen (H) and oxygen (O). The most common carbohydrate is $C_6H_{12}O_6$, which is glucose or fructose. This is the sugar that plants compose out of air and water. After building up glucose, the plant combines the sugar molecules into more complex carbohydrates, forming the starches, which we eat as cereals or flour. Later, the plant combines the molecules of the starches into more highly developed units called cellulose. Paper and wood are forms of cellulose. Since the human digestive system is incapable of breaking cellulose down to simple sugars, cellulose cannot be absorbed. The carbohydrates are sources of energy, providing fuel for the body machine.

Proteins. These are the basic material for building up protoplasm, the material of living substance.

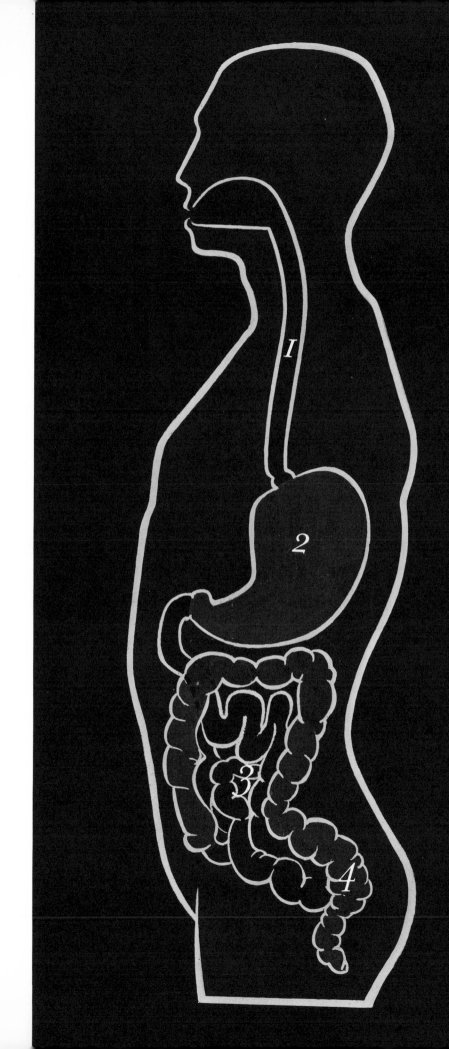

The principle parts
of the digestive tract:
1. the mouth and esophagus
2. stomach
3. small intestine
4. large intestine

We might even speak of the body as a machine built of protein protoplasm and driven by the combustion of sugars and fats. Chemically, proteins are formidable chains of amino acids. There are more than one hundred amino acids known to occur in nature, but only about twenty-three of these join in forming protein chains and twenty are important for human proteins.

These chains are not simple. The first correct analysis of a protein took the English chemist Sanger and his collaborators about ten years—and the protein was a relatively simple one, the hormone known as insulin. Insulin is composed of two parallel chains of amino acids held together by two atoms of sulfur. Metallic atoms as bridges that connect elements are apparently typical of the atomic structure of hormones. The first part of the investigation was directed toward finding out which amino acids were participating in the formation of insulin. This was tedious work in which calculation, imagination, patience, and, of course, luck each played a part and led finally to the solution. After insulin, other protein chains were analyzed; and so began the new science of protein analysis. The beginning of this investigation can be dated, but not the end, for the number of possible proteins is without limit. The possible combinations of amino acids goes into the billions and trillions, like the possible combinations of pieces in a chess game.

The American chemist Linus Pauling has estimated that the human body manufactures from fifty thousand to one hundred thousand different protein molecules. One example is the hemoglobin molecule which is made up of ten thousand atoms. And as we have seen, this must be constantly manufactured to replace the hemoglobin molecules of red cells that are constantly being used up. This, among countless other examples, is why we must have proteins daily just to keep up with the body's demands.

Fats. Fats are compounds of one molecule of glycerol and three molecules of fatty acids. The fatty acids consist of long rows of atoms, so that the breakdown of the molecule releases the considerable amount of energy contained in the bonds between atoms. Thus the body can use fat as a kind of high octane fuel. Its high energy value makes it good for a time of hunger, for winter storage and for cold seasons. In the fall the animal about to

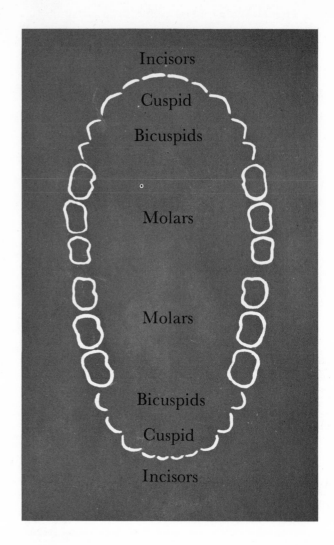

(Above) The teeth of the upper and lower jaws. The incisors are adapted for cutting; the cuspids, or canines, are adapted for holding and the bicuspids and molars are adapted for grinding.

The teeth. Embryologically teeth are products of the skin rather than of the skeleton. They are nourished by (1) arteries in the soft connective tissue core, or (2) pulp, which also contains nerve fibers. The pulp is covered by two hard layers: (3) the dentine which is a modified bony mass, and outside this (4) the enamel, an extremely resistant armor. A cavity results when the enamel and dentine layers wear away.

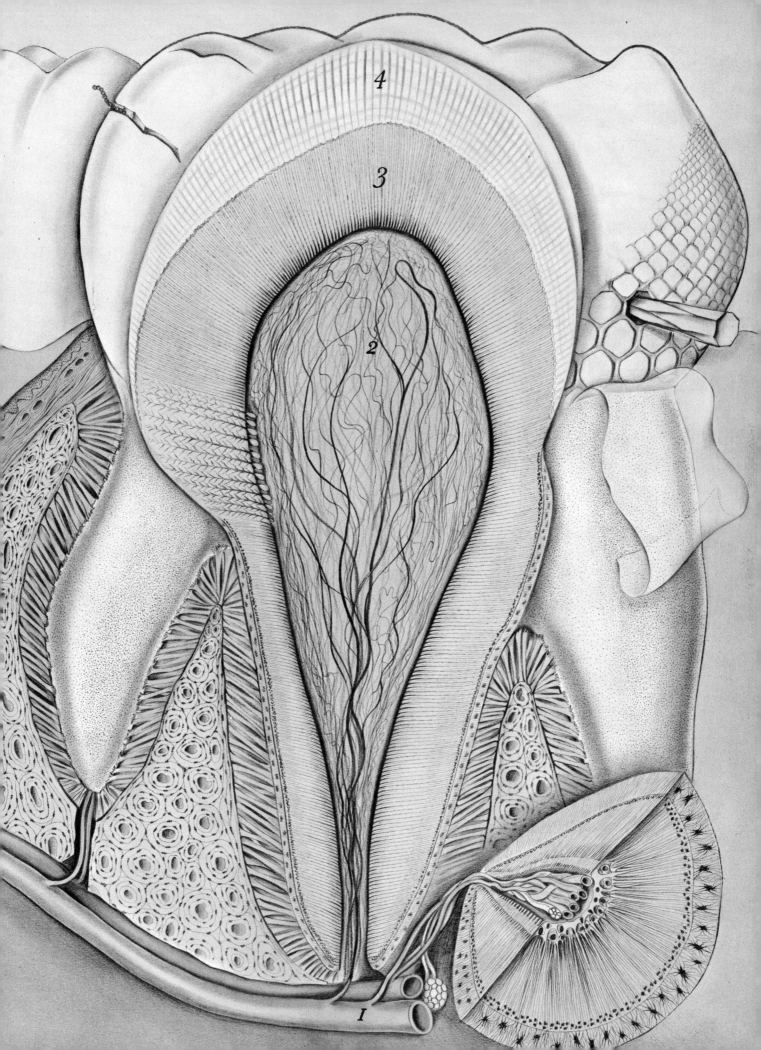

hibernate collects fatty grains and nuts. Burning slowly but intensely, like candles, whicn are also made of fat, the fats yield more than double the energy of equal weights of carbohydrates and proteins. Sugars are a quick-burning "instant" fuel; fats are a slow-burning high octane fuel; proteins are the builders of protoplasm.

The Function of the Mouth

The mouth performs five functions:

1. *Collecting food.* The mouth collects food in preparation for the act of swallowing.
2. *Salivation.* The mucous membrane of the mouth is padded with hundreds of tiny glands that take part in producing a slimy juice, the saliva, which converts food into a doughy mass that can be kneaded by the digestive system.
3. *Mastication.* The teeth grind the food.
4. *Bolus formation.* The moistened and ground mass of food is formed into a bite, or bolus, that can be swallowed.
5. *Starch digestion.* The saliva contains enzymes that start the chemical digestion of starches.

At six locations in the mouth there are especially large salivary glands. The two largest, the parotids, are located in the cheeks just in front and under the ear. During childhood almost everyone develops a virus infection of these glands and gets a case of parotitis, called mumps. The infection lasts only a few days and thereafter the individual is generally immune to this affliction.

A second, smaller pair of glands is situated between the lower jaw and the tongue (the submaxillary glands) and a third pair under the tongue on the floor of the mouth (the sublingual glands). The three pairs of glands have ducts opening into the mouth and produce most of the saliva. These salivary glands also secrete an enzyme called amylase that begins attacking the molecules of starch present in food.

The saliva does more than moisten the food and provide an enzyme for starch digestion. We taste food only because chemicals in it go into solution and can then stimulate the taste buds in the mouth. Speech and swallowing are possible only because of the moistening and lubricating action of the saliva on the surfaces of the mouth and pharynx.

(Right) The surface of the tongue is covered with hundreds of tiny projections, called papillae, which contain taste buds. Mucus-secreting glands open into the furrows between the papillae.

(Below) The tongue mixes food ground by the teeth and forms it into a mass that can easily be swallowed.

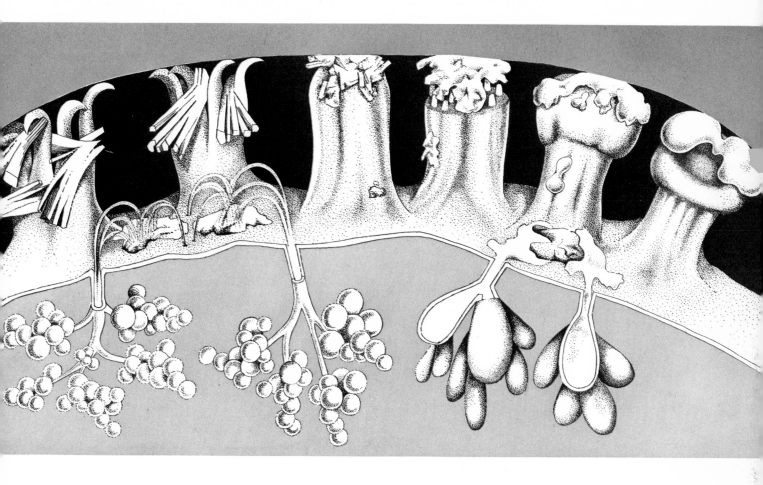

The saliva also serves as a cleansing agent for the mouth and its contents and helps reduce the growth of bacteria.

The glands continuously secrete saliva, enough to keep the mouth moist. When we eat, the amount is markedly increased. Even when someone thinks of food, his mouth waters; this is called a "conditioned reflex." The Russian physiologist Pavlov became famous for his work on such reflexes and based many of his experiments on the action of the salivary glands. A well-known experiment was one in which he trained a dog to expect food after a bell was rung. Soon the dog would salivate automatically when the bell was rung, even though food was not forthcoming. Conversely, Pavlov showed that he could terminate this conditioned reflex by repeatedly denying food to the dog after the bell had been rung.

Such work, together with the psychiatric investigations of Sigmund Freud, led to the development of psychosomatic medicine, the appreciation of the reactions of the organs of the body to psychological stimuli. An awareness of the relationship of the body to psychological reactions is of course very old: the Bible, Homer and Shakespeare all have it. But psychosomatic medicine and psychoanalysis have made a science of it.

The Teeth

The mouth also has two other instruments to compress the food into a package that can be swallowed by the throat: teeth and tongue.

Although the teeth look and feel as though they were bones and thus part of the skeleton, they are in fact, like nails and hair, products of the original embryonic layer which formed the skin. Historically, they are the equivalent of the scales of fish. Among the most primitive of present-day fishes are the sharks: their scales and our teeth are basically identical. Teeth consist of a soft core of connective tissue, the pulp, which is rich in blood vessels that nourish the teeth and contain nerve fibers, and a

159

hard cover composed of two layers of tissue. The inner layer is the dentine, a bonelike mass. When this dentine is worn through, the tooth becomes sensitive and a "cavity" results. When the decay reaches the pulp, the invading bacteria feeding on the pulp cause acute pain and if the dentist can no longer fill the cavity, he may have to extract the tooth. He may burn out the pulp, whereupon the tooth is no longer nourished by the body and becomes a lifeless shell.

The dentine of the tooth is capped by a layer of calcium salt crystals, the enamel. Enamel is the hardest of all tissues in the body. It sometimes takes lifelong use—and abuse—without wearing out. The lower part of the tooth, called the root, is held tight in the jaw bone by strong fibers, and it goes down deep to a nourishing blood vessel. Fish grow and discard teeth in limitless numbers, just as we do our hair. However, higher vertebrates, such as man, develop only two sets of teeth: the "milk" teeth of childhood, which are replaced only once, during the years of growth. There are twenty "milk" teeth in a child and thirty-two "permanent" teeth in an adult. The incisor teeth bite and cut, the canine teeth hold, and the premolars and molars grind.

The Tongue

The tongue is an organ whose primary use is for mixing and combining the foods we eat. It is basically a muscle; and an operatic singer who sings the six hundred and fifty syllables of the "champagne aria" in thirty-five seconds, as José d'Andrado did, or a Demosthenes who trains his voice by putting a pebble in his mouth and then making himself heard above the thundering of the surf, has developed this organ into the finest musical instrument. Buy a few slices of smoked tongue and admire the intricacy of their muscle fibers. The fibers run not only from the tip to the base but also from side to side, and others vertically, up and down. The whole organ is fixed to a muscular cushion whose fibers fan out symmetrically. The undersurface of the tongue is attached to the floor of the mouth by a fold of tissue. When this is unusually short a person is said to be "tongue-tied" and has difficulty in speaking. In such a case a physician may cut the tie in childhood.

The tongue has, moreover, about a thousand

The esophagus. Food leaving the mouth moves down the esophagus in peristaltic waves. The esophagus is like a collapsible pipe that expands to accommodate food (upper) and contracts just above the food (lower) in order to push it down.

(Right above) The pancreas. This long gland lying across the posterior abdominal wall secretes digestive juices containing enzymes that break down proteins, starches and fats. The pancreas also secretes a hormone, insulin, into the blood stream.

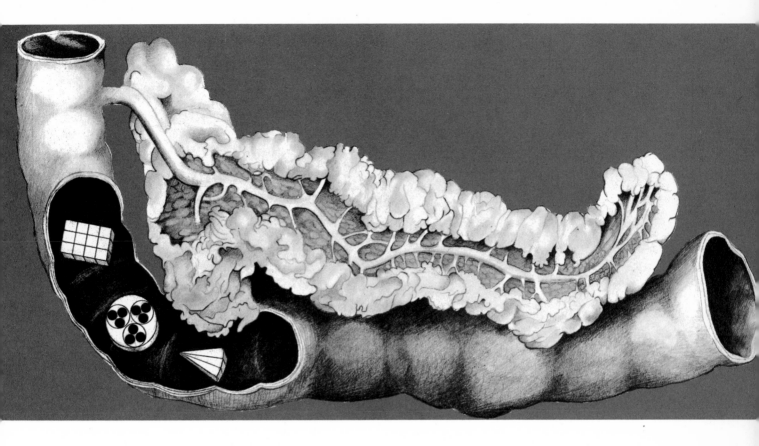

taste bulbs set on the end of countless nerves. It is not easy to decide whether the diaphragm or the tongue deserves the prize as the most perfect construction of muscle.

The Throat

After the food taken into the mouth has been sufficiently moistened with saliva, ground up by the teeth, and formed by tongue and cheeks into a shape that can be swallowed, we push this nutritive cartridge, called a bolus, down our throat and start it on its journey through the intestinal tract. At first the bolus must pass a dangerous crossing—the opening of the trachea, or windpipe. It passes the movable bridge known as the epiglottis. Thereafter the bite moves down through the gullet. It does not fall freely but is thrust along by peristaltic waves until it reaches the stomach. The entrance into the stomach is normally kept closed through the tension of the sphincter muscle that rings the opening. The ring relaxes long enough to let the bolus of food pass through.

The Stomach

The stomach is a sac woven from muscle fibers and lined with a mucous membrane containing glands that produce a digestive juice. Like the mouth, the stomach works mechanically through its muscle fibers and chemically through its glands. The muscle fibers exert a certain tension and a healthy stomach has a muscle tone of medium strength. If the muscle tone is too weak, the muscle fibers cannot withstand the weight of the food, the stomach sac stretches too far, and we have a condition known as gastroptosis.

The basic function of the stomach is the further moistening of the food, churning and grinding it and partly dissolving it in the gastric juice. A quart to a quart and a half of gastric juice, containing both hydrochloric acid and the protein-digesting

161

Digestion in the stomach. In (1) the stomach is empty and inactive. In (2) food has entered the stomach and together with air has formed a bubble. Some stomachs have a long, vertical shape (3) because of poor muscle tone. A powerful ring of muscle fibers, the pylorus, keeps the lower exit of the stomach closed. In (4) the pylorus has opened where small portions of food, acted upon by the gastric juice have reached it. The stomach is controlled by autonomic nerves so that anxiety and tension may lead to (5) a nervous stomach. Doctors are able to observe an ulcer in the stomach by inserting (6) a gastroscope, which has a lens system and a lighting device.

enzyme pepsin is formed each twenty-four hours. Pepsin acts only in the presence of an acid. Everyone knows how bitter the gastric juices are when they rise from the gullet into the mouth. The stomach glands are lined with two kinds of cells, those that produce the enzyme pepsin, and those that secrete hydrochloric acid. The production of the gastric juices is a complex process. Among other things, the stomach itself must be completely protected against being digested by its own juices.

The length of time that food stays in the stomach depends on the digestive powers of the stomach and the nature of the food as well as the volume and the acidity. Warm fluids tend to move through the stomach most easily and rapidly. Thus the first food we give an exhausted or starving person is of a kind that does not require a major digestive effort; for example, warm tea, warm milk, a clear broth. Cold food is less digestible. Fats require much more work than lean dishes; legumes such as peas, beans, and lentils are difficult to digest in comparison to spinach. There are timetables that show the time required by different foods, ranging from a few

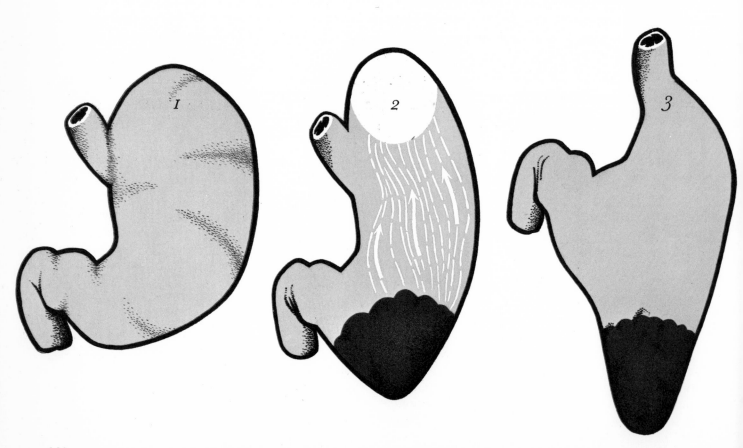

minutes for a broth to the twenty hours for a fatty dish like goose.

After the food is ready to be transported further, it moves along a row of folds called the "stomach road." The lower exit of the stomach is automatically kept closed by a powerful ring of muscle fibers, the pylorus—another sphincter. It was once believed that this ring opened by a chemical reaction when the food has been sufficiently saturated with the acid of the gastric juices. It is now thought that the pylorus opens as soon as the food in the stomach becomes fluid enough to pass through. There is little absorption of food or water through the stomach. That takes place lower down in the alimentary canal.

The protection against the stomach digesting itself probably depends upon the layer of mucus coating the stomach surface and also on its blood supply. When these fail, self-digestion does take place and a peptic ulcer forms, the pepsin having digested the protoplasm of the cellular wall. When the ulcer forms in the stomach itself, it is called a gastric ulcer. When it forms just beyond the stomach

in the part of the small intestine called the duodenum, it is a duodenal ulcer.

The Small Intestine

After passing out of the stomach exit in small portions, the food enters the intestine, which is a tube almost thirty feet long; the first section of this is narrow and is called the small intestine (color portfolio plate 21) although it is much the longer section about twenty-five feet in length. The second and wider section of the tube is the large intestine (color portfolio plate 18). The intestine is a muscular tube and is lined, like the mouth, gullet and stomach, with a mucous membrane. A look at the intestines of a chicken will give you a good impression of its appearance. Despite the fact that the small intestine is confined in a tight space and that the loops intertwine and are in almost constant motion like a netful of eels, the loops manage not to become entangled.

Food must move from loop to loop deliberately

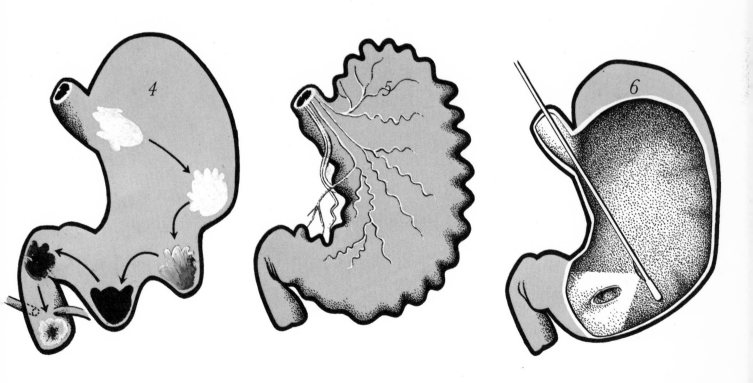

enough to allow it to undergo the process of being mixed and chemically decomposed. It may take hours before the food we took in has become a soup from which the molecules can be absorbed through the walls of the intestine. This absorption takes place through the villi, which are finger-like organs that line the inside of the intestine. There are about four million of these villi, each containing a network of arteries, veins, lymph vessels and nerves. Especially during the period of digestion they are in constant motion, like the fingers of sea anemones, dipping into the digestive broth, sucking up molecules from it, and making them part of the body. Yesterday salmon or meat or milk; today human blood and tissue!

The Duodenum

One part of the small intestine merits special attention. This is the initial curve, called the duodenum, which means simply "twelve," its length being roughly equal to the width of twelve fingers. It could much more appropriately be called "the horseshoe" because that is its shape and size. It is the most important segment of the intestine because there the three main glands of the digestive system, the stomach, liver and pancreas, empty their secretions for their attack on the three types of nutritional substances: starches, proteins, fats.

The action that takes place in the valley of the duodenum is like a battle. First the stomach sends forward its contents in peristaltic waves. Then this acid soup is neutralized by the products of the three duodenal forces: the microscopic glands of the duodenum itself and the two large glands at the sides of the intestinal tube, the pancreas and liver.

The Pancreas

The pancreas (color portfolio plate 22) is the most effective of the digestive glands. We might even assert that if a man's pancreas is functioning, he can live without the salivary glands of his mouth, or the glands of the stomach. No juice in the digestive system is so powerful or has such far-ranging effects. Its various enzymes break down the starches into glycogen, the glycogen into malt-

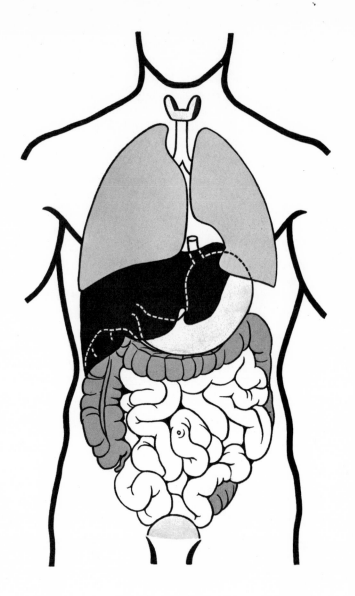

ose, and the maltose into glucose, which is the dollar bill in the commerce of the body. It breaks the proteins into their simpler parts: first into polypeptides, then peptides and even into amino acids—a tremendous task!—although most of the final formation into amino acids is done by enzymes coming from intestinal glands. In addition, the pancreatic juice contains an enzyme, pancreatic lipase that splits the complex molecules of the fats into glycerine and fatty acids. Finally, the tissue of the pancreas is interspersed with islets of a hormonal tissue, which produce insulin. Like all organs, the pancreas is protected against its own product. The human stomach digests the proteins of the food but it does not digest itself. Only in rare cases does the protective barrier within the pancreas break down and the gland dissolves itself; it melts and disappears like butter in a heated pan. In a few days the victim dies from necrosis of the pancreas.

The Liver

The liver is best understood if we start with the basic fact that it has several entirely different functions. The liver serves as a filter from the intestines upward toward the heart. All blood vessels from the intestines, constituting a thirty-foot pipe, concentrate in one central vein, the portal vein, and flow into the liver. Inside the liver this vein divides into millions of blood vessels among the liver cells.

Like the customs officials the liver cells swarm around the blood from the intestines and filter it. This blood contains the amino acids and the sugar derived from the proteins and the carbohydrates and the multitude of other ingredients of all the foods we take in. An exception is the fats, which go through the lymph vessels, not directly to the liver. The liver cells test all the "imports" and decide whether to admit or reject them. The liver becomes the storehouse of digested food. It also detoxifies them. And it is an enormous chemical factory for the metabolism of carbohydrate, protein and fat.

The liver also acts as a digestive gland, producing a digestive juice, the bile, which is important for digestion and absorption of fats. The bile drips through a fine hose into a sac, the gall bladder, which hangs on the underface of the liver. The gall bladder is not essential, and if it gives trouble it can

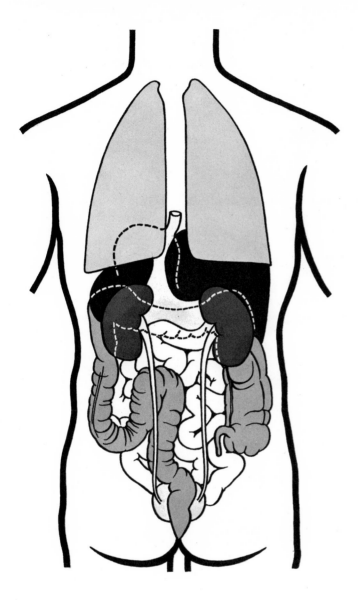

Intestines (front and rear views). After passing from the stomach, food enters the small intestine (in white), a narrow tube about twenty-five feet long, and then the large intestine or colon (in gray), which runs about five feet and ends at the rectum.

165

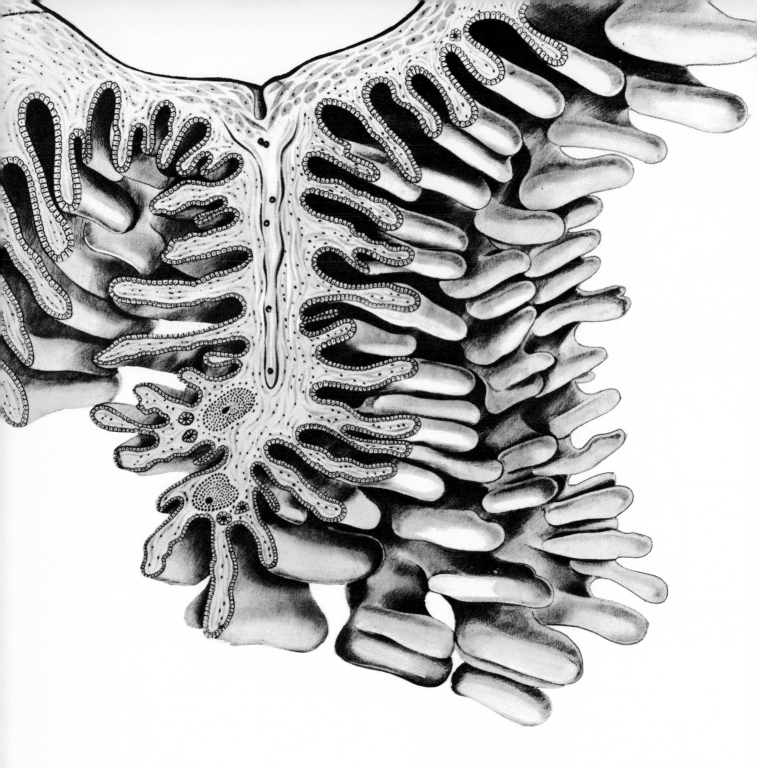

Villi, millions of fingerlike projections, waving to and fro on the inside of the small intestine, absorb the digestive broth.

be removed without harm to the patient. In some persons the bile remains in the gall bladder for hours and in time may form concretions or "stones," sometimes as tiny as diamonds, but sometimes as large as marbles. Like the petrified walls of the arteries, gall stones are a product of life and especially of age. We might almost say that all humans, if they live long enough, are condemned to gall stones. Autopsies reveal that of those who die at age thirty, one per cent have gall stones; at age fifty it is twenty per cent, and at sixty-five even more. Not every carrier of stones suffers. Most persons do not even know that they carry these dubious gems.

The Stages of Digestion

Our food passes through the following stages in the course of digestion:

1. The mouth mixes and chews the food and gulps it down in small masses.

2. Inside the stomach the food is permeated with gastric juices and becomes that sour and acid mixture we know from vomiting.

3. After passing through the stomach the churned and half-dissolved contents enter the duodenum, where it is saturated with bile and pancreatic secretions and becomes a greenish soupy mass called chyme.

4. As the chyme progresses slowly through the intestines, much of the water and fluid substances in it are absorbed; at the same time, water is added by the secretions of the intestinal glands. The nourishing components are slowly extracted and absorbed by the body.

5. In the last part of the digestive tract, the large intestine, there is much absorption of water and salts and the chyme becomes the semisolid mass we evacuate as excrement. Digestion is a stairway leading down from flight to flight and ending with the waste matter called feces.

The Large Intestine

The final section of the intestine is the colon; since its diameter is twice that of the small intestine, it is called the large intestine although it is only about five feet long. In contrast to the labyrinthine maze of the small intestines, the large intestine has a relatively fixed shape. It begins as the caecum and ends as the rectum, which conducts excrement through the anal opening and out of the body.

Where the small intestine meets the colon it forms a valve. Passing through this valve the chyme enters the caecum, a sac or blind pouch that is as wide as a fist. Projecting from its blind end is a worm-shaped finger-like tube called the appendix. The appendix serves no function in man although in lower animals it probably takes part in digestion. In man it often becomes infected, leading to appendicitis. The treatment is surgical and appendectomies are, along with tonsillectomies, probably the most common surgical operations today.

Inside the Colon

The digestive process from mouth to caecum is a series of enzymatic processes, breaking down the carbohydrates, fats and proteins. In the colon an entirely new process begins: the fermentation of the "indigestible" residue of food by microorganisms.

The first portion of the small intestine is practically sterile, that is, devoid of bacterial life. About twenty-five species of bacteria can live in the mouth of man, but most of them die when they pass into the acid juices of the stomach. With the movement of the chyme farther along the small intestine, bacteria begin to appear. At last, the residual chyme passes into the area of the colon, the waste-receiver of the body. There, bacteria in the form of microscopic fungi, yeast cells, and algae thrive undisturbed by acids and enzymes. Human feces is a semiliquid mixture of several hundred million microorganisms, with a negligible amount of undigested hulls of grains and other residues.

Here we come to an unsolved problem: Is there a purpose for these microorganisms in the colon? Metchnikoff, the discoverer of the wandering cells of the blood, declared that they were parasites of decay that thrive on the residues of our meals. He believed that they produced toxins or poisons that hasten the aging of the body and that mankind would be infinitely better off if we could get rid of them. Other biologists think that these microorganisms are not parasitic enemies but peaceful

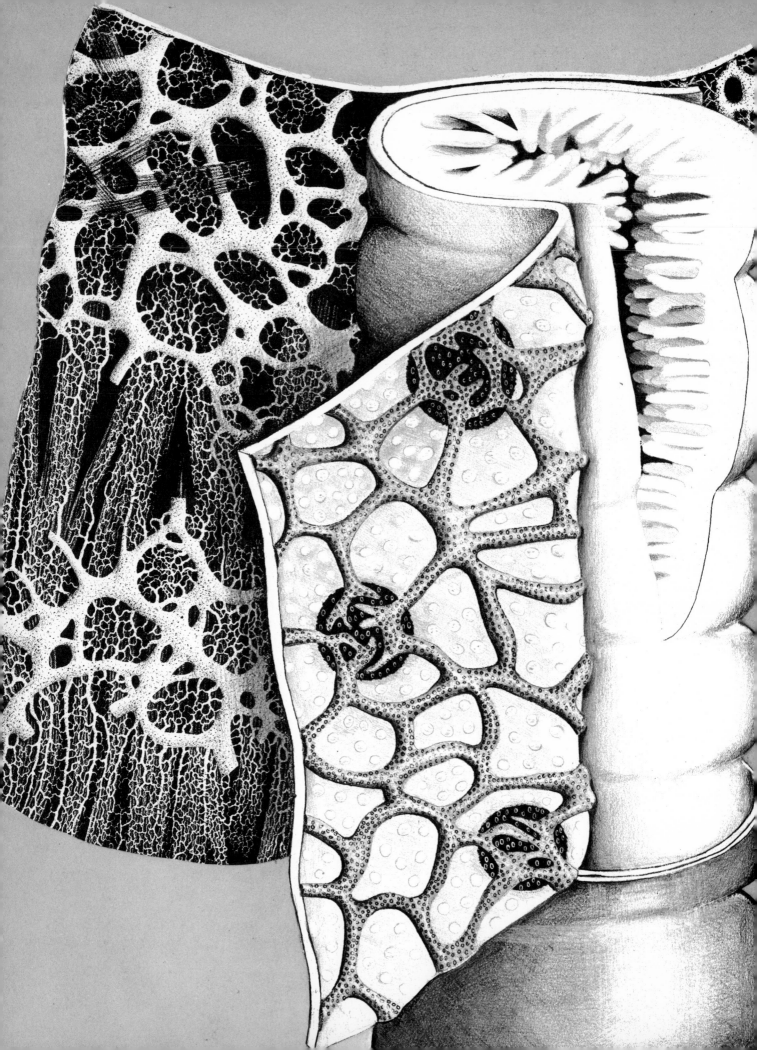

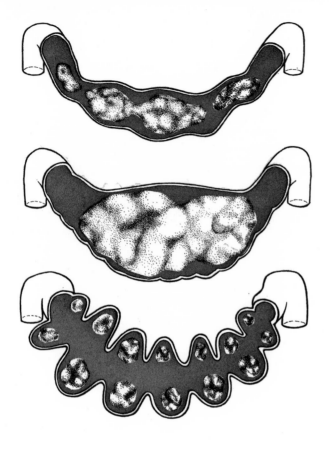

Constipation. Normally the large intestine pushes feces along to the rectum (top). In the sluggish condition known as atonic constipation (center) the large intestine does not react to the feces and retains them in the colon for several days. Hypertonic or spastic constipation (bottom) occurs when the intestinal tract reacts violently, pressing all the water out of the feces and leaving hard clumps that are excreted with difficulty.

(Left) The lymph vessels in the wall of the small intestines serve mainly to absorb fatty substances while the lymph nodes and patches act as a defense against bacteria.

symbionts, that is, organisms that live in amicable coexistence with us and protect the intestines against invasion by dangerous microbes. These scientists claim that such organisms produce some beneficial vitamins, and this seems to be true. Perhaps the answer is that they are a little of both— parasites and yet producers of helpful vitamins.

Constipation and Diarrhea

Two irregularities in the function of the intestines— they are irregularities and not ailments—are common: excessively slow or too rapid action. The first is called constipation, the other, diarrhea.

Constipation can take two completely different forms: atonic constipation and hypertonic, or spastic, constipation. Atonic constipation results when the intestinal tube does not react promptly. A normal intestine responds to digested foods either when these foods press against the walls of the tube or stimulate them chemically. But if the intestinal tube does not react even when the feces have been reduced to waste, and carries this waste around in the colon for four or five days at a time, the individual is suffering from atonic constipation.

Constipation may also result from too great a sensitivity of the intestinal wall. The intestinal pipe contracts too violently, and the contracted pipe does not move its contents toward the rectum, but holds it like a baby that will not give up something it has grasped. If we take an x-ray of the spastic-constipated patient, the colon shows up as a string of pearls.

Diarrhea is caused by too much activity in the digestive tract. The half-digested food arrives at the end of the colon much too early and there is a premature urge to release the excrement. The feces are not sufficiently digested and contain too much water, so that the excrement is watery and contains half-digested fats and proteins that give off a characteristic odor. Occasionally diarrhea is a process of self-help; the body has taken in something poisonous and will get rid of the noxious intake as quickly as possible. But in the other cases, the diarrhea may simply be the result of oversensitive intestines, a nervous disturbance, an aggressive bacillus like that of dysentery, or of ulcerations of the digestive tube. It is the doctor's art to find out what the factors are and to counteract them wisely.

169

16

Metabolism

By a remarkable chemical process called metabolism the food and water we take in is converted into energy and tissue.

(Facing page) Metabolism of protein. (1) During diges- tion food proteins must be broken down into their amino acids before they can be absorbed. (2) After absorption in small intestines, the amino acids are conveyed to (3) the liver and elsewhere, to be converted into body proteins. (Adapted from Illustrated Physiology by Ann B. McNaught and Robin Callander, E. & S. Livingstone Ltd., 1963)

If we can imagine ourselves undertaking to build the body of an average adult we would need the following ingredients: first, eleven or twelve gallons of water, then a number of tablespoons of four salts, sodium, potassium, calcium and magnesium, as well as chlorides, phosphates and sulphides. The salts are those we find in the ocean, where life first arose. We would also need a pinch of other materials, such as iron, manganese, copper, iodine, cobalt, zinc and molybdenum, and even traces of such elements as fluorine, aluminum and boron, although we do not know what their function is.

We would then still need the principal ingredients of the body: proteins, carbohydrates and fats. We are constantly using up or losing these ingredients and replacing them daily by eating and drinking. Our meals are the stops at the gas stations of our journey through life. The chemical process by which the food and water we take in is converted into energy and tissue is called metabolism.

The Basal Metabolic Rate

Even if an individual were completely at rest twenty-four hours a day he would still require eight hundred to twelve hundred calories daily for the maintenance of the life processes. This is called the basal metabolic rate, or BMR; it is of course related to the individual's size. The BMR is meas- ured when a subject is at complete rest early in the morning, before having eaten breakfast; he is in- structed to breathe the air from the cylinder of a BMR machine. The machine records the amount of oxygen he uses up; it is then easy to calculate the amount of energy produced by the subject and, from that, his BMR.

Since the thyroid gland controls the metabolic rate, it is assumed that if the BMR is higher than normal for the patient, he probably has an over- active thyroid, or a hyperthyroid condition. If the BMR is lower than normal, he probably has an un- deractive thyroid, that is, a hypothyroid condition.

The Body as a Combustion Machine

It has long been fashionable to compare the body with a combustion machine. The comparison is

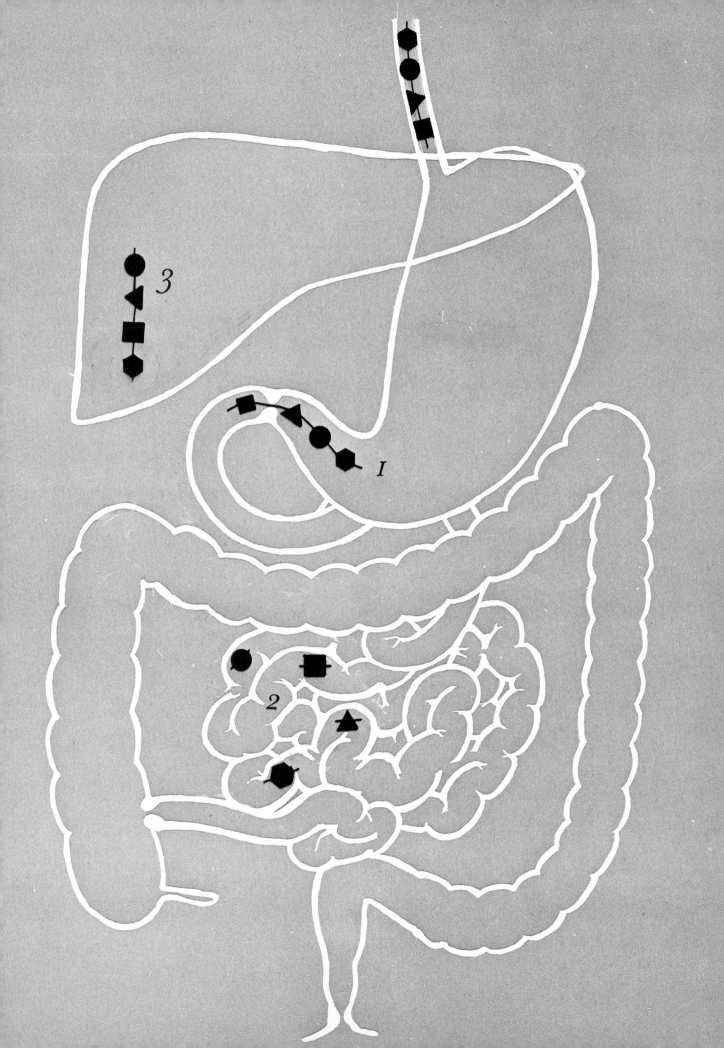

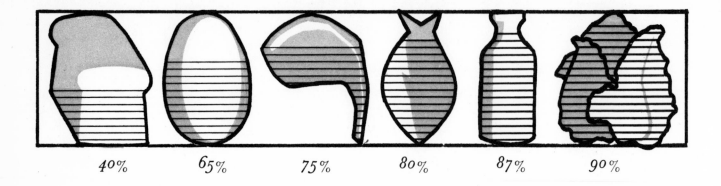

40%   65%   75%   80%   87%   90%

The water content of food. Water is the vehicle for almost all metabolic processes and is a major constituent of almost all the foodstuffs man consumes.

persuasive but it must not be taken too literally: the body does not genuinely parallel any machine we are familiar with. But let us for a moment accept the analogy.

One striking similarity between the body and a machine is in their use of oxygen. We breathe in air twelve to sixteen times a minute during sleep as well as when we are awake. The fresh air contains twenty-one per cent oxygen when we inhale it but only sixteen per cent oxygen when we exhale it. Our body has absorbed five per cent of the oxygen and has replaced it with carbon dioxide and water vapor. In exactly the same way, an automobile engine that burns gasoline must have oxygen to operate. The carbon and hydrogen in the gasoline is turned into carbon dioxide (CO_2) and water (H_2O), yielding energy in the process. The body burns the carbon and hydrogen in its food with the aid of oxygen and also turns it into CO_2 and H_2O in order to obtain energy. We can see the H_2O in the form of water vapor in the exhaust of the automobile as we can see it in the vapor in our breath on a cold day.

As engineers can tell us how much energy is yielded by gasoline, medical scientists can now determine how much energy is obtained from food. Just as we measure length in feet and miles, and heat in degrees, so we measure the energy value of

foodstuffs in terms of calories. One *large* calorie is the amount of heat required to raise one thousand grams of water (about a quart) one degree centigrade. In nutrition, however, we use the *small* calorie, the amount of heat necessary to raise one gram of water one degree centigrade.

The three main fuels in our food are carbohydrates, fats and proteins. For our purposes, it is sufficiently accurate to say that the energy output of carbohydrates is four calories per gram and of the fats about nine calories per gram. Proteins—that is, those not used to replace tissue—can supply us with four calories per gram.

The Calories Needed by the Body

A human adult weighing about one hundred and fifty pounds needs somewhat less than one calorie per minute at complete rest, which means about twelve hundred calories in twenty-four hours. Add to that the fact that our movements when we sit, stand, or walk—the act of eating, the secretions of glands, every breath, consume calories, and it is easy to see why the human body, even of a man who is a "sedentary worker," burns over two thousand calories per day. A child uses about twice as much as an adult in proportion to body weight. A person who does fairly hard work burns about four thousand to five thousand calories daily, and someone who does strenuous work, such as a farmer, coal miner or stevedore, may use as much as seven thousand calories per day.

172

Metabolizing Water

Our body is made up of almost sixty per cent water; we carry from ten to twelve gallons of water in us. It is not pure water but a solution of 0.1 per cent salts, a kind of warm, dilute sea water. We are constantly losing water: we exhale vapor, so that on cold days the windows of a room or a car are quickly covered with frosting from the vapor given off by the bodies of the occupants. On warm days we lose a considerable amount of water through the sweat glands. The main organs that throw off body water are the kidneys and the intestine; our excrement is at least sixty per cent water. Water is the vehicle for almost all metabolic processes and first on the list of our foodstuffs.

About a quarter of an hour after we drink a liquid, some of it appears as urine in the bladder. To get there it must pass not only through the kidneys but also the liver and the heart, putting a burden on these organs. The heart must pump every gulp of fluid, the liver must do the work of screening, and the kidneys must do the job of filtering the urine into the bladder.

Metabolizing the Carbohydrates

In order to be absorbed from the intestines, the carbohydrates we eat as starches in the form of potatoes, rice, bread or noodles, or even as sugar, must be broken down to the simplest sugars. Each simple sugar molecule contains six carbon atoms, twelve hydrogen atoms and six oxygen atoms, or $C_6H_{12}O_6$. There are three such simple sugars: glucose, galactose, and fructose, each with the same overall formula $C_6H_{12}O_6$ but with a different organization of atoms. Glucose is the basic sugar, the "white coal," of the body machine.

The sugar we use to sweeten our foods is called sucrose and is a double sugar, made up of glucose and fructose linked together. This double sugar does not contain exactly twice the number of atoms of carbon, hydrogen, and oxygen; it lacks two hydrogens and one oxygen. Special digestive tools called enzymes break up double sugars into simple sugars, but to complete the simple sugar, the body adds a molecule of water, H_2O, which provides the missing atoms of hydrogen and oxygen. This proc-

ess, hydrolysis, takes place in all the stages of the breaking up of starches.

After the simple sugar glucose is absorbed into the blood stream, it may be built up again into a starch called glycogen and stored in the liver and in muscle. Otherwise, glucose is used directly by the body cells to provide energy. The liver's stores of glycogen can be called upon by the body cells whenever needed. The liver cells turn the glycogen into glucose, which then makes its way through the blood stream to the various organs and cells. Whenever it is needed, muscle glycogen is also broken down into sugar by the muscle cells. All of these steps take place through the action of enzymes and, as we shall see in a later chapter, hormones.

But the body is not a simple engine. The energy provided by burning glucose is stored as a kind of chemical energy, as in a battery. This chemical energy is contained in one of the most powerful compounds found in nature, adenosine triphosphate, called familiarly by biochemists ATP. The atoms in molecules are either loosely held together by what is called a low energy bond or are tightly held together by high energy bonds. When such a high bond is broken, a burst of energy is released that, for example, permits muscles to contract. The conversion of the energy provided by burning glucose and forming ATP takes place in the mitochondria of the cells. Because energy is important for muscles, muscle cells have many mitochondria.

Metabolism of the Fats

The simplest of the fats is made up of molecules consisting of glycerol and three molecular chains of fatty acids. The chains of fatty acid vary in length. Fat digestion in the intestine begins in the duodenum. Here the bile of the liver flows into the intestinal tube and transforms the fat into an emulsion by dispersing it into microscopic droplets of milky fluid. After the fat inside the duodenum is dispersed, the enzymes from the pancreas and the intestinal glands start the chemical digestion. The drops of emulsified fat, broken down into glycerol and the fatty acids, are then apparently picked up by the thousands of lymph channels in the intestinal villi, and reach the lymphatic tubes.

If the intake of fat is copious, the droplets fill the lymphatic vessels like a milk, and this is visible through the transparent walls of the great lymph tube that ascends along the spine towards the heart. From there the fat circulates with the blood stream and after a time it reappears in the tissues that store fat. One of the main storehouses is the liver. Gourmets highly esteem the fat-filled livers of geese that are forcibly overfed with corn and kept as inactive as possible. Besides the liver, the chief storehouses of fat are the muscles, the skin, the hips and, in women, the breasts. Fat can easily be transformed into sugar, and vice versa, sugar into fat. We feed our pigs, and the Hungarians their geese, with carbohydrate cereals such as corn and leave it to the animals to assimilate the corn and transform it into fat.

Although fats can be manufactured from carbohydrates, we cannot live on a fat-free diet. Certain fatty acids—linoleic, linolenic and arachidonic—which make up some of the fats cannot be manufactured in adequate amounts by the body and must be present in our food. Furthermore, certain essential vitamins occur in fatty foods.

Proteins

Although one gram of protein provides four calories, proteins are mainly necessary in the diet to help make up the cellular protoplasm. Fats and carbohydrates can provide energy for the body but the body cannot manufacture protein out of them because they lack nitrogen.

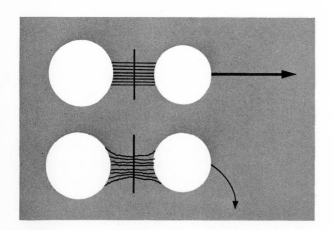

The building blocks of protein are the amino acids, which are made up of carbon, oxygen, hydrogen and nitrogen. Of the hundred or so amino acids in nature, some twenty-two or twenty-three can be found in proteins; about twenty are important in the body. The proteins in our food can be short in some of these amino acids but the body suffers no harm because it can manufacture the missing amino acids out of the others present in our food. According to recent information, there are ten amino acids indispensable for normal growth.

After the protein in our food is digested and hydrolyzed into amino acids, these are absorbed into the blood stream and can reach all the organs and cells of the body. Within the cells, the amino acids can be used to manufacture needed proteins. This process requires energy, which is provided by ATP.

But protein is not only built up in the body: it is also destroyed, as when cells die. Unnecessary protein material is taken care of mostly by the liver, one of the busiest organs of the body. The liver not only manufactures proteins—for example, the proteins in the blood plasma—but it breaks up excess amino acids, producing urea from the nitrogen, which is excreted in the urine. It can convert the remaining portion of many of the amino acids into glucose, which can then be readily utilized for energy.

Since protein foods are generally the most costly, and the lack of protein is the primary cause of undernourishment, scientists have long discussed how much and what kind of proteins the human body needs. It was found that the "calorie" yardstick used to measure carbohydrates and fats was not useful in measuring proteins. The body needs specific amounts of amino acids to compose those

Energy is chemically stored in the body in a compound, adenosine tryphosphate (ATP), containing high energy bonds. The illustration contrasts the spurt of energy released when there is a breaking apart of two molecules held together by high energy bonds (above) with that of molecules held by low energy bonds (below). (Adapted from The Chemicals of Life by Isaac Asimov, Abelard-Schuman Limited, 1954)

Caloric Values in Foods

	Measure	Calories
Butter	1 tbsp.	100
Buttermilk	1 cup	86
Cheese, cottage	1 oz.	27
Cheese, cream	1 oz.	106
Cheese, Swiss	1 oz.	105
Eggs	1 medium	77
Ice cream, plain	1 slice	167
Margarine	1 tbsp.	100
Milk, evaporated, cnd.	1 cup	346
Milk, malted	1 cup	281
Milk, whole	1 cup	166
Apple pie	1, 4″ sector	330
Bread, rye	1, ½″ slice	57
Bread, white	1, ½″ slice	63
Bread, whole wheat	1, ½″ slice	55
Corn flakes	1 cup	96
Crackers, Graham	2 medium	55
Doughnuts	1	136
Farina, ckd.	1 cup	105
Noodles, (egg) ckd.	1 cup	107
Pancakes, buckwheat	1, 4″ diam.	48
Puffed wheat	1 cup	43
Rice, white	1 cup	692
Rolls, sweet	1 roll	178
Spaghetti, ckd.	1 cup	220
Wheat germ	1 cup	246
Bacon, fried	2 slices	97
Chicken fryer, raw	1 breast	210
Chicken roaster, raw	4 oz.	227
Frankfurter, ckd.	1	124
Goose	4 oz.	420
Ham, cured, ckd.	3 oz.	340
Hamburger, ckd.	3 oz. ground	316
Lamb leg roast, ckd.	3 oz. roast	314
Lamb rib chop, ckd.	4 oz. chop	480
Liver, beef, fried	2 oz.	118
Porterhouse, ckd.	3 oz. steak	293
Tongue, beef	4 oz.	235
Turkey	4 oz.	304
Veal cutlet, ckd.	3 oz. cutlet	184
Veal stew meat, ckd.	3 oz.	252

	Measure	Calories
Clams, raw	4 oz.	92
Halibut, ckd.	1 fillet	230
Lobster, raw	½ average	88
Oysters, raw	13–19 medium	200
Salmon, cnd.	3 oz.	120
Swordfish, ckd.	1 steak	223
Tuna fish, cnd.	3 oz. drained	170
Apples, raw	1 medium	87
Bananas	1 medium	132
Cantaloupes	½ melon	37
Dates, dried	1 cup pitted	505
Grapefruit, raw	1 cup sections	77
Olives, green	10 "mammoth"	72
Oranges	1 medium	70
Orange juice, fresh	1 cup	108
Peaches, raw	1 medium	45
Pears, raw	1 medium	95
Raisins, dry	1 cup	430
Strawberries, raw	1 cup	54
Strawberries, frozen	3 oz.	82
Tomato juice, canned	1 cup	50
Asparagus, ckd.	1 cup cut spears	36
Carrots, raw	1 cup grated	45
Celery, raw	1 cup diced	18
Corn, sweet, ckd.	1 ear	85
Lettuce	2 large leaves	7
Lima beans, green, ckd.	1 cup	152
Lima beans, dry	1 cup	610
Mushrooms, raw	½ cup, diced	8
Peas, green, ckd.	1 cup	111
Peas, green, cnd.	1 cup	145
Peas, dry, split	1 cup	689
Potatoes, white, baked	1 medium	97
Potatoes, boiled	1 medium	120
Spinach, ckd.	1 cup	46
Tomatoes, raw	1 medium	30
Beer	12 oz.	72–173
Chocolate, plain, sw.	¾″ × 1–½″ × ¼″	28
Cocoa beverage	1 cup	236
Coffee, black	1 cup	9
Cola beverages	6 oz.	83
Fudge, plain	2″ sq. × ⅝″	185
Jams, marmalades	1 tbsp.	55
Peanuts, roasted	1 cup	805
Peanut butter	1 tbsp.	92
Sugars, cane or beet	1 tbsp.	48

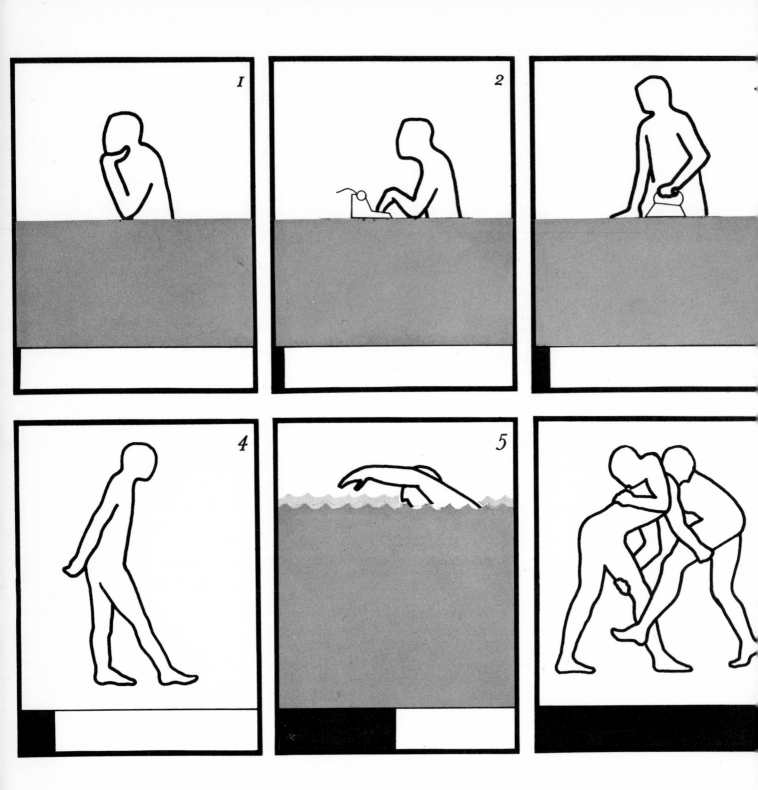

Amounts of energy expended in various activities in terms of calories per hour: (1) mental work, 7–8; (2) rapid typing, 16–40; (3) ironing, 59; (4) walking, 130–200; (5) swimming, 200–700 and (6) wrestling, 980. To estimate daily calorie requirements, an individual must take into account his size and the work he does.

proteins that are indispensable for the replacement of the worn-out machinery of life. Such proteins as those produced by potatoes and corn are "cheap"; but the essential amino acids are found only in such relatively expensive foods as meat, liver, brains, hormone glands, milk, cheese, butter and eggs. Populations that live only on such cheaper products as potatoes and corn suffer a lack of the essential amino acids even if the intake in calories or grams is large.

Diet

There has been endless discussion about the quantities of food the human body needs. When contact has been made, especially during wars, with the inhabitants of remote countries it was found that man can survive on diets of astonishingly poor composition. The Eskimos, the Aleutian fishermen, the people of the Kalahari desert, or the Andes of Peru live on diets that nutritionists would declare absolutely inadequate. A celebrated example of a man who lived on an extremely simple diet is Mahatma Ghandi.

The human body is immensely adaptable in terms of diet, especially if such psychic factors as religious and ethical forces encourage a particular approach. Usually people today follow a diet composed of 300 to 500 grams of carbohydrates, 100 grams of fats and a minimum of 50 grams of such high-grade proteins as we get from milk, eggs, butter, meat, brain, liver, and various glands. If, like any well-fed modern individual, we add legumes, salads, nuts, fruits, occasionally a little olive or fish oil, herring, salmon or sturgeon, and some spiced foods, we will not suffer from any lack of proteins or vitamins.

17

Vitamins

Vital for health, stamina and growth are certain substances called vitamins. A lack of them causes such ailments as rickets, scurvy, night blindness and catarrhs.

Besides the basic food substances—proteins, carbohydrates, fat, water, minerals—a healthy diet must contain substances called vitamins. These were discovered only as recently as the late 1890's. For centuries before that, a relationship between certain ailments and nutrition had been suspected. The first important discovery in this field was made by a Dutch doctor, Eijkman, in a government prison on Java. He observed that not only the prisoners but also the pigeons around the prison, which depended on the prisoners to feed them, suffered from a dreadful endemic nervous ailment and degeneration called by the Javanese *beri-beri*. In beri-beri, one of the most common maladies in East Asia, the victims grew increasingly weak and gradually became paralyzed. The Dutch spent large sums for hospitals to treat the endless rows of beri-beri sufferers but it was all in vain—until Dr. Eijkman decided to find out why the prisoners and the pigeons developed beri-beri. His finding: the staple food of the Javanese population was rice, rice shorn of its hulls. When the hulls are removed, he found, the rice produced beri-beri. As soon as the hulls were added to the rice the Dutch had no more cases of beri-beri and they were able to convert the beri-beri hospitals into schools or into hostels for sailors.

Eijkman's discovery and the wonder cures at Java created a great stir. Scientists realized that, in addition to proteins, carbohydrates and fats, food must contain quantities, however minute, of other ingredients. In the hull of the rice grain was a substance that was necessary if maladies such as beri-beri were to be avoided. Like proteins, the substance was found to contain nitrogen in the combination of the amine NH_3: it was therefore called the vital amine, or vitamin. In fact, what the rice hulls contained was the vitamin thiamine. Later it was found that not all of these substances were NH_3 compounds; but we still refer to the whole group as vitamins.

Other endemic illnesses seemingly connected with nutrition were suspected to be the result of "avitaminosis." Long known and dreaded was scurvy, an ailment that haunted sailors and presumably was associated with the lack of fresh food on ships. The British fleet needed twice as many mariners as they had, because half the sailors were always ill. The English doctors found that the only food that controlled scurvy was fresh fruit, so the warships were loaded not only with cannon balls but with lemons and limes. And this was the custom in the British fleet a hundred years before Eijkman investigated pigeons with beri-beri on Java.

The Importance of Vitamins

Vitamins do not have a specific composition like proteins but are all of different and unrelated origin. They are as different as ants and woodpeckers in a forest.

Since vitamins are not part of a logical system and scientists at first did not even know their chemical structure, they have been labelled A, B, C, D, and so forth, in the order in which they were discovered. Some vitamins are elementary chemical compounds: for example, vitamin C is a rather simple substance, ascorbic acid. Another substance of simple molecular composition is niacin or nicotinic acid. Others are mixtures and are therefore called complex, such as B-complex. Still others have proved so elusive that scientists are not certain whether they exist. But we have apparently detected most vitamins, or at least the important ones, and no further major discoveries may be anticipated.

How the vitamins acquired such importance in the metabolism of mammals is not clear. They act as co-enzymes, or helpers to enzymes, which, as we said in an earlier chapter, direct and speed up the chemical reactions of the body. The body manufactures its own enzymes, for these are proteins and are needed in fairly large quantities. But the body does not manufacture vitamins, although these are needed in remarkably small quantities; for example, only one two-thousandth of an ounce of niacin is needed by the body daily. Other vitamins are required in even smaller amounts. We must therefore obtain our vitamins in our food since they are essential for good health.

Vitamins have become one of the most widely used medicaments of our time. It is estimated that at least one hundred million vitamin pills or drops are being taken daily and that much of the improvement in health, stamina, growth, and the records being set in sports is intimately connected with the "vitaminization" of the modern diet.

Vitamin A

Vitamin A belongs to a family of substances called carotenes, because the best known of them are of the yellow dye that colors carrots. All yellow vegetables like squash and sweet potatoes and many green vegetables are rich in carotene, which is a long molecule containing forty carbon atoms. Our body breaks this up into two and obtains two molecules of vitamin A, each containing twenty carbon atoms. The human body needs a minimum of about one one-thousandth of a gram of vitamin A daily as part of its diet; otherwise the skin becomes dry and scaly, nails break, the lacrimal or tear-producing glands dry up and fertility decreases. The surface cells of the respiratory tract also dry up and the cilia disappear.

The average night, especially under an open sky, is not absolutely black; we are able to see in twilight with the help of an enzyme known as visual purple. This is a purple-colored substance related to vitamin A, which sensitizes the cells of the light-sensitive screen in the rear wall of the eye. The storehouse of vitamin A is the liver. If the liver does not provide sufficient quantities of vitamin A, the vitamin-starved eye becomes "night blind." The night-blind person sees well enough in full light but poorly in twilight.

Carotenes are soluble only in oil. Therefore, in animals vitamin A is found particularly in products and organs—such as the liver—that are rich in oil. The best source of vitamin A is the liver of the codfish, which is ten times as rich as the liver of land animals. Our daily vitamin A requirement is provided by milk, eggs, butter, and such vegetables as carrots, squash, sweet potatoes, radishes, cucumbers, tomatoes and green peppers. The citizen of the Western world-who enjoys a normal diet need not worry: he will not suffer from a vitamin A deficiency and will not be plagued by night blindness, inflammation of the eyes, or catarrhs of the respiratory tract.

Vitamin B

Vitamin B is a complex of a dozen chemical compounds with labels from B_1 to B_{12}. The most important is B_1, or thiamine, which is rich in brewer's yeast. The meat of pork also provides ample amounts of B_1; other sources are the hulls of grains of wheat, rice and rye. It is an enzyme helper that the embryo of the plant needs in order to build itself up. If the embryo is discarded with the hull, the vitamin is lost and the body gets a food lacking in vitamin B_1. If we feed a laboratory animal bread made of white wheat, it gets beri-beri, but if we then give it one drop of yeast, it recovers. In the United States, all flour must by law be artificially enriched with B_1; Americans therefore need not worry about this vitamin.

Vitamin B_{12}

B_{12} is a co-enzyme which cooperates in the manufacture of the blood cells, a process that takes place inside the bone marrow. The structure of this molecule contains an atom of the mineral cobalt and is more complex than any other vitamin. Individuals who suffer from pernicious anemia lack this vitamin: what is strange here is that their diet is not lacking in vitamin B_{12}—they are simply unable to absorb the vitamin from their intestinal tracts. The stomach has to secrete a substance called intrinsic factor before the vitamin can be absorbed through the intestinal wall. Patients with pernicious anemia cannot form intrinsic factor and thus they cannot absorb vitamin B_{12}.

Vitamin B_{12} is stored in the liver, and as far back as forty years ago it was known that the lives of patients with pernicious anemia could be saved by giving them injections of liver extract. Today vitamin B_{12} can be synthesized and the vitamin itself injected once a month so that the patient can lead an entirely normal life.

Another compound of the B-complex was analyzed in 1935. It was at first called lactoflavin because it was extracted from milk; it is a yellow-green fluorescent pigment. Later it acquired its present name, riboflavin. It is one of the co-enzymes that cooperate in the respiration of the tissue cell. Respiration in man consists of two acts: first the blood inside the lungs absorbs oxygen from the air and transports it into the body via the blood cells. After the blood cells have carried the oxygen to the capillaries, it is transferred to the cells of the tissues. The flow of oxygen into the lungs, the external respiration, is followed by the transporting of the oxygen in the blood into the tissues. The use of the oxygen by the tissue cells is internal respiration and is called oxidation and reduction. The latter requires the help of riboflavin.

Vitamin C

As we have said, vitamin C is a chemically simple substance—ascorbic acid. In contrast to the yellow color of the carotenes, foods rich in vitamin C are green. Most mammals synthesize their vitamin C; but man as well as the anthropoid apes, monkeys and guinea pigs, must import it from outside the body. Human babies are born with an adequate amount of vitamin C present in their bodies, but they lose this after a few weeks if they are not breast fed; the modern mother then provides the child with vitamin C by means of small doses of lemon, tomato, or other fruit and vegetable juices.

Although we do not know how vitamin C acts, we do know that it is present in high concentration in the adrenal gland. The major ailment resulting from a deficiency of vitamin C is scurvy. This disease starts with a leakage of blood from the capillaries and the appearance of black and blue spots under the skin. The gums begin to bleed, swell and ulcerate and the teeth become loose. Blood also seeps out from the intestines and the bladder. Besides vitamin C, a co-enzyme called "factor P" (for permeability) plays a part in the leakage of blood. Little is known about this factor except that it is found, along with vitamin C, in lemon peel and red peppers. In scurvy, ultimately the bones and cartilage become weakened and the intercellular substance, in general, becomes defective. For this reason, wounds and fractures heal slowly and badly.

Descriptions of what sailors and soldiers have suffered from scurvy forms one of the most harrowing chapters in the history of illness. As the Greeks spoke of the punishment the gods meted out to those who were too proud, so we may say scurvy was the punishment of those who dared leave their natural habitat and venture out on the sea. One of the most heroic pioneers of the oceans was the Portuguese Magellan, the first man to circumnavigate the globe. Of the two hundred men who sailed with him, less than twenty returned to Lisbon.

It must have been a pitiable spectacle to see those emaciated scurvy-ridden wretches, like phantoms from a picture by Breughel, making their way to church with candles in their trembling hands to give thanks for their "happy" return.

Similarly, it is said that the British navy did not lose half as many soldiers and sailors in battles and invasions as it did through scurvy.

Vitamin D

Vitamin D is a sterol, that is, a fatty substance. Sterols are always present in protoplasm and are therefore found in every cell of the human body. One of these sterols is cholesterol; a close relative of cholesterol, 7-dehydrocholesterol, is abundant in the cells of the skin. It is light-sensitive, and if the skin is exposed to sunlight or light rich in short waves, as, for example, from an ultraviolet lamp, the 7-dehydrocholesterol is transformed into vitamin D. We are not sure how vitamin D acts but we know from innumerable observations what a deficiency of it does. The two main building materials the body uses for manufacturing bones are calcium and phosphorus; they are combined into a compound, a calcium phosphate salt. If vitamin D is not present in the body, the calcium phosphate salt will not be deposited in bone. The child will suffer from rickets: the bones will not harden, the legs will become bowed under the weight of the body, and the spine will bend, leaving the victim a hunchback. Before 1900 the streets of all slums were filled with rickety, malformed children, with an unhealthy pallor, bad teeth, and oversized heads. Rickets was the bane of the poor—poor in money, poor in education, poor in vitamin D. Like beri-beri and scurvy, rickets disappeared when scientists discovered vitamins, the mysterious action of ultraviolet radiation, the sterols of the skin, and the transformation of these sterols into vitamin D.

"More light," cried the physicians, and the modern age began with the widening of dark, narrow streets, the increase in the number and size of windows, the establishment of national parks, the movement out-of-doors, the popularity of water and snow sports and other open-air activities. The whole of mankind was treated with one cure, a vitamin D cure.

The surface of the sea, especially in warm waters like those of the Gulf Stream, teems with minute animal and plant life called plankton. Plankton abound in vitamin D because they live in the range of the strongest radiation and the clearest sunshine. Plankton are the pasture of fishes and whales. The gigantic whale feeds on plankton soup! The codfish stores the vitamin D in its liver, and codfish liver oil is the classic remedy against rickets. From sunshine to plankton to cod liver oil—this is the story of vitamin D and the treatment for rickets.

In investigating the vitamins it was found that some are partly sensitive to aging, oxidation by air, light, heat. Some are so sensitive to heat that rats cannot be raised on cooked foods alone—bits of uncooked fresh food must be added. Our knowledge of the vitamins is still incomplete. Therefore, the nutritionists say: Don't rely on dried fruits, but eat fresh fruit, including green fruits, with their undiminished content of vitamins A and C. Don't cook food too long. Don't reheat food; it loses value with every heating. Eat young plants, young salad greens, and not those that are too well-grown. Modern nutrition was inaugurated. The result was: no more rickets, scurvy, or hunchbacks, and a new generation taller in stature and with longer life expectancy.

Vitamin D is a miracle substance. It should be administered either in the form of food vitamins or of vitamin-producing sunlight. But overexposure of the body to sunlight has its dangers too. An intelligent person need only observe the warnings of nature. The skin tells us when we have passed the safe period and reached our limit. The skin should never be exposed so long that it produces sunburn or blisters. If the body is overfed with vitamin D over a period of months, chalk deposits appear in the arteries or inside the kidneys and elsewhere in the body. Man walks a narrow path between a deficiency of vitamins and the hazards of overdosing. But it is an easy path to keep to if one has a normally balanced diet and takes the sun in moderation.

18

The Kidneys

An extraordinary pair of organs, the kidneys, filters waste products out of 180 quarts of blood fluid every twenty-four hours.

(Facing page) The kidneys filter 180 quarts of water daily out of the blood plasma, which reaches them by means of renal arteries. The final filtrate, urine, moves down through long tubes, the ureters, to the bladder.

The kidneys are twin, bean-shaped glands (color portfolio plate 24) suspended from the back wall of the abdomen to the right and left of the spinal column. They are connected with the blood stream through large arteries. After filtering the blood plasma, they send the final filtrate, urine, through the ureters, a long tube leading from each kidney down to the bladder. In one of the methods of studying kidney functions, the physician administers a dye that colors the urine. He then inserts a cystoscope into the bladder and observes how the ureter ejects a few drops of urine into the bladder every few seconds.

If we had to choose the most remarkable creation in the human body, it would be the kidney. Each human kidney is composed of a million filters called glomeruli, attached to a million long, twisted tubules. As the filtrate flows through the tubules, the cells of the tubular wall reabsorb over ninety-nine per cent of the water and send it back into the blood stream.

In the course of twenty-four hours, man's extraordinary kidneys filter a total of 180 quarts of water—and everything dissolved in it—out of the blood plasma, which reaches them by means of the renal arteries. With the exception of one to one-and-one-half quarts of water—the normal amount of urine excreted in a day—all this fluid is reabsorbed, together with the valuable substances in solution such as sodium, potassium and glucose. Only the waste products are left for excretion from the body, along with any excesses of the salts that the body uses.

Evolution of the Kidney

The primitive animals that first developed in the sea had no problems with the salts and water in their bodies because the concentration of the salts inside them was the same as in the sea around them. As these animals grew more complex, a primitive kidney developed that could get rid of waste matter, but it had no glomeruli, for there was no need to excrete water. When these sea animals first entered the fresher water in river estuaries they were faced with a much smaller concentration of salts in the water around them. Water from the river must have forced its way into their bodies by osmotic pressure, seeking to make the concentration of salt

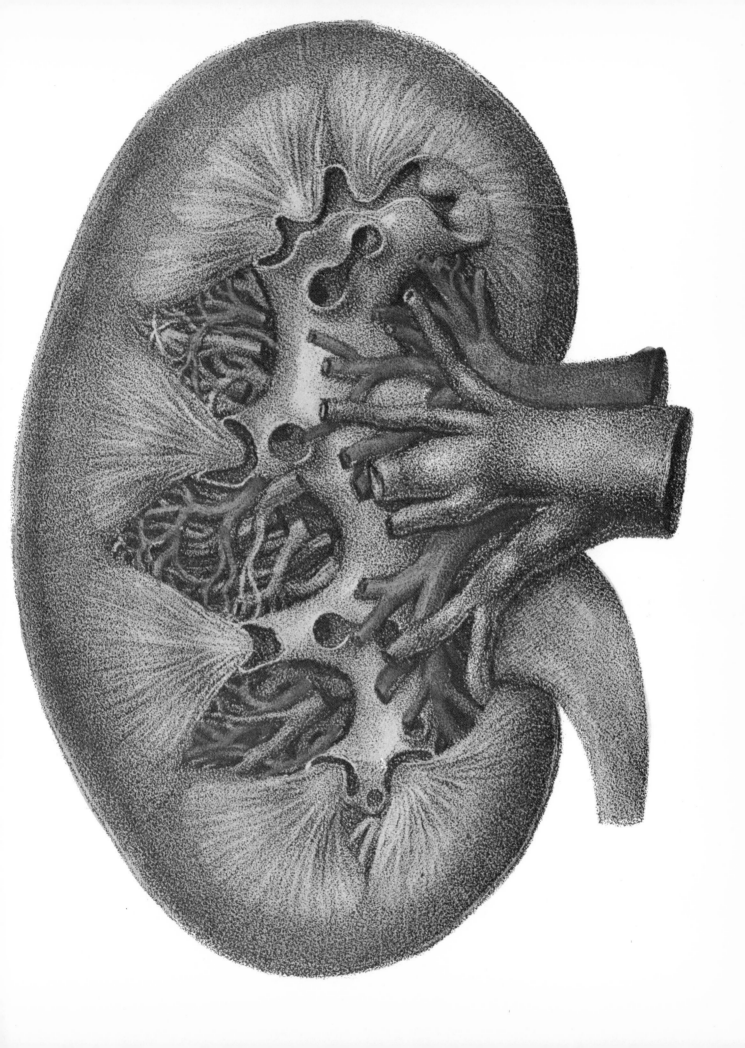

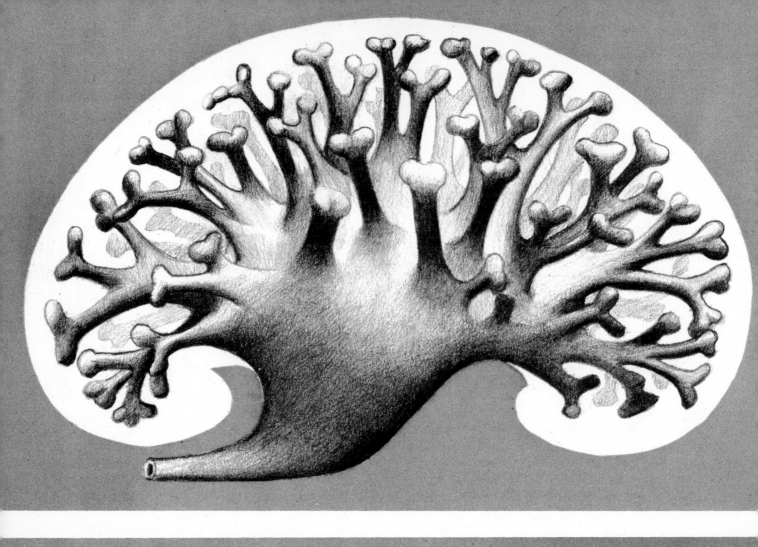

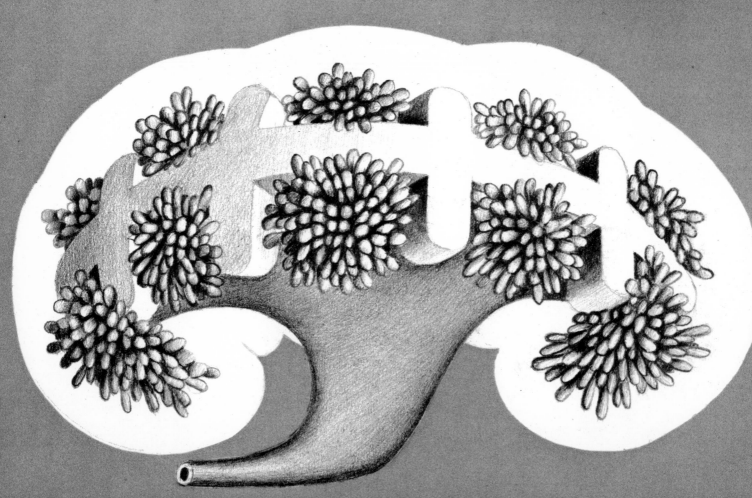

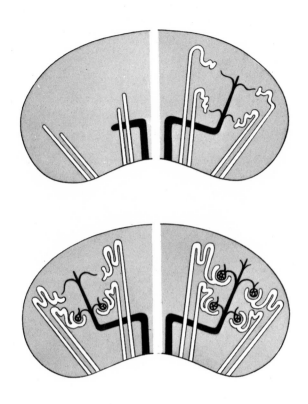

(Above) Development of the kidney filters. As the kidney develops, microscopic blood vessels (in black) intertwine with the urinary tubules. Each filter consists of a urinary tubule, one end of which envelops a grapelike mass of blood vessels from which blood plasma liquid filters into the tubule.

(Left) Kidney tubules. Millions of filtering units in the kidneys lead into collecting tubules which join and ultimately empty into the ureter leading out of each kidney.

in their bodies as dilute as it was in the estuary. The first animals must have been blown up by the water much like an egg that cracks when it is boiled in water without salt.

Then some mutant species probably developed a kidney containing glomeruli that could get rid of excess water. The glomerular kidney enabled later species to crawl out on land and permitted their gills to change into lungs.

Kidney Disorders

A trained investigator can see many significant things in the urine the kidney produces. If he lets the water evaporate, crystals appear. If he examines the urine microscopically, cells are seen. Most of these cells come from the walls of the bladder or of the urethra, through which the urine ran. The experienced doctor knows that the walls, like all skin, normally shed a small number of dead cells. If the number the investigator sees is excessive he will recognize that the urinary system is irritated or even inflamed. If the filter sheds whole rows of cells, if protein is lost in the urine, or if phagocytes are visible, the investigator knows that the kidney is ill and the patient may be suffering from a nephritis—an inflammation of the kidney. In a urinalysis, a centrifuge tube is filled with urine and centrifuged for ten minutes; the sediment is then examined under a microscope. If the kidney is inflamed, red blood cells or white blood cells may be seen. The trained investigator can even tell whether the inflammation is recent or chronic.

The kidneys filter about a hundred compounds, the end products of metabolism. The most conspicuous are the nitrates, the ashes of the amino group NH_3, which characterize the amino acids, the chain links of the proteins. The chemical group NH_3 appears in the urine as urea, $CO{<}^{NH_2}_{NH_2}$. Because it is so strong in nitrogen, urea is used as fertilizer. Since time immemorial, farmers have fertilized their fields with the manure of the cows because it also contains nitrogenous wastes. Today we use the artificial, but not necessarily better, nitrogen products of our chemical factories.

The human body produces approximately thirty grams of urea daily. It was a great event in the history of chemistry when the German chemist

185

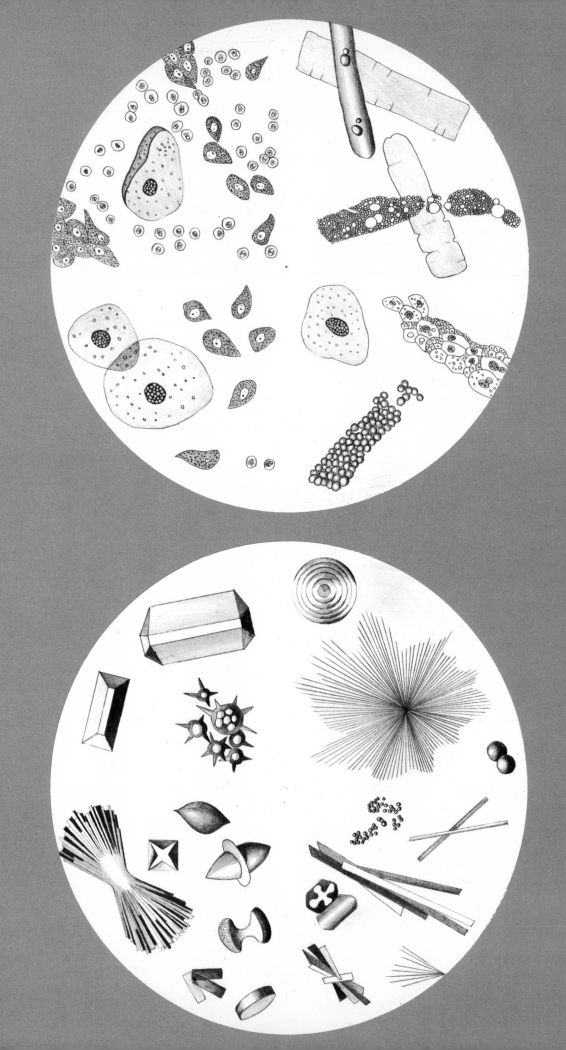

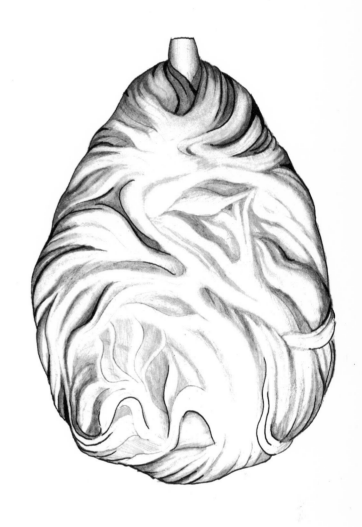

(Left) Microscopic view of urine. The presence of red blood cells and white blood cells in addition to epithelial cells in a drop of urine (above) indicates an inflammation in the kidneys. If the urine is allowed to dry (below), many crystals of waste products become visible.

(Right) The urinary bladder. When moderately full (above), the bladder contains about half a quart of urine. When it is emptied (below), the muscles are firmly contracted.

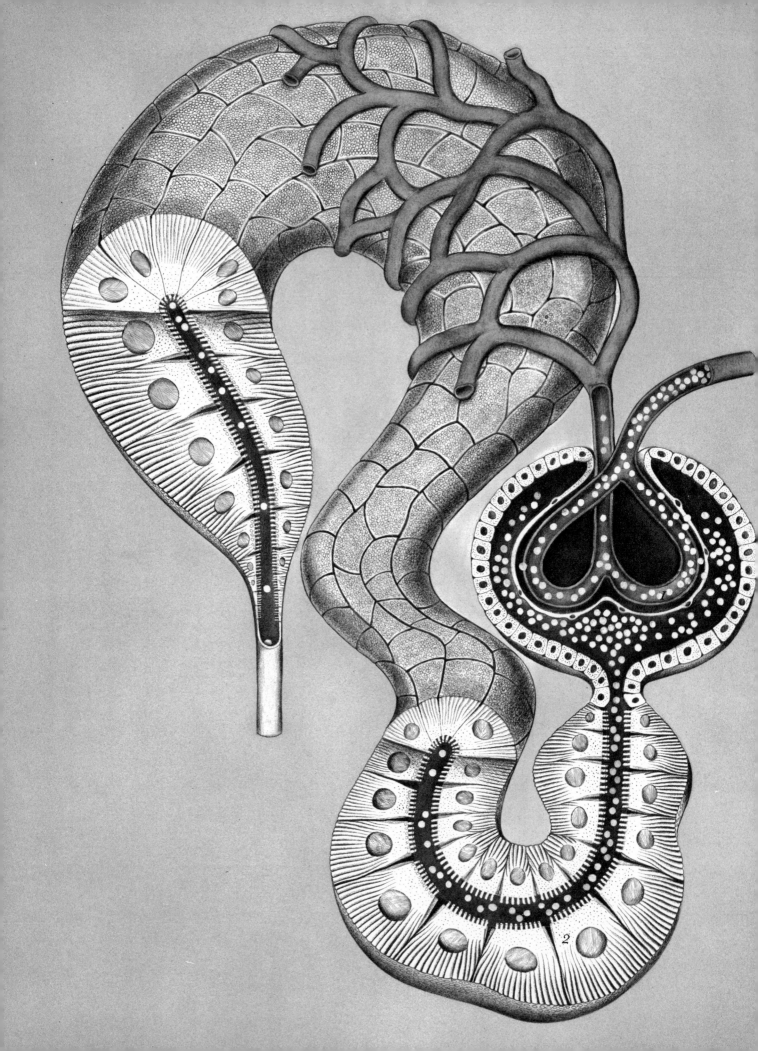

2

Friedrich Woehler emerged from his laboratory and exhibited urea that he had produced chemically. Up to that time it had been asserted that only a living organism could synthesize an "organic" compound. On that day the age of organic syntheses dawned and modern chemistry was born. One of its proudest achievements is artificial urea. In one sense, the economic standard of a country can be measured by the amount of artificial nitrogen compounds its farmers can afford.

Kidney Stones

If urine is exposed for hours to the open air, ubiquitous bacteria, including those that feed on urea, settle in it and convert it into ammonia, resulting among other things, in the penetrating odor of stale urine. Under certain conditions the minerals of the urine form incrustations inside the kidneys, the ureter, or the bladder, appearing either as coarse grit or as solitary kidney or bladder stones. Sometimes these stones remain so inactive that they are not noted; only by chance or by an autopsy are they detected.

The removal of bladder stones is one of the oldest operations in the history of medicine. In medieval times, special "stone removers" traveled from fair to fair and performed their operations in public to demonstrate their skill and win patients. If the operator was a clever showman, he won as much applause as an acrobat or an actor. Since the operation was not performed under antiseptic conditions, the patient often developed an infection. The applause of the townspeople then turned quickly to anger, and if the "stone cutters" had not left town, it is very likely that they ended up on the gallows.

Transplantation of Kidneys

It is relatively easy to remove kidneys. It is also technically possible to transplant the kidney of one human being into another, hooking up the necessary artery and vein and attaching the ureters. The difficulty—at least at present—is getting the body to accept the foreign kidney. After a few days, the body of the patient may reject the implanted kidney unless the donor is an identical twin of the patient. As we have seen in an earlier chapter, it will put its immunization apparatus in motion and mobilize its phagocytes against the invader kidney. Normally this would be a healthy reaction, but unfortunately in this case it conflicts with the surgeon's strategy.

A nephron, one of a million such units in the kidneys. Water and other substances in the blood plasma pass through a filtering apparatus, the glomerulus (1), and reach the tubule of the nephron (2). As the various substances, such as glucose, then pass along the ureter, most of the water and all the glucose is absorbed by the cells of the tubule, and return to the blood stream.

19

The Hormones

The substances secreted by such endocrine glands as the pituitary, thyroid, thymus, adrenals, pancreas, ovaries and testes regulate some of the most important functions of the body.

(Facing page) Double role of the pancreas. The digestive secretions (in white) of the pancreas pass into the intestine to break down proteins, carbohydrates and fats. The islets of the pancreas (in black) produce the hormone insulin, which passes into the blood stream and regulates the burning of sugar for energy. If too much insulin is produced the result is low blood sugar. If too little insulin is produced or if the insulin is defective, the result is high blood sugar, a condition known as diabetes.

Of all the ideas that Ernst Haeckel, leading zoologist of the second half of the 19th century, developed, the most fundamental was the "biogenetic principle." He said in effect that in its individual development as an embryo every animal passes through the same stages as did its ancestors in their evolutionary history. The embryo is at first like a gastrula, just as its ancestors were gastrulas. Later it floats like a fish in the womb of its mother, and for a time gills such as fish use for breathing appear on its throat.

Most of these biogenetic organs are only ephemeral and have no practical function. They appear and disappear like phantoms. Because they are a throwback to primitive stages of evolution, we call them atavisms. Some of these do not disappear entirely but are transformed. Our hormonal or endocrine glands are such transformed atavistic organs. In contrast to ordinary glands, they do not send their product through ducts into the surrounding areas, like the saliva from the salivary glands into the mouth or those of the liver into the gall bladder and the intestines. Instead, the hormones from endocrine glands directly enter the blood stream and, through the blood, all parts of the body. They are therefore called the glands of internal secretion or the ductless glands.

Because their secretions are minute and are dissolved in the blood and lymph, they are difficult to detect. In the early years of hormone research, it took an enormous effort to isolate usable amounts. Those who chose to work with sex hormones made contracts with slaughterhouses for the sex glands of thousands of lambs and steers. Three drops of hormone were finally extracted from a hecatomb of steers, not as a sacrifice for Olympian Jove but for the Goddess of Science!

The Hormonal Glands

One of the characteristics of the hormonal glands is their wanderlust, their tendency to leave their source and look for work elsewhere. The human embryo develops gills like those of primitive fishes, but parts of these turn into hormonal glands and leave their birthplace at the sides of the throat in the course of their embryonic development. The pituitary gland, the thyroid, the parathyroids and

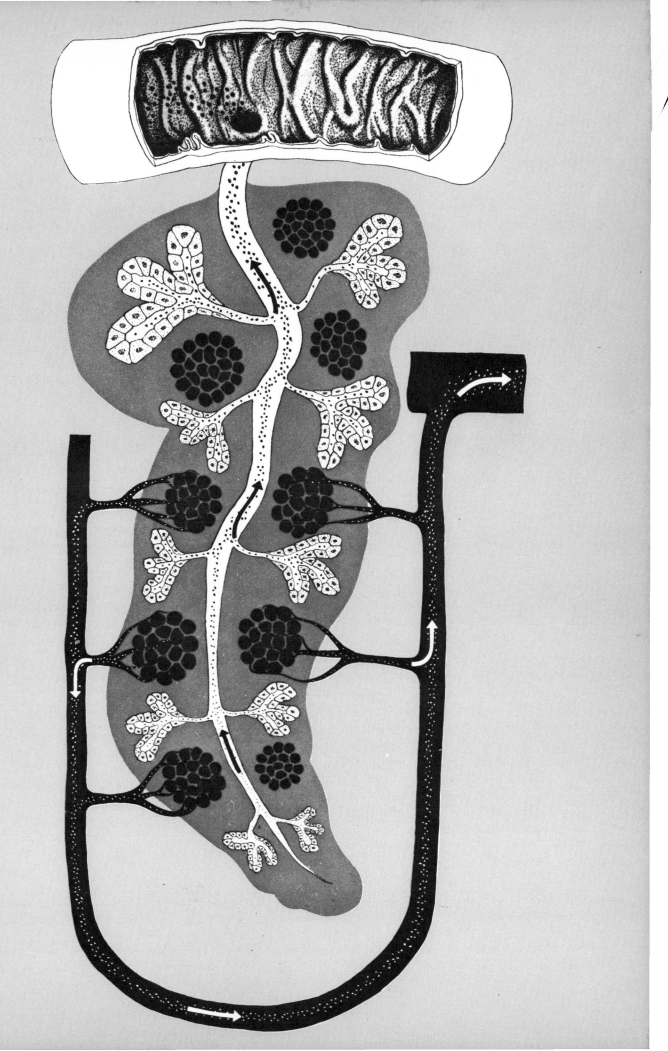

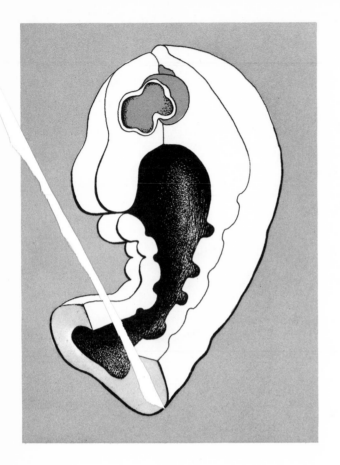

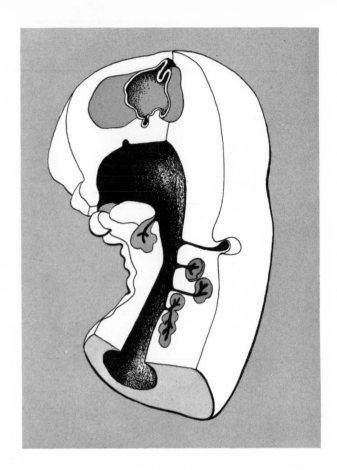

the thymus develop in part from these primitive gills.

The two adrenal glands do not migrate far. They form in the peritoneum of the abdomen and then settle on top of the kidneys. A group of cells from the neighboring sympathetic nervous system migrates into the adrenal glands and forms a core there. Thus the adrenal glands become double organs, with a nervous core and a glandular cortex. The cortex produces a series of steroids, the corticosteroids, which have wide-ranging effects. The core functions in cooperation with the sympathetic nerve system, regulating the blood pressure, the heart action and other activities of the body, through the secretion of adrenalin.

Another double organ is the pancreas. Its ordinary glandular tissue produces the various enzymes that serve to open the molecular chains of proteins, carbohydrates and fats. Inside this digestive gland there settled a hormonal gland in the form of little

Hormonal glands in the embryo. The embryo forms gills much like those of primitive fishes (left). Parts of these gills are transformed into hormonal glands (right) and migrate to form the thyroid, parathyroid and thymus glands.

islets of tissue that fabricate the hormone called insulin. Similar double organs are the sex glands. These produce the germinating cells, the sperm cells in the man and the ova in a woman; they also produce sex hormones that flow through the blood and give rise to such secondary sexual traits as the beard of the male and the breasts of the female.

One gland, the hypophysis, which in the embryo has its origin in the roof of the mouth, migrates to the brain. The hypophysis, or pituitary gland (color portfolio plate 28), hangs under the brain like a fire bell, serving to regulate all the endocrine glands. It is, as we shall see, one of the most amazing organs in the body.

An outstanding example of the transformation of an old organ is the pineal body. Among the ancestors of man there must have been a reptile that spent its days lying lazily in the mire of primordial swamps, looking toward the sky through a third eye that developed out of the middle brain. Only some reptiles of an almost vanished prehistoric past around Australia still retain faint remnants of such an eye. In man this remnant has been transformed into a small cone-shaped body on the roof of the brain, the pineal body. The origin of the pineal body is truly one of the strangest stories in the history of the human body. Its function in man is unknown; some believe it is merely vestigial while others believe that it is an endocrine gland whose secretion affects the sex glands.

The Rhythm of Inner Secretions

Unlike the heart or skin or stomach, the hormonal glands do not work in the same way from the birth of the body to its death.

The life of man has three divisions. The first part is childhood, during which he grows; in this period the growth hormones from the pituitary are particularly active, while the sex glands are at rest. Then comes puberty, so called from the pubes, the hair around the genitals. This hair appears only after the genital glands begin to work, and they start only after the growth hormones are slowing down and the body has almost stopped growing. In the first third of life the body grows under the influence of the growth hormones. After that the sex glands govern an important part of the activity

of the body. About thirty years later these glands usually begin to wither, and the last part of life starts: old age. A woman's menstruation ends and with it her fertility; the man loses his potency and therewith the power to fertilize a woman. The hormonal glands determine the fate of man. A child with an underactive thyroid gland remains stunted physiologically, a cretin in mentality and sluggish in temperament. The hormonal glands may well be called the glands of our destiny.

The Thyroid Gland

The first organ recognized as a hormone gland was the thyroid. It consists of two bodies like small walnuts; they are connected by an isthmus and are located beside the larynx. It is the most conspicuous of the hormonal glands because it is directly under the skin and can be felt by touch when it becomes enlarged. When the thyroid develops one of the various disturbances to which it is subject, it becomes especially prominent. When one of the most frequent of these disorders, known as a goiter, occurs, it becomes enlarged.

In earlier times in some Alpine valleys, a considerable part of the population suffered from a strange ailment. They were afflicted with hard throat tumors that were sometimes as large as melons. In severe cases the victims sometimes showed more than the visible swelling on the throat, and tended to be physically dwarfed, sluggish in action and of borderline intelligence. Rarely did a girl with a severe goiter mature to the point of being able to bear children. All such victims invariably became a burden on the family and the community.

When surgical science had advanced to the point where operations could be performed with chloroform and aseptically, a courageous Swiss surgeon, Theodore Kocher, undertook to cut out such tumors, and did so successfully. Realizing that a goiter in a child was a sign of a diseased thyroid gland and could lead to the retarded state known as cretinism, Kocher decided to try to prevent this development by removing the gland itself. He did so, but after a promising start the child stopped developing mentally as well as physically. It degenerated into complete helplessness. The full

 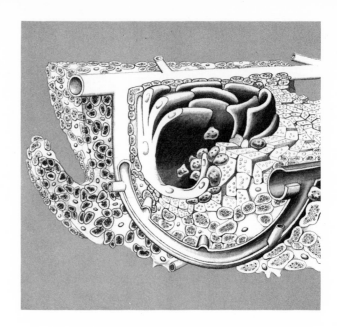

importance of the thyroid gland became immediately evident.

Thus the science of hormonology started with a very dramatic chapter. More than a thousand publications about goiter and cretinism followed. Entire congresses of scientists were devoted to it, but the mystery was not solved. The best answer to the problem is summed up in one word: iodine. The hormones produced by the thyroid gland, of which thyroxin is an example, all contain atoms of iodine. When iodine is deficient or lacking in the diet, the thyroid gland becomes enlarged in the desperate effort to produce its hormones. If no iodine at all is available, a baby becomes a cretin and an adult develops hypothyroidism or myxedema, a condition marked by serious underproduction of thyroid hormones.

Alpine valleys are relatively poor in iodine, and after long investigation of the goiter problem, scientists provided the whole population of Switzerland with a table salt enriched with iodine. This iodinization of the population doubtless had beneficial effects. The number of endemic cretins were reduced, as were goiters and myxedema, but cretinism itself was not erased. Other agents, in-

Details of three hormonal glands. The pineal gland, or body (left), hidden in the brain, is believed by some to secrete a hormone affecting the sex glands; others believe it to be merely vestigial. The thymus gland (center) has only recently aroused interest as a hormonal gland. It is largest in infancy and childhood and then atrophies with age. There is evidence that the thymus gland is of great importance in the development of immunity mechanisms and the formation of antibodies. In the adrenal glands (right), which cap each kidney, the inner layers of cells manufacture adrenalin while the outer, cortical layers produce corticosteroids such as cortisone.

cluding hereditary factors, are involved. In some families cretinism is frequent; others seem to be free of it. But so far that is all we know.

Basedow's Disease or Hyperthyroidism

Seemingly independent of regional influences is a disturbance of the thyroid first called Basedow's disease after the 19th-century physician who first described it.

Like all glands, the thyroid consists of the epithelium or producing tissue, and the connective tissue. The connective tissue does no work, but through it run the blood vessels, lymph vessels and nerves; it thus provides the epithelium with the means of producing its hormones. In healthy organs there is a proper balance between the two tissues. In the cretin, the unproductive connective tissue is, so to speak, overgrown and suffocates the epithelium so that the gland becomes immense and hangs dead on the neck. In Basedow's disease, it is the epithelial tissue that is hyperactive. The gland is again oversized but soft like a plum and only moderately swollen. The hyperactive thyroid gland overproduces the thyroid hormones which control the basal metabolic rate. The hyperthyroid patient is overactive, nervous, his heart beats too fast, he loses weight even though he eats a great deal and his eyes bulge to the point of making him appear pop-eyed.

There are three ways of treating hyperthyroidism today. In one the patient is given antithyroid drugs, which slow down the production of hormones. In a second procedure, enough of the overactive gland is removed so that the remainder produces a normal amount of the thyroid hormones. In the most recent procedure the patient drinks a solution of radioactive iodine which collects in the thyroid gland and destroys enough of it to reduce the hormone production to normal.

Parathyroid Glands

Besides the thyroid, or enveloped in it, there are the tiny parathyroid glands. These regulate the metabolism of phosphorus and calcium in the body through the parathyroid hormone. When the parathyroids are overactive, there is a loss of calcium and phosphorus from the bones and they develop cysts, or holes, and break easily. The amount of calcium in the blood increases and calcium is lost in the urine. Calcium in the blood is necessary for normal nerve function but when the blood calcium rises too high, nerves react sluggishly to stimuli. The patient loses his appetite, is nauseated and his muscles and ligaments lose their tone. Overactive parathyroid glands must be removed by means of surgery.

When the parathyroid glands are underactive, the blood calcium falls and calcification develops in various parts of the body. As a result of the lower blood calcium, the nerves become oversensitive to stimuli, muscles twitch, and convulsions, known as tetany, may follow.

Thymus

Until recently, the thymus gland was a mystery. It was known to be large in infancy and then to diminish steadily until only a remnant remained in adults. It has now been demonstrated in animals

195

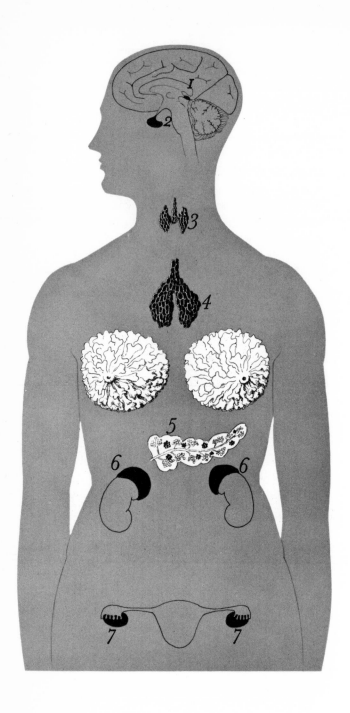

that the thymus is necessary in the late stages of embryonic development and in early infancy to develop the immunity mechanisms possessed by man and animals. The thymus sends young lymph cells and probably a hormone to the lymph nodes and spleen. As a result, the lymph and spleen become capable of producing antibodies—the method by which we combat infection.

The Islets of the Pancreas

The islets of the pancreas are marked by the wanderlust that is characteristic of hormonal glands. In the course of, say, a billion years, hormonal tissues immigrated in small groups into the big digestive gland behind the stomach. There they became islets of hormonal tissue producing insulin, the "island" hormone. Insulin controls the burning of sugar in the cells for the production of energy. How it does this is not completely known but it is believed that it permits sugar to pass through the walls of cells so that it can undergo metabolism inside the cell.

When the pancreas cannot manufacture enough insulin, or manufactures a chemically abnormal insulin, the body develops diabetes. Diabetes is an inherited disease but it is not an extremely dominant trait and it may not show up until late in life. The body of a diabetic patient is unable to burn sugar normally and the blood sugar becomes abnormally high. As a result, sugar is lost in the urine because the kidney tubules are unable to reabsorb the large amount of sugar that reaches the kidneys.

The most easily detectable sign of diabetes is sugar in the urine. The medieval doctor put his finger in the urine and tasted it; today precise chemical tests are used. A patient with diabetes is like a man who carries a bag of sugar with a hole in it: he buys five pounds but comes home with only four. The diabetic eats, but he does not have normal strength because he loses part of the energy in his food, and he remains hungry. The sugar he loses in the urine carries water along with it, so that the diabetic passes a great deal of urine and is constantly thirsty.

Ever since the Canadian doctor Frederick Banting extracted insulin from the pancreas of an animal, insulin injections have been available for the treat-

Location of the hormonal glands (in black): (1) pineal; (2) pituitary; (3) thyroid; (4) thymus; (5) pancreas; (6) adrenal and (7) ovary. The parathyroid glands are tiny and are either enveloped in the thyroid gland or are close beside it. The ovaries of a woman are paralleled by the testicles of a man, the latter being located in the scrotal sac. The mammary glands secrete milk and are not hormonal glands.

ment of diabetics. Since that time, antidiabetic drugs have been discovered; these can be taken by mouth and in some patients seem to stimulate a sluggish pancreas so that it secretes an adequate amount of insulin.

The Adrenal Glands

The adrenal glands, each perched over one of the kidneys, are double glands. The core, or medulla, manufactures adrenalin. Anger or fear stimulates this gland to secrete adrenalin into the blood stream. As a result, the heart beats faster, the liver sends sugar into the blood, the blood supply to the intestines is reduced and digestion stops, the blood supply to the muscles is increased, and the body burns sugar faster. In short, adrenalin makes it possible to meet an emergency by fight or flight.

As we have seen, the adrenal cortex secretes hormones called the corticosteroids. One such hormone is cortisone; the isolation and synthesis of this hormone was a sensational event. Cortisone affects the storage of the starch glycogen, thus of sugar in the liver, and it combats inflammation as well. The latter explains why cortisone and its chemical derivatives are used to treat rheumatoid arthritis.

Just as the islets of the pancreas may fail to function properly and permit diabetes to develop, a failure in the adrenal cortex may lead to Addison's disease. In this condition the patient loses sodium chloride through the urine and has difficulties with his glucose-glycogen metabolism. The outward manifestations are excessive weakness and fatigue, loss of weight, darkening of the skin, nausea, vomiting and diarrhea. The patient is also irritable and nervous. He is treated with corticosteroids.

The Pituitary Gland

The pituitary gland (also called the hypophysis) is the master gland of the body. Compared with other endocrine glands, it produces the largest number of hormones, including some that control the other endocrine glands of the body. For example, it produces a hormone, called ACTH. This hormone stimulates the functioning of the adrenal cortex. The pituitary gland also secretes a hormone known as TSH, and which stimulates the thyroid gland.

One of the most important hormones manufactured by the pituitary is a growth hormone. If too much of this is produced by the pituitary, a growing child becomes a giant. If not enough growth hormone is produced, the child will become a midget, a lilliputian, such as P.T. Barnum's most famous human curiosity, Tom Thumb. In rare cases the pituitary begins over-secreting growth hormone after the end of childhood; when this happens the bones of the hands, feet and chin continue to grow until they become abnormally large and produce a condition known as acromegaly.

Still another pituitary hormone sends commands to the uterus of a pregnant woman to start those spastic movements called labor that will help her to expel the child. The notice it sends out is: the child is ripe for birth. At the same time another pituitary hormone activates the breast of the mother to produce milk.

Other hormones of the pituitary gland work in other ways to serve the sex functions. One of them, the gonadotrophic hormone, ripens the gonads, or sex cells—the spermatozoa of the male and the eggs of the female. This hormone will be discussed in a later chapter.

20

The Basic Nervous System

An unimaginably complex network of nerve fibers carries sensory impressions to the spinal cord and brain and conveys messages back to all organs and tissues.

After they have passed through the gastrula stage, the embryos of all vertebrate animals develop into a fairly long oval plate divided into three layers, called the germinal layers. The final inner layer is the mother substance of the digestive system, and the middle layer forms the connective tissues, including blood vessels, heart, muscles and bones. The outer layer forms the skin and the nervous system.

The nervous system develops from a groove running along the middle line of the back. The cells of this groove are at first typical epithelial cells. Later they send out processes and become star shaped. The fully-developed nerve cell is large, has a sizeable nucleus in the center and sends out branches, or dendrites, in all directions. One of the dendrites is stronger and longer than the others and later becomes the axon. The special function of the nerve cell is to transmit stimuli. The dendrites, numerous but comparatively short, collect stimuli and carry them toward the cell; the axons, the cables we call nerves, carry the collected stimuli away from the cell.

Between the fine fibers of the nerve cell are bodies (which stain readily with basic aniline dyes) called the Nissl substance or Nissl's bodies. It is not certain what these bodies do but it is believed that they provide a specific nutritive substance for nerve cells that is rich in proteins. The Nissl substance is presumably "the daily bread" of the nerve cell. After a night's sleep we get up with our nerve cells full of fuel. Contrariwise, after a day's work we say: "I am worn out; I need rest and something to eat," or as a biologist might express it: "My nerve cells are drained of nucleic acid and I need proteins, vitamins and carbohydrates to replenish them."

As the daily increase and decrease of the Nissl substance indicate, the nerve cell is the nutritive center of the dendrites that carry the impulses produced by the cell. Under a microscope a nerve cell of the autonomic nervous system appears as a large globe surrounded by smaller, satellite cells. It is a sensory cell that collects impulses and responds to them by sending a message on through the main dendrite, the axon.

The central feature of the axon is a bundle of fibers. These are wrapped in a sheath that is the product of special cells present along the axon. These cells secrete a fatty substance, myelin, that evidently acts as insulation. To hold the butter-like

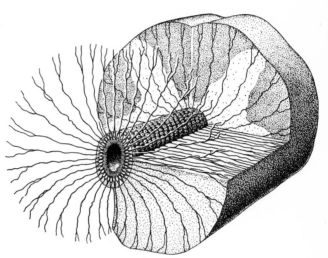

(Above) Embryonic neural tube. Neuroglia cells and the long fibers extending from them define the form and structure of the primitive neural tube.

(Left) Nerve cell. Various staining techniques reveal structural elements in the cell: nerve fibers (top); the nucleus (center), and the nutritive substance known as the Nissl bodies (bottom).

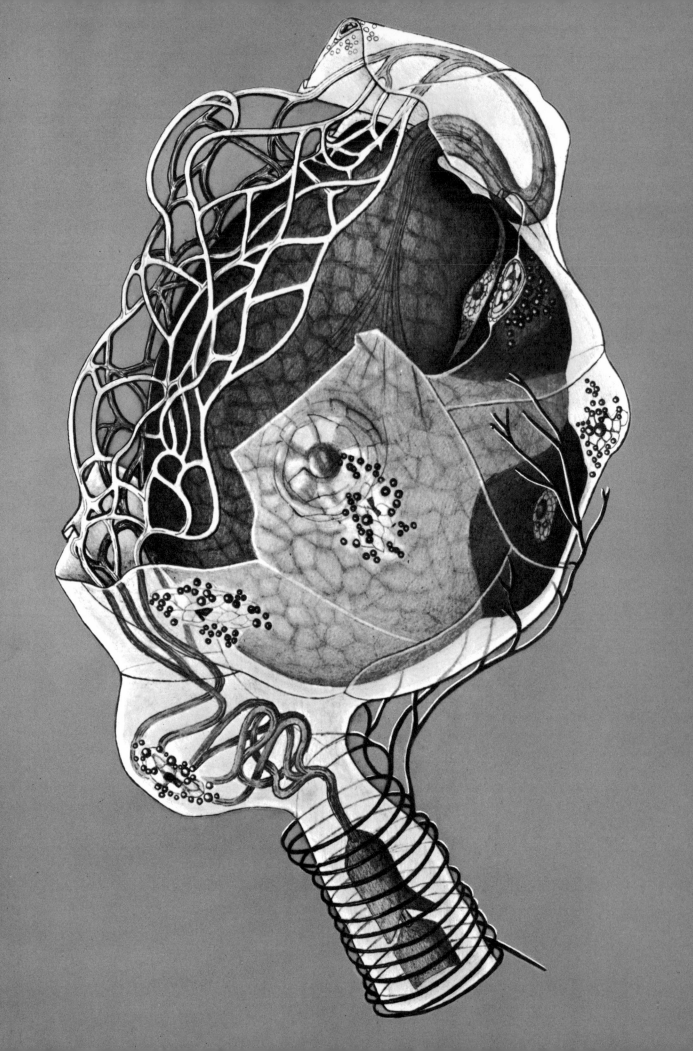

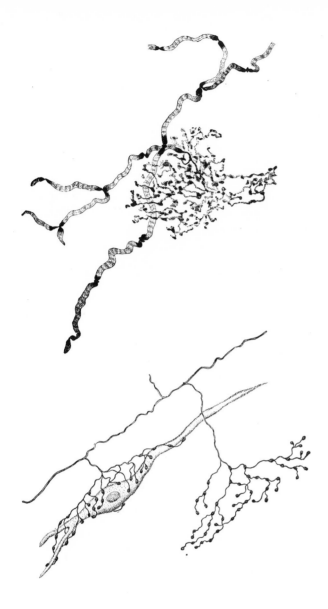

myelin together, it is wrapped in a net. At intervals of a millimeter or less, it is divided by narrow rings. A horny substance is also interwoven in the axon so that it is a masterwork of microscopic craftsmanship.

The axon carries an impulse a considerable distance, often as far as from the brain to a striped muscle fiber in a finger or toe. The device that connects the axon to the striped muscle is called the motor plate, and the place of contact between two nerve cells is a synapse.

The Neuroglia

In the last quarter of the 19th century the Italian anatomist Golgi discovered that *argentum nitricum*—the same compound of silver and nitrogen that we use in photography because of its sensitivity to light—colors the fatty substance of animal tissues black. The "Golgi" method became standard in staining microscopic slides. Investigators suddenly saw among the nerve cells a network of cells that had been thitherto invisible. All spaces between the nerve cells and fibers are filled with these cells; they are labeled "neuro-glia," from *glia*, the Greek word for glue. All we know at present is that a part of the neuroglia cells serve as messengers between the blood vessels and the nerve cells, play a part in the metabolism of nerve cells, and probably eat up dying nerve tissue.

Nerve Currents and Hormones

The most common terminal of nerves is the motor cushion that transmits the nerve impulse to the muscle fiber. It is amazingly similar to the electrodes of an old-fashioned electrical apparatus. Entering this cushion, the nerve loses its myelin sheath, and the fibrils end in naked knobs. It is here that the nerve current is transmitted to the muscle fiber. The presence of many mitochondria in the cells is a reliable indication that this is an area of great activity.

The electron microscope together with microchemistry have made possible revolutionary new discoveries concerning the mechanism of the nerve impulse. In the 19th century it was believed that

Transmission of stimuli. The nerve cell sends out many tiny branches of fibers (upper) to receive stimuli. The impulse is then either relayed to other nerve cells or transmitted to an organ (lower) so that an action can be carried out in response to the stimulus.

(Left) A nerve cell of the autonomic nervous system. This very complex cell helps collect impulses from the body's internal sensations and sends them to the central nervous system. It resembles a large globe surrounded by satellites, with fine nerve fibers wound around it as in an induction coil in an electrical relay.

201

Path of nerve fibers as seen in a cross-section of a nerve cell (1) and in a schematic drawing (2). A more complex path is shown in a longitudinal section (3) and a corresponding schematic drawing (4).

the nerve transmitted its impulse like an electric current. Now we know that the electric current is caused by an exchange of sodium, potassium and chloride ions that are the "electrolytes" of the body fluid.

The axis of the nerve is rich in potassium ions, whereas its exterior is rich in sodium ions. The resting cell has ions of opposite signs, positive and negative, equally distributed on both sides of the cell membrane. When a stimulus comes, an interchange of sodium and potassium ions takes place, as well as an exchange of the charges on each side of the cell membrane. This exchange, which lasts one millisecond, manifests itself as a current. Thereafter the nerve remains "depolarized" for eight milliseconds while the ions return to their original places. This exchange is repeated at the rate of 120 cycles per second (the alternating current which feeds our lamps works at about half as many cycles). After the revelation of this microchemical action came the discovery that the so-called electrodes at the ends of the nerves were—glands! These produce a substance called acetylcholine.

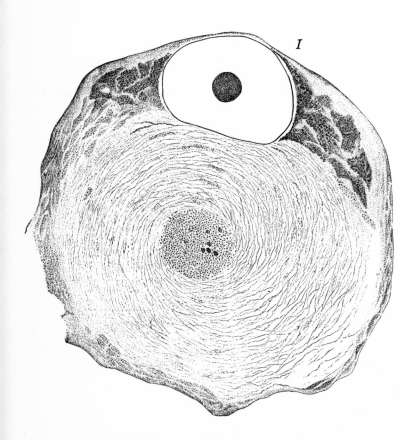 *I*

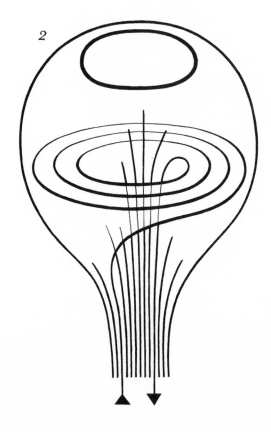 *2*

The exchange of the electrolyte atoms, the ions, which produces an electric current along the nerve to the muscle fiber, triggers the release of acetylcholine.

The Autonomic Nervous System

Few persons have a clear idea of the human nerve system because it is so complex. We start with the fact that the primordial part of the nervous system is the spinal cord, which runs through the central canal of the spine. But even older than the spinal cord, from an evolutionary point of view, are groups of nerve cells outside of the cord, called ganglia. Some of the ganglia are arranged in two chains along the spinal column; others are scattered among the tissues and organs of the body. These ganglia and their connections form the autonomic or involuntary nervous system (color portfolio plates 29–31).

It is not easy to say where the autonomic nervous system begins because its roots are buried deep in the brain, especially in the centers at the base of the brain. These centers act as the thermostats of temperature, and govern metabolism, the combustion of sugar, the distribution of body fluids, the tension of the arteries, perspiration, the digestive fluids, the excretion of the kidneys, and so on. There must be myriads of these roots, like those of an old vine.

Sympathetic and Parasympathetic Systems

The autonomic nervous system has two divisions: the parasympathetic and the sympathetic. Generally speaking, the internal organs, such as the heart, the lungs, the intestines, the uterus, the bladder and the glands, receive fibers from both divisions. The impulses traveling in the fibers of one division are antagonistic to those traveling in the other. For example, the smooth muscles of the intestines are relaxed by the sympathetic, but are stimulated by the parasympathetic; the heart beat is speeded up by the sympathetic, and is slowed

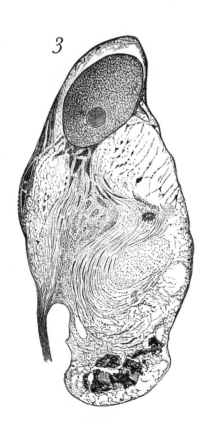

3

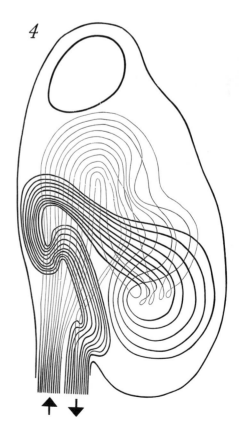

4

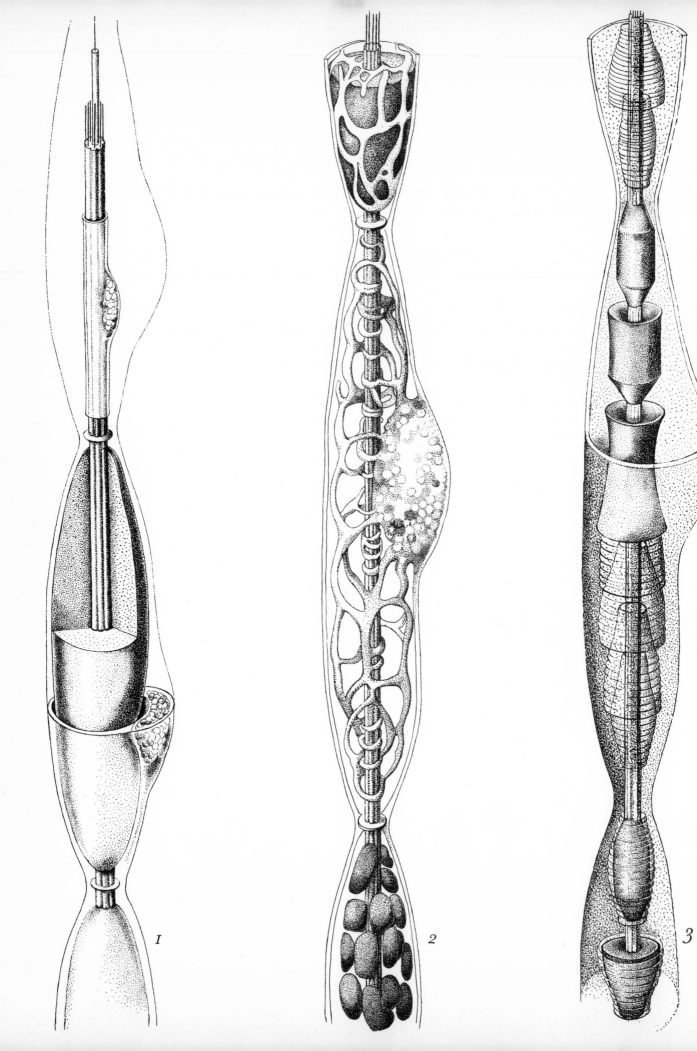

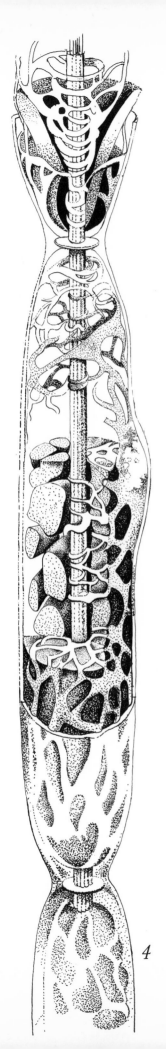

4

Structure of the axon. The axon is the only branch sent out by a nerve cell that conducts an impulse away from the cell. The fibers in an axon are contained in a sheath (1) produced by special cells which secrete a fatty insulating material called myelin (2). To hold the myelin together, the axon is wrapped in a net. It is also divided by narrow rings (3) and interwoven with a horny substance (4).

down by the parasympathetic. One of the cranial nerves, the vagus, carries parasympathetic nerve fibers along with it to many of the internal organs.

We are governed by sympathies and antipathies like a balloon that is at once blown by winds and held by gravity. Just as every vehicle has a brake as well as an accelerator, so we have an inhibiting force as well as an activating nerve impulse. We could not play a piano, drive a car or speak a word if we could not brake or restrain the muscles after stimulating them.

The sympathetic system was so called because it seemed to govern the sympathetic emotions. The vagus got its name from the way the vagus nerve wanders vagrantly through the intestinal organs, the heart, lungs and diaphragm and all organs of the abdomen. There is no corner where sympathetic and vagus fibers are not to be found. As vasomotor nerves, they follow the arteries from their great trunks down to the microscopic arterioles, regulating the flow of blood by opposed constriction and dilatation.

Two Phases of Personality

The sympathetic and vagus nerves act respectively like spurs and reins. The two systems do not act side by side, or in mutually exclusive areas, but are interwoven and entangled. There are areas where the sympathetic nerve behaves as if it were the vagus, and vice versa; we do not know why. And because it is so, we ourselves are not simple in our reactions but full of contradictions. In one area of our personality we are vagic and in another sympathetic; we are both good and bad, both generous and avaricious.

In general, the sympathetic nerve is the nerve of action and productivity; the vagus is the nerve of rest and relaxation. The sympathetic nerve opens the pupil of the eye, whereas the vagus closes it. The sympathetic accelerates the action of the heart; the vagus decreases it. Drugs that increase respiration are sympathicotonic; those that diminish the intake of air are vagotonic. Coffee stimulates the sympathetic current; a sleeping pill does not. Personalities can be classified as sympathicotonics or vagotonics. The sympathicotonic person is prone to excitement; the vagotonic reacts more slowly

and is inclined to depression. Like the two nerve fibers, the two personalities are interwoven. Most persons may be said to be both sympathicotonic and vagotonic.

Tonus and Blood Pressure

When we look at a plant and see that its leaves stand out firmly, we feel that it is in good condition. What we see is its "tonus." The same is true of the human body. When a friend's cheeks become pale and flabby, he has lost his "tonus" and we think of him as looking ill. Tonus is the tension characteristic of a living organism. In the human body all muscles are in a constant state of effortless tension that holds the skeleton upright and gives us the impression of a living human being and not of a manikin.

Tonus is, of course, necessary in all parts of the body. It holds the entrance to the stomach closed as if it were the valve of an oyster; it holds the ring of the anus tight so that we do not emit excrement; it holds the urinary bladder closed. Tonus is vital in our circulatory system, heart and arteries. Our blood system is an elastic tube regulated by a constant and specific pressure. The heart needs a certain resistance to work correctly. It wants exercise and work. It needs to be exerted to stay fresh. No trainer says to a boxer: rest. He must train to the limit to get the most out of his punch. The tonus of the arteries is measured by the pressure necessary to stop the flow of blood in one of the medium-sized arteries, and this is called blood pressure. Since the blood pressure gives invaluable information about the condition of the circulatory system it has become very important in modern medicine.

Neuroglia cells. Brain tissue stained by the Golgi technique reveals a startling network of cells in the central nervous system. These cells are important as structural elements but some undoubtedly also play a role in nerve metabolism or in disposing of broken-down nervous tissue cells.

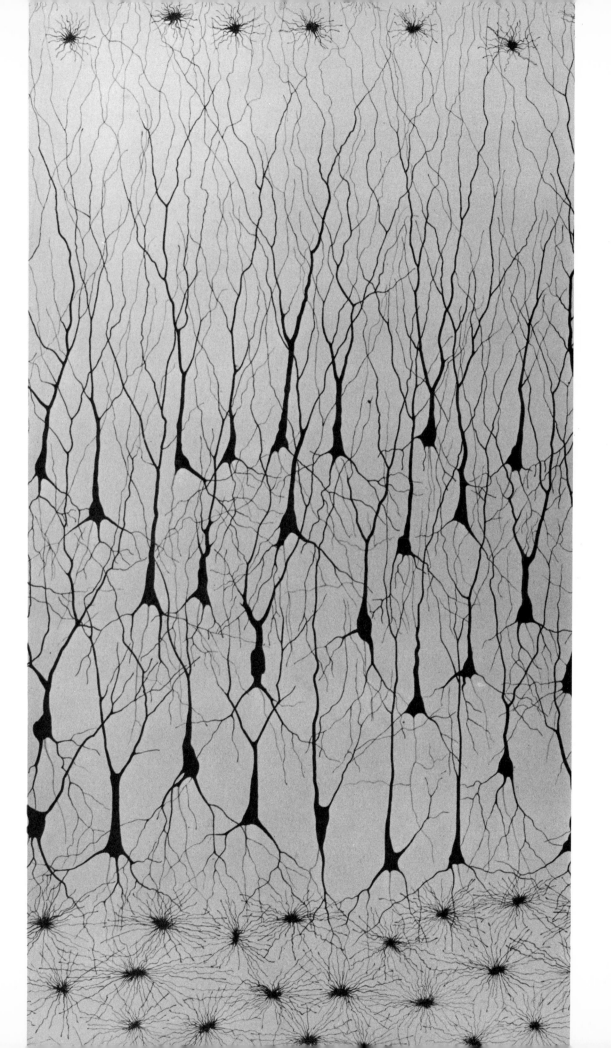

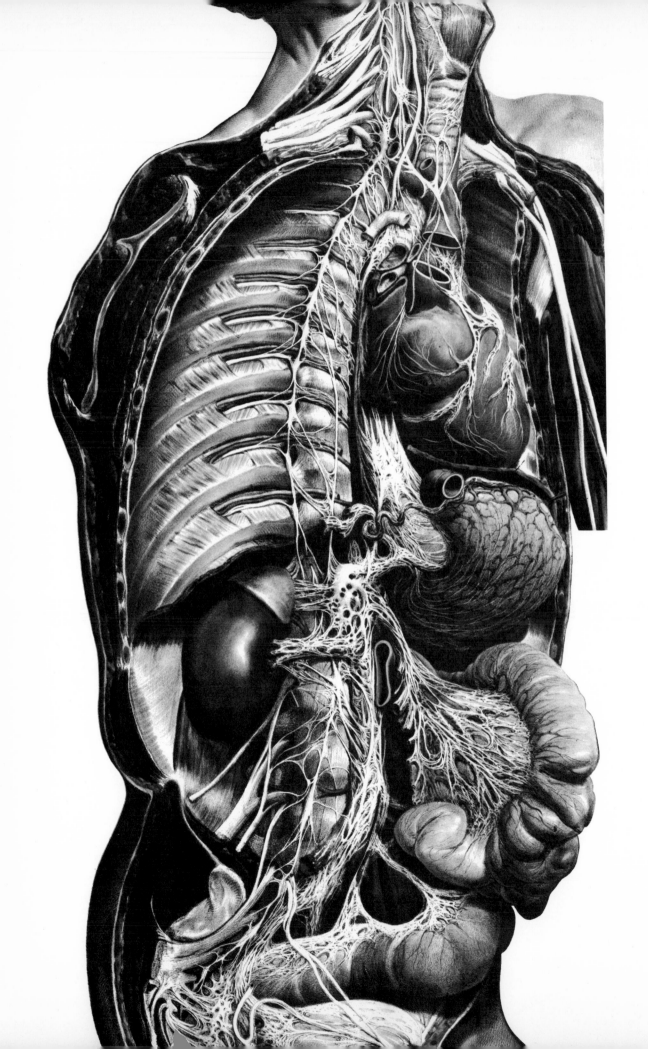

How Is Your Tonus Today?

We are accustomed to greet a person with the question, "How are you?" We should really say, "How is your tonus?" because what we call "feeling" is the state of our tonus. If our tonus is strong, we feel well; we love the whole world. During an average day, the tonus diminishes, and by evening we often feel "dead tired," like a violin with the strings loose. We say, "I have no pep," meaning "I have no tonus." The loss of tonus is visible in the face. Members of our family say: "You look tired." We try to raise the tonus by taking a warm bath or a cold shower, walking in fresh air, playing golf or tennis, drinking cocktails or coffee. All of these we call "tonics"—that is, stimulants to the tonus.

Shock

Shock is the sudden breakdown of the finely balanced equilibrium of the sympathico-vagus system. It is an earthquake in the realm of the autonomic system. The solar plexus, located on the rear wall of the abdomen, behind the stomach and in front of the aorta, is a collection of ganglia of the autonomic nervous system. It is highly sensitive. One of the fundamental points of boxing is the effectiveness of a blow in this center. A hard blow in the solar plexus is almost always a knockout blow because the blood pressure of the victim sinks, the heart misses its beat, the capillaries of the skin empty, and the reeling victim immediately loses consciousness.

The autonomic nervous system includes the sympathetic ganglia lying along the spine and the parasympathetic plexuses of the heart, stomach, intestines and the urinary system.

21

The
Spinal Cord

A cable of nerves in the spine collects sensations and relays many to the brain. It also carries messages from the brain to every part of the body.

(Facing page) *The spinal cord is a pathway carrying information to the brain and messages or commands from the brain to the muscles.*

Our nervous system is basically a relay system of neurons, that is, nerve cells that send their stimulus from cell to cell, through a long axon. It is based on four types or stages of neurons. The first one carries an impulse, a sensation: for example, from the hand up to the spinal cord. There the neuron ends, transferring the impulse either as a "reflex" to another neuron, which transmits the message to a reacting muscle, or the impulse continues along the next neuron up to the brain. The neurons to and from the brain form a cable twenty inches long—the spinal cord (color portfolio plate 25).

Just above the neck the spinal cord enters the brain and widens into the medulla oblongata (color portfolio plate 28), which is the lowermost portion of the brain stem. The medulla oblongata is one of the most important nervous centers in the human body. It may be compared to a central railroad terminal where the main streets of a city converge. From the medulla oblongata the neurons of the spinal cord radiate out on various paths to enter the structures of the brain. The widening medulla has a central cavity forming a kind of viaduct known as a ventricle. Here many of the ascending neurons end or make a connection with the next series of neurons that run to other areas or to the so-called brain stem.

Among the most important centers at the base of the brain are the thalami and hypothalami. The pituitary gland which is partly a hormonal gland and partly a nervous center is also attached to the base of the brain. In these deep centers of the brain are rooted the animalistic impulses: the urge to aggress and to kill, to dominate and to subject, the sexual urge, the desire to rape or to be raped, to love or to hate, to be a mother. Here lives what Freud calls the "unconscious." Here is the birthplace of the so-called more primitive passions.

The medulla oblongata is the upper terminal of the spinal cord. Here about half of the spinal neurons end, and a new neuron, which is usually the third or fourth, carries the impulse to the end station in the cortex of the brain.

Afferent, Efferent, and Inhibitory Nerves

Nerves that carry impulses from the outer parts of the body to the brain are called afferent or sensory

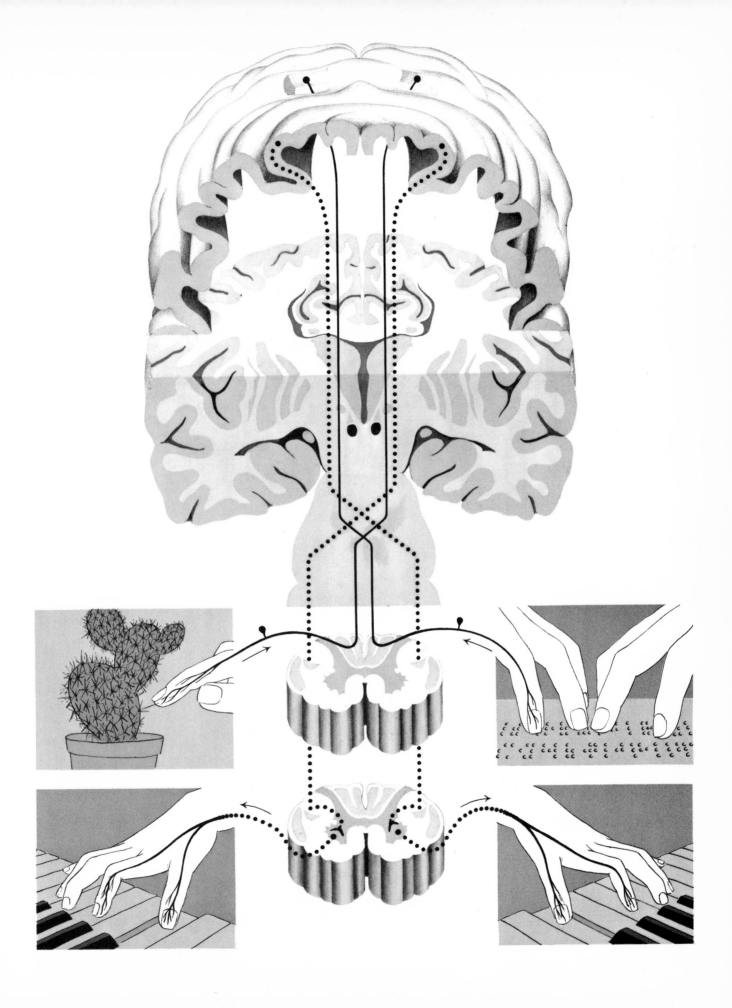

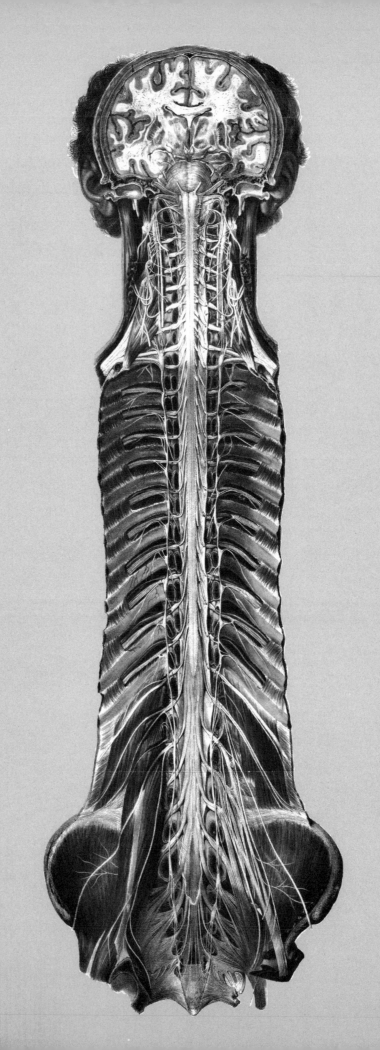

nerves. Nerves that carry impulses from the brain down to the muscles or glands are called efferent or motor nerves. The spinal cord and the brain form the central nervous system. The peripheral nervous system consists of twelve pairs of so-called cranial nerves directly attached to the brain and thirty-one pairs of nerves issuing from the spinal cord. The cranial nerves include the nerves of smell, sight, hearing, taste, the vagus as well as others.

It has been found that nerves contain not only motor and sensory fibers but also fibers of the autonomic nervous system. "Tonus fibers" send out a steady current that holds in tonic tension the fine smooth muscles of the skin, the openings of the stomach, of the bladder, the anus, the vagina, and the windpipe. Besides stimulating motor fibers, every motor nerve also carries inhibitors, just as our autos have brakes as well as accelerators.

The Reflex

Generally the impulse of a nerve—for example, the feeling of pain after touching a hot stove—is carried through the relays of neurons in the spinal cord upward to the medulla and the brain, and is thereafter registered by the cells of the cortex. But not all impulses travel this way. The nerve cells of the spinal cord are connected through dendrites (numerous short branches of the nerve cells) with other nerve cells nearby. One or more of these dendrites may lead to a neuron that conducts the efferent motor impulse from the brain back to the muscles, the original area of sensation. It is a kind of "short circuit"; the impulse does not reach the cortex of our brain, which is the sole organ of conscious feeling. In such a case we react before we become aware of what has happened. This short circuit of the nerves is called a reflex.

We walk in a dusty city street and a speck blows into one of our eyes. Our eye "window," the cornea, which is extremely sensitive, immediately reacts: our eyelids close and tears flow over the eye to wash away the intruder. The reaction is almost instantaneous; we have no time to think or deliberate. We are the subject of a reflex. Other familiar reflexes include coughing when food gets into the windpipe, and vomiting and sneezing. Hundreds of such reflexes are working steadily within us without any conscious direction from us; they are in fact the most common type of action in the body. Almost all the activity of our visceral organs, such as breathing, the pumping of the heart, the movement of our intestines and stomach, and the flow of the bile and the pancreas, are reflex actions. The reflexes ease the burden of the brain. We do not have to think about breathing; reflexes do this work for us. It is estimated that more than twenty thousand reflex relays are constantly at work to keep the machinery of the body operating without waiting for special commands from the cortex.

The spinal cord contains two main elements: the sum of the reflex arcs that run out horizontally, and the tracts that ascend to and descend from the brain in the form of sensory and motor nerves. The neurons are grouped, according to their function and destination, in a motor tract, a sensory tract, the anterior, posterior, and lateral tracts, and the tract that leads to the cerebellum. Many neurons end at the top of the spinal cord in the medulla oblongata, the most complex "traffic center" of the nervous system. Here the spinal cord passes through the narrow ring of the uppermost vertebrae, and we come upon one of the most wonderful and mysterious creations of nature—the brain.

The spinal cord, central cable of the nervous system, is about eighteen inches long. Thirty-one pairs of nerves run out from its sides to all the peripheral parts of the body.

22

The Brain

Like the master controls of a computer system, a cluster of nerve centers in the brain coordinates all the basic physical functions, from heart action to metabolism, and all mental processes, from remembering to imagining.

The human brain (color portfolio plates 25–28) is a partly fluid and partly solid mass. (A calf's brain, available at any butcher shop, will give a good idea of the basic features of the human brain.) Surprisingly more than eighty per cent of the brain is water. The rest consists of proteins of a high order, rich in phosphorus, intermingled with molecules of lipids and certain complex sugars called cerebrosides. As might be expected, the brain has a very vigorous metabolism and needs an almost constant supply of sugar. Its need for oxygen is almost twenty-five times as great as is that of muscles.

Dreams

The brain seems never to rest. During sleep it continues to be active, and we have the illusion that what we experience in sleep resembles what we experience when awake. We describe this sleeptime activity of the brain as dreams. In waking periods we can experience only the actual events of life. During our dreams, however, the nerve cells raise havoc with reality; they behave like children when their parents are away from home. All order, sense and control are gone. Vision follows vision as it pleases. We become the victims of the memories and images in our cortex cells.

Modern science has begun to explore sleep and dreams with the help of electrical devices. The pupils of our eyes, the window through which we look at the world, are closed by muscle rings that are very sensitive and react by opening and closing during excitement. Every movement of these muscle rings can be registered by electrical devices. These devices record electrical impulses that indicate whether or not we are experiencing dreams. The curves of these "dream currents" reveal that we dream during sleep much more than we are able to remember the following morning. They also allow us to measure the effect of sleep and tranquilizers. Maybe one day we may even be able to photograph the contents of our dreams.

The Brain Stem

The brain stem is a firm mass at the base of the brain which holds that sensitive and vulnerable

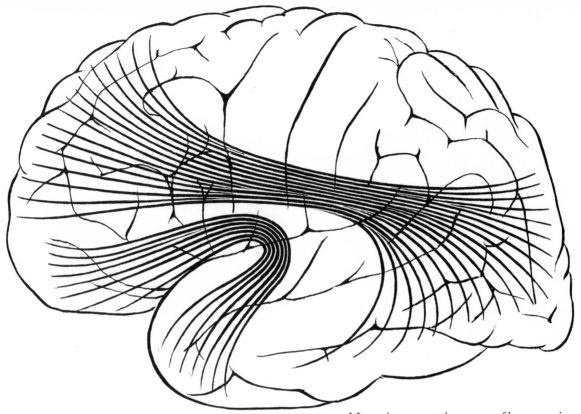

Many interconnecting nerve fibers running between the different parts of the brain carry on a multitude of integrative functions.

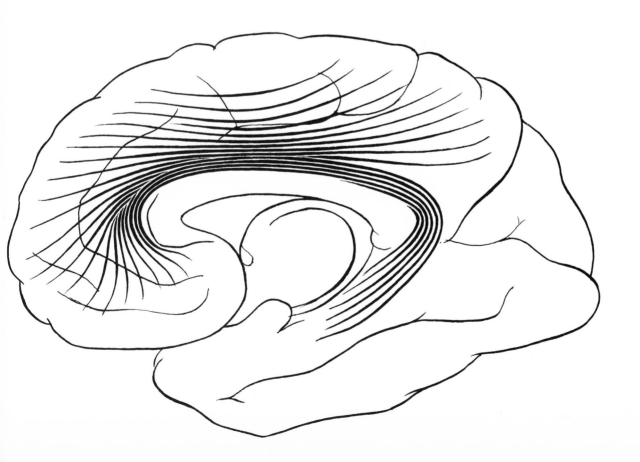

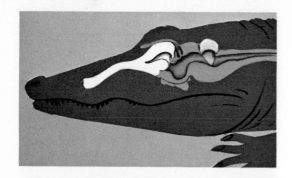

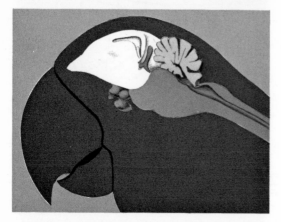

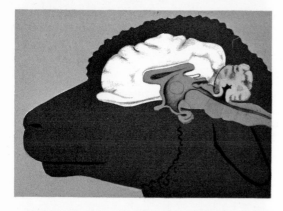

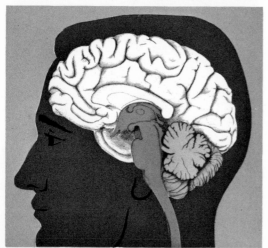

Evolution of the brain from reptile to man. A comparison of four brains, crocodile, parrot, sheep and man, reveals the importance of the brain stem (shown in gray), the controlling center of the automatic functions in reptiles and animals. The cerebellum, the center of balance and equilibrium is most highly developed in birds. In man the cerebellar mass is enveloped by the highly developed forebrain (in white), or cortex, which is peculiar to higher mammals and particularly man.

Topography of the brain, showing (1) the cerebrum; (2) the corpus callosum; (3) the thalamic and hypothalamic areas; (4) the cerebellum and (5) the medulla oblongata.

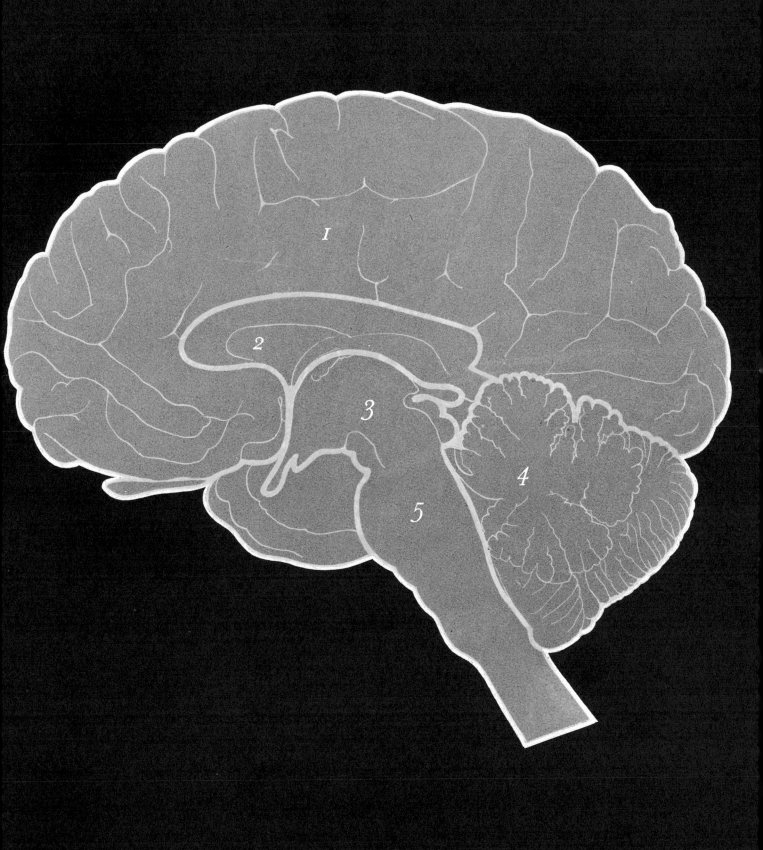

organ securely like a crown at the top of the body. The fishes, ancestors of the mammals, had no "brain" but only such a brain stem. After the fishes came the amphibians and the reptiles; in them the old fish brain developed the neopallium, which we call the brain.

The brain stem of man is a conglomeration of centers. When the brain stem was still the brain of our ancestors the fishes, the "soul" resided in its brain stem. Later the "soul" rose into the higher spheres, and today we regard the cortex of the brain behind the marble wall of the forehead as the "palace of the soul." We thus have two souls; one deep in the brain stem, the animal soul, or thalamus soul, and one high up on the surface of the neo-brain. The former is, so to speak, the "animal" in us, the strong but not easily defined urges we call instincts. They can be good and bad: the extremes are illustrated in the very beginning of biblical history where on the one hand Eve seduces Adam, Cain murders his brother, and Lot rapes his daughters, and on the other hand in Abraham and Jacob, who strive to fulfill the ideals of humanity.

Body Heat and Fever

Centers in the brain stem control the autonomic nervous system; this is the master of the whole complex of automatic functions that keep the body going without a moment's interruption. One of those functions is control of the body temperature. Unlike the cold-blooded animals, the human body maintains a constant temperature, normally 98.6° Fahrenheit when measured inside the mouth (it is somewhat higher in the blood, and somewhat lower on the skin). The thermostat that makes sure that the heat produced by the metabolic process in the body will be balanced by the heat loss, is the hypothalamus. On a hot day, or when heat production in the body increases—as after a meal— the hypothalamus directs an increased flow of blood to the skin, our capillaries dilate, our sweat glands become active and we lose heat. The reverse action takes place on a cold day, and we shiver in order to stir up increased heat production.

During illness, the thermostat sets itself at a higher level and we develop a fever; in some degree this may be a defense mechanism since certain

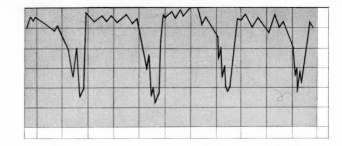

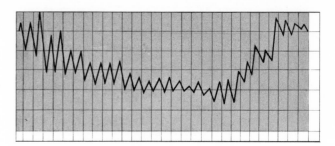

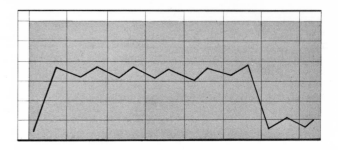

Body temperature. One function of part of the brain stem, the hypothalamus, is the thermostatic maintenance of a constant body temperature, normally 98.6° Fahrenheit. The hypothalamus insures a balance between heat produced by metabolism and heat normally lost by the body. During illness, the thermostat adjusts to a higher level and we develop a fever.

(Facing page) Crossing pathways to the brain. All nerve fibers carrying messages to and from the parts of the body converge at the spinal cord or above it and there cross to the opposite side. This crossing of pathways explains why disturbances on one side of the brain are revealed by abnormalities in the opposite half of the body.

invading bacteria probably cannot withstand a high body temperature. Fever therapy used to be a popular method of treatment before the days of antibiotics: and patients would be placed in heated boxes to raise their body temperature two or three degrees. But the body cannot stand a temperature of even eight or ten degrees above normal for any length of time; 108° Fahrenheit for even a short period is fatal.

During the past few decades, scientists have been investigating the various areas of the brain stem to discover what functions they control. The investigators have worked with animals such as cats and monkeys and have tried drugs, electric currents and surgical operations. First, surgeons isolated the thalamus from the neighboring centers, cutting the connections between it and the neo-brain. The cats or monkeys that were operated on showed the kind of symptoms we observe in mentally disturbed persons, such as instability and aggressiveness.

With the greatest care trained specialists began to perform comparable operations on ailing mental patients. One such operation is a lobotomy, in which the connections between the frontal lobe and the brain stem are severed. The results were not uniform and proved unpredictable. In some cases the effects were miraculous: patients who had been so withdrawn that they had to be committed to mental hospitals returned home and became peaceful and socially acceptable members of society. But in other cases the personality was radically changed. A hitherto asocial person who had avoided social gatherings became so uninhibited and indiscriminately gregarious that his family grew alarmed.

One operation of this kind has proved promising in the treatment of aging persons suffering from Parkinson's disease, a malady marked by a tremor of the hands and sometimes also of the head. The physician injects a freezing solution into the thalamic region in order to counteract the nervous rigidity that grips the victim. In many instances this has been very successful.

The Cerebellum

A major center of the brain stem is the cerebellum, a word that is a diminutive of the Latin *cerebrum*, meaning brain.

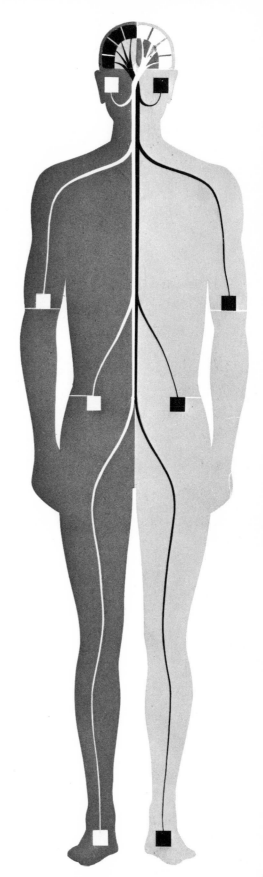

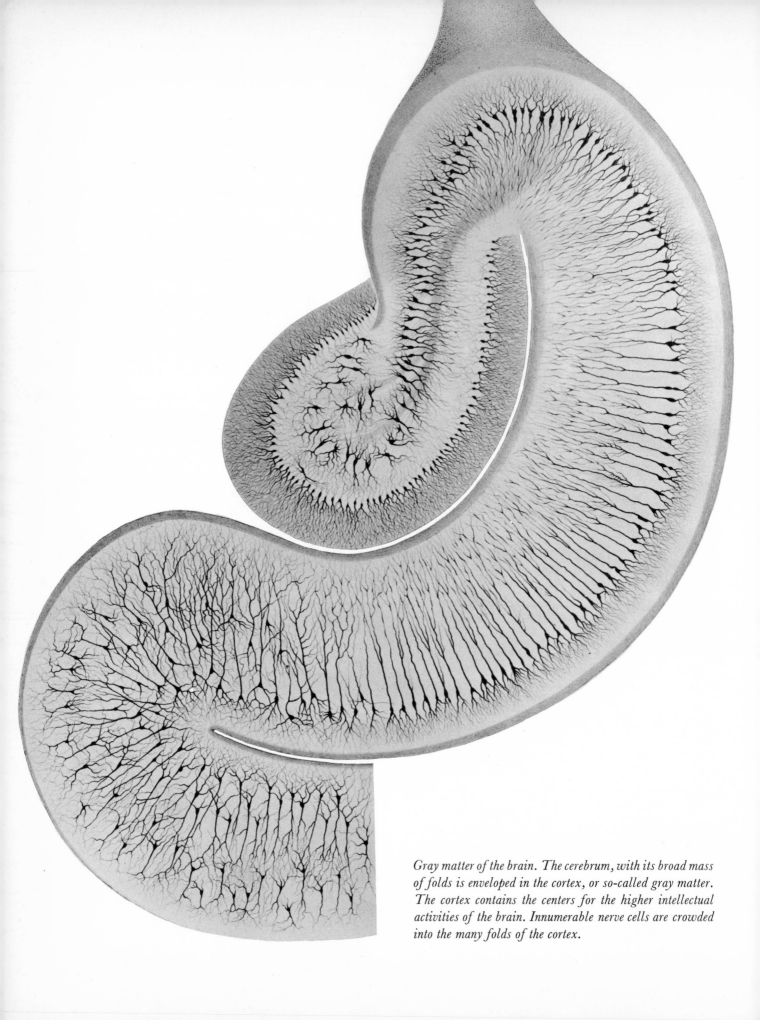

Gray matter of the brain. The cerebrum, with its broad mass of folds is enveloped in the cortex, or so-called gray matter. The cortex contains the centers for the higher intellectual activities of the brain. Innumerable nerve cells are crowded into the many folds of the cortex.

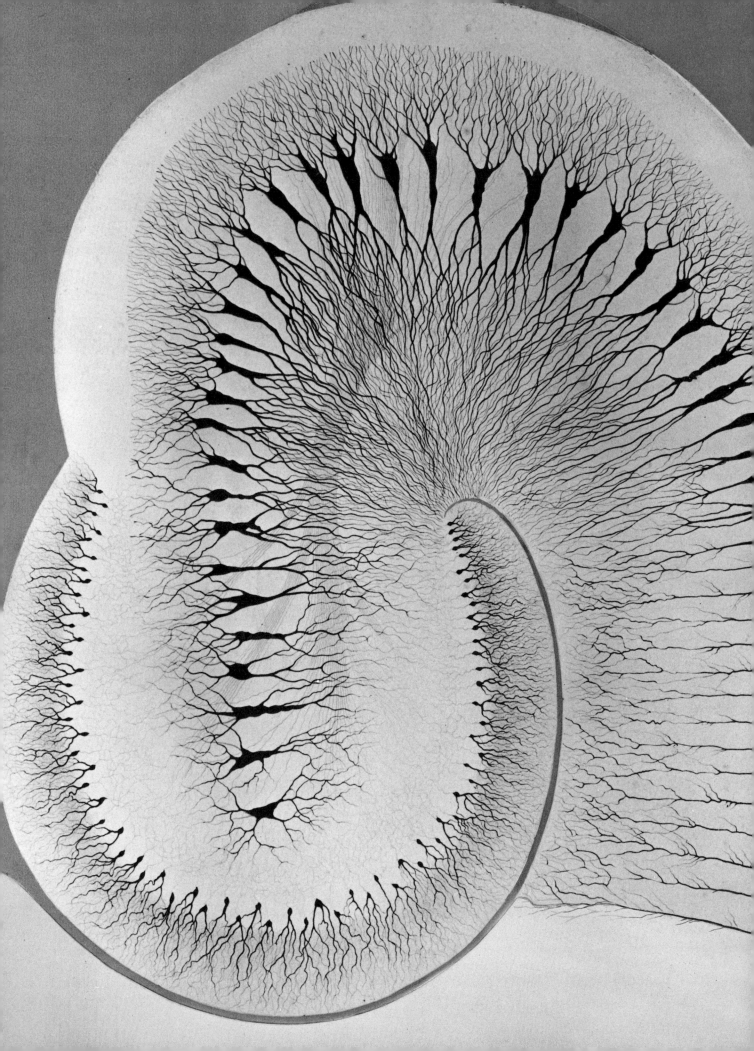

The cerebellum is the central gyroscope of the human body. It may be compared to the instrument board of an airplane. Since it is not, so to speak, a psychic or intellectual part of the brain, it is not a new acquisition but one that developed far back in the history of fishes. It was already highly developed among fishes that were good swimmers and jumpers and it reached its highest development among the birds (who are not forerunners of man but members of a side-genus). Birds use the cerebellum more than any other genus because flight and air acrobatics depend so heavily on it.

In man the expanding brain has engulfed and overshadowed the cerebellum, shunting it into a corner between spine and brain, like a Cinderella. The cerebellum collects impulses arriving from the semicircular canals, and from hundreds of muscles and ligaments. The tension of the muscles informs it of the position of the body. These impulses are registered, classified and are then transmitted through the spinal cord to the muscles of the skeleton so that the body can be brought into balance.

After we have studied the delicate organization of a dozen different cells with their complex inter-relationships—there are at least ten million in the cerebellar mass—we are not surprised that maladies of the cerebellum, such as tumors or hemorrhages, cause major disorders. If you deprive a dog of half of its cerebellum, it loses its powers of balance and when it tries to run in a straight line tends always to the left or right.

The Forebrain

What we call the brain is the neopallium, which covers the ancient fish brain with a curving, cauliflower-like mass of gray substance. It is enveloped in a cortex, or rind—the gray matter—of about ten billion nerve cells distributed in about six layers. The network of connecting fibers in the human brain is too complex and fine for us to disentangle.

The brain is composed of two elements: the gray matter and the white matter. The spinal cord contains relatively little gray matter; most of the cord consists of white matter in the externally located axon fibers. In the brain, the gray matter, consisting of nerve cells, makes up a major portion of the cortex. Beneath the gray matter, which is like the shell of a walnut, is the white matter, again made up of axon fibers and constituting the tracts running to different centers of the brain and out of the brain to the spinal cord.

We perform the principal part of our brain work, thinking, feeling and reacting, in the cortex. The combining and testing of ideas take place in the association areas of the cortex. These are such moments as when in a chess game a player studies the table and considers his next move as well as the possible moves of his opponent. At such a time, the association areas of the cortex, as well as the sensory and motor areas, are brought into play.

The ten billion cortex cells and the white fibers—white because the fibers are covered with whitish myelin sheaths—are logically organized. All sensory cells collecting impulses from the outside are concentrated in what is known as the sensory area. All the voluntary motor cells that respond to these impulses and send a current to start action in the muscle fibers are just behind the sensory area.

In terms of evolutionary history our forebrain is a very modern organ. In the age of the fishes the nerve tracts conducted the sensory impressions of the eyes to the stem of the brain. During the era of the reptiles these tracts were enlarged and the optical impressions that had previously been carried to the brain stem were conducted to the cortex. In higher mammals such impressions were carried over new paths to the rear end of the cortex. The way human beings perceive images on the retina of the eye, using cells in the rear of the brain that combine the processes of seeing, memorizing and associating, constitutes an entirely new principle found only in the higher mammals.

This new development in man's forebrain is as revolutionary a step forward as a computer is over an abacus. It is the organ whereby a Toscanini can look at the printed score of a symphony and be able to conduct a hundred-man orchestra years later without having the score in front of him.

A curious feature of the central nervous system is the crossing of pathways from one side to the other. The afferent nerve fibers that carry the sensations of pain, heat, cold, touch, pressure and position from various parts of the body reach the spinal cord by means of the spinal nerves. On their way these fibers from one side of the body cross to the other side of the spinal cord or the brain stem and thus go to the brain centers and cerebral cortex of the opposite side. The motor fibers making their way from the motor areas of the cerebral cortex also cross.

This crossing of the motor fiber takes place in the pyramidal tracts, so called because these tracts have the shape of pyramids. About three quarters of the way down the medulla oblongata the pyramidal tracts cross and then continue on down the spinal cord to the various spinal nerves and the various muscles of the opposite half of the body. Thus a hemorrhage or tumor on one side of the brain causes a paralysis in the opposite half of the body.

There is an additional system of motor fibers that arises in centers of the brain stem, rather than in the motor area of the cortex. Known as the extrapyramidal system, its fibers do not cross as they pass down the spinal cord. In birds, amphibia and reptiles the extrapyramidal system is the highest control center for purposeful motor activities. In man, the extrapyramidal system is still present but its function has been taken over mainly by the pyramidal tracts. What function the extrapyramidal tract performs in man is still in the realm of Nature's mysteries.

23

Psychosomatics

Vital in the health of the individual is the influence that thought and emotion have on the body, and, contrariwise, that the body has on the mind or psyche.

The term psychosomatic is a composite of the Greek *psyche,* the mind, and *soma,* the body, the combination referring to the interaction of mind and body in the functioning of the human organism. The intimate relationship between psychic disturbance and physical illness is something that has long been known. A tale from ancient India tells of a princess who fell ill of a sickness that no physician could diagnose. Finally, a doctor famous for his wisdom and skill was called to the palace. He ordered all the men in the royal court to pass the girl's bedside. While this was taking place the doctor held her hand and observed the beat of her pulse. As the thirty-sixth man passed by, the physician cried, "Stop!" and announced that the girl was sick for love of this youth. A similar scene is painted by a Flemish artist. In it one sees a doctor with his hand on the pulse of an ailing woman. The family looks worried, but the doctor is smiling and in the background a woman is making familiar gestures indicating that the source of the trouble is only love.

All of us have had experiences in which a thought or emotion has had a strong effect on body functions, as, for example, when we are so frightened that we tremble or break out in a cold sweat or get "goose flesh" or cold chill. There are times when we are so shocked that we cannot speak or catch our breath, or when we are so apprehensive that we get stomach cramps. But the best-known example of a psychosomatic reaction is blushing. We feel embarrassment or shame and in a moment the blood vessels of our face dilate, our cheeks redden— and reveal our thoughts and emotions. Or there is the opposite effect: we receive sad news, the blood vessels of the face contract and we grow pale. Psychosomatic reactions are not restricted to such visible manifestations. If we connect a manometer to the urinary bladder and tell the patient: "Now think of a holdup man jumping out at you on a dark street," the bladder immediately contracts and the needle of the manometer goes up. We are not *soma* alone or *psyche* alone: we are *psychosomatic.* All the organs of the body are affected by the mind.

The body also affects the mind. We all know how our spirits fall when we are ill. This is true even when the illness is a minor one and of short duration, such as a cold. And how anxious and fearful we become when we are seriously ill! The problem of the physician in many instances is to decide whether the mind is affecting the body or whether an ailing body is affecting the mind. Are the patient's difficulties *psychosomatic* or are they *somatopsychic?*

Modern medicine looks upon certain diseases as especially influenced by the mind, and perhaps even caused by the mind. These are diseases where all tests show no physical cause. An example of this are ulcers of the duodenum and the stomach. These are called peptic ulcers because the enzyme pepsin, together with hydrochloric acid secreted by the stomach, does not confine its digestive powers to food but also digests a part of the wall of the duodenum or the stomach and causes an ulceration.

Peptic Ulcer

Individuals with peptic ulcers are usually anxious and tense by temperament and develop their ailment during periods of great stress. It is believed that anxiety and tension in the cortex of the brain affect the autonomic nervous system; the center in the brain stem controlling the stomach glands is overstimulated and causes an oversecretion of hydrochloric acid and pepsin, which leads to the ulcer. The doctor treats the patient with antacids to neutralize the hydrochloric acid. He also prescribes a drug that acts against the parasympathetic nerves and possibly a tranquilizer to relax the patient's mind.

Hypertension

Another example of a psychosomatic ailment is hypertension. This is a complex disease because sometimes a specific organic cause for the hypertension can be located. Usually, no such cause for the hypertension is found. It is then assumed that stress and tension are affecting the autonomic nervous system and causing the center controlling blood pressure to react abnormally. The doctor treats such hypertension with tranquilizers and with drugs that counteract the effects of the sympathetic

nervous system. Among the other disturbances now thought of as psychosomatic are ulcerative colitis, migraine and other types of headache, and irregularities in menstruation.

Even such a disease as asthma, where a specific cause such as an allergy to pollen, house dust, or animal fur can be identified, has important psychosomatic aspects. Typical is the girl of five who suffered from asthma. Every few weeks there is a night of terror. The whole family must comfort her. A specialist is consulted. After much testing, the cause of the asthma, an allergy, is found: horsehair. The girl is sent to live with distant relatives and after three months the attacks subside; in another few months they disappear entirely. But as soon as the girl returns the asthma recurs. The physician begins to study the case from a psychosomatic point of view. The girl is an only daughter, intelligent but demanding attention, especially from her father. But he goes bowling several nights a week and golfing on weekends. One day he has an accident and has to give up his sports. He begins to spend much more time at home and devotes more attention to his daughter. The asthma attacks dwindle and finally disappear.

The psychological aspects of disease are well recognized today but we are only at the threshold of understanding the factors involved. The brain and its dynamics are staggeringly complex. Some investigators assert that man's brain is actually a composite of three brains. First there is the brain stem, which is still pretty much the reptilian brain. Over this is the simple cortex that the lower mammals developed and that man has retained. Superimposed on this old cortex is man's splendid new cortex with its massive cerebral hemispheres. When Eve in the garden of Eden said that the snake tempted her, she may have meant that it was the reptilian brain within her that tempted her. When we talk of the animal nature in man, we are referring to the old cortex and its connections with the brain stem. And when we talk of psychosomatic disease—or of mental diseases generally—we may be talking of conflicts among our brains and the effects these conflicts have on us—the proud possessors of three brains.

24

The Skin

A tough, self-rejuvenating layer of cells covering the body protects it and helps control its temperature and secrete its wastes.

The skin, the cover of the body, is made up of two tissues, a strong underlying one of connective tissue, the dermis, and an outer covering of epithelial cells, the epidermis. Under the dermis is a layer of loose connective tissue that enables the skin to move easily on the muscles or bones over which it lies.

Epithelial cells occur as a layer, called epithelium, covering all the outer and inner surfaces of the body. In the tongue, for example, the epithelium is the mucous membrane. The characteristic formation of the epithelium is a gland. First the epithelial cells form a cavity and then the walls of the cavity produce secretions. The glands specialize: some excrete watery products like sweat, while others produce a fatty product like the oil on our skin, or a mucous fluid like saliva. The glands of the stomach produce the acid gastric juices, the liver glands the bile and the hormonal glands the hormones.

The Epidermis

The dermis and the epidermis are knit together by plugs, millions of microscopic cones called papillae. In the apes and man, the papillae of the palms and the soles of the feet are arranged in ridges. If you look at the skin on your fingertips, you will see that it forms a fine pattern of whorls: these are the ridges. Each individual finger pattern is unique, so that it can serve for identification. Such "fingerprints" were used long before written signatures became common. In the ruins of Nineveh we find fingerprints as signatures on commercial and marital contracts.

In the 19th century the French introduced a clever system of identification of criminals by the criminologist Bertillon. It depended on careful body measurements, scars, and personality characteristics. Then an Argentinian, Juan Vucetich, decided that the Bertillon system was clumsy in comparison with the simple fingerprinting method, and he utilized the latter for criminal identification. His technique was refined by E.R. Henry and became widely used in English-speaking countries. A bitter fight raged between the English and French criminologists until finally the dactyloscriptists of the English school won. The criminologists agreed to restrict themselves to twelve characteristics, and a formula was developed that can be telegraphed

(Facing page) The skin, a magnified view showing: (1) outer layer of the epidermis containing horny cells; (2) the inner layers of the epidermis containing pigmented cells; (3) the dermis; (4) blood vessels of dermis; (5) lymph vessels; (6) a sensory nerve ending to register touch; (7) a shaft of hair with its membranes, surrounding lymph vessels, and the nerve fibers around the shaft; (8) a pair of sebaceous glands, which provide oil; (9) sweat gland spiraling to the surface pores; (10) a deep, insulating layer of fat cells.

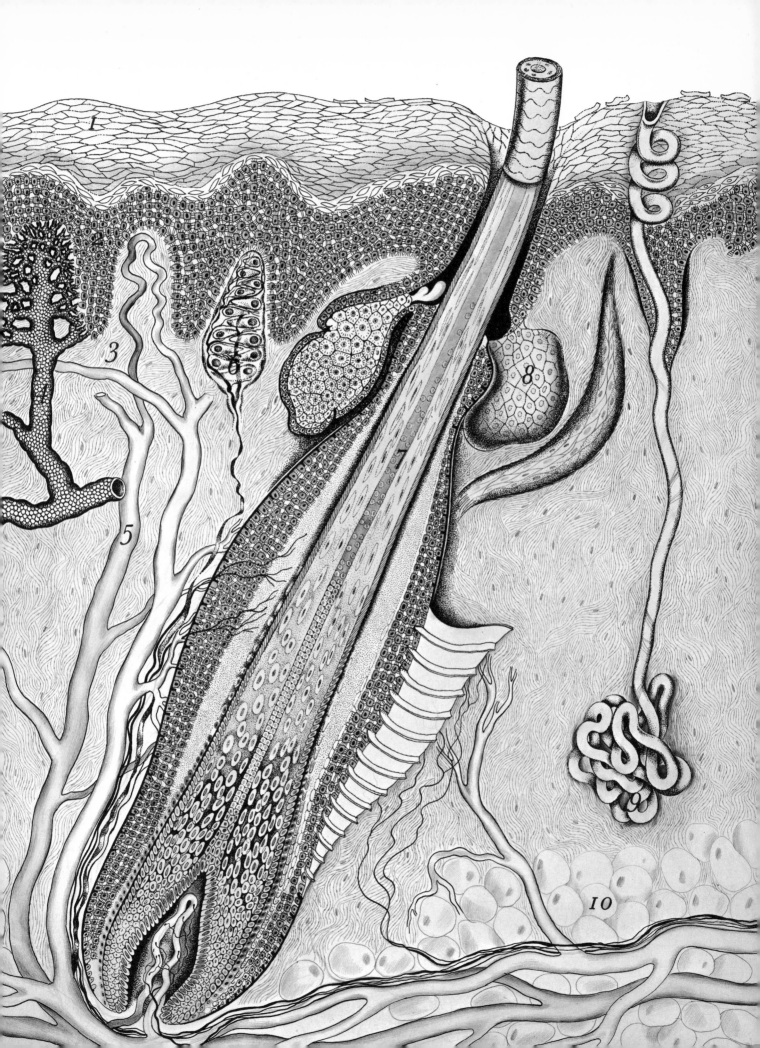

and can identify an individual in a matter of minutes. If the fingerprints of everyone on earth were registered, it would, according to the laws of probability, require four billion years before one would find the same fingerprint.

The epidermis consists of epithelial cells making up about four main layers. The lowermost layer, nearest to the blood vessels, is productive, and proliferates new cells uninterruptedly. As the new cells appear, the outer cells, pushed outward, die, dry up, and form, like the fallen leaves of an autumnal forest, a layer of dead and horny cells. These dead cells are daily brushed away and replaced by the new cells underneath. The continual sloughing off of the outer layer and its replacement is the secret of the persisting youthfulness of the skin.

The lowermost level of the epidermis is also important because it contains cells with a pigment—melanin. The color of a Negro is due to the fact that he has more melanin in these cells. The activity of such pigment cells is increased by ultraviolet rays of the sun—which is why men are tanned by the sun. Albinos have no pigment at all, whether in the skin, the hair or the eyes.

The Dermis

Below the thin epithelial epidermis, a thicker fundament of connective tissue, the dermis, forms. A burn on the skin is classified as of the first, second, or third degree. A burn of the first degree affects only the epidermis; the epidermis replaces the injured tissue in a few days. A simple sunburn is such a burn. A burn of the second degree injures the skin down to the border between the epidermis and the dermis. The lymph vessels exude lymph, and a characteristic blister raises the epidermis in the area of the burn. If the damage penetrates into the lower layers—the dermis itself—and destroys the connective tissue, its fibers, fat, blood and lymph vessels and nerves, or even chars the bones or muscles beneath, the burn is of the third degree.

The dermis is a strong tissue; therefore men throughout history have used the skin of beasts—or even man—as material for cover, clothing and carpets. The skin of a dead animal is processed by scraping and then tanning with a mild acid, such as tannic acid, procured from the bark of a tree.

Criminologists can identify an individual by a formula based on his fingerprint characteristics. The pinpointed area (above) is further magnified (above right) and the patterns can be broken down according to a certain number of characteristics that are of special interest to the investigator.

(Right) Fingerprints. The pattern of ridges on each fingertip is unique. The six patterns shown are the prints of only one person, but of different fingers of the two hands. Fingerprints served for identification long before the written signature.

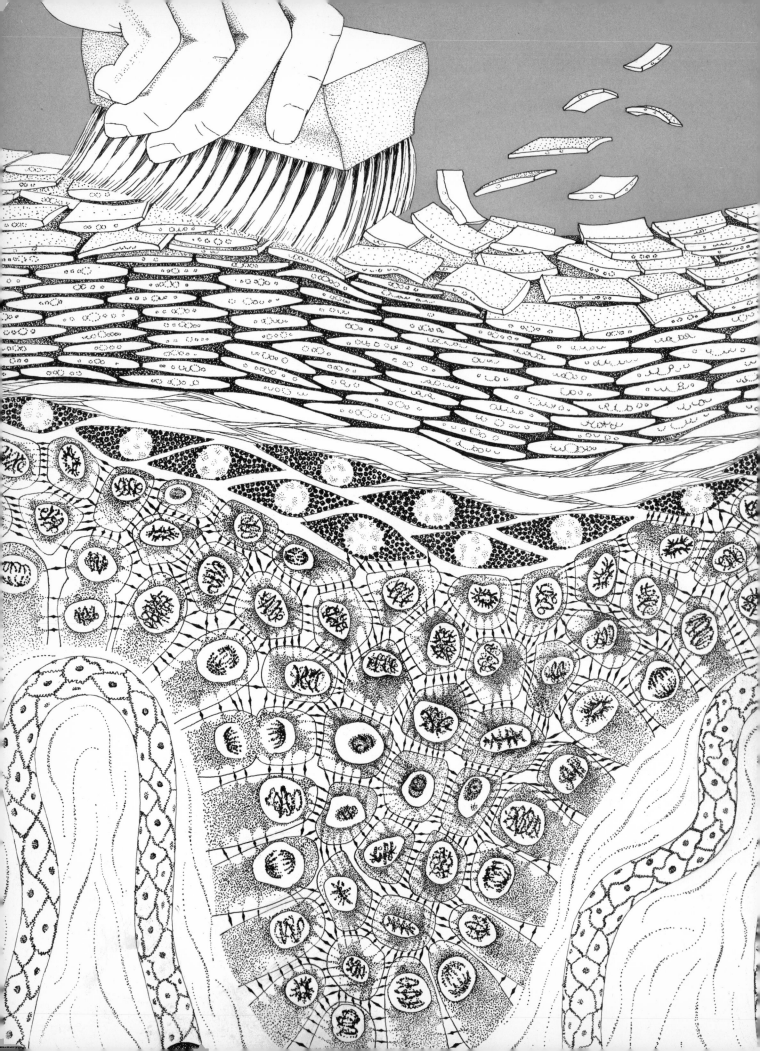

Human skin can be tanned like that of an animal; it becomes a fine leather such as that of young goats used in kid gloves. In prehistoric times it was the ambition of barbaric warriors to come home with coats made from the skin of their enemies. Revolutionists in France bound books with the skin of their aristocratic oppressors. Johann Ziska, the Bohemian leader of the Hussites, left an order in his last will that a drum be made from his skin so that he could continue to encourage his followers in their fight against the Pope.

All the organs of the skin are embedded in the dermis. The blood and lymph vessels of the dermis penetrate out to the papillae and then return to the interior. Also deep down in the epidermis we find the two kinds of characteristic skin glands: the sweat and the sebaceous glands. The sweat glands are isolated, but the sebaceous glands are always connected to a hair. The sweat gland lies deep in the connective tissue and spirals through layers of horny epidermis cells to emerge on the surface through a tiny hole called a pore. In ordinary sweating, about one pint of liquid evaporates each day invisibly and is called invisible perspiration. If the body produces sweat in visible quantity, the amount given off may rise to two, three, or even, in extreme cases, ten quarts a day. The skin of the human body is perforated by about two million sweat pores with a combined length of six miles. The sweat glands are not distributed evenly but are set closer together on such areas as the forehead, the palms of the hands, the soles of the feet and in the armpits.

Since the body maintains a heat of about 98.6° Fahrenheit, the difference in temperature between the body of a mammal and the surrounding air is generally considerable, often reaching as much as 70 degrees on a winter's day. Every animal tries to stabilize its body temperature in a variety of ways. Birds open or close their feathers; a snake lies on a boulder in the sun; a cat stretches out in the sunshine in the morning, in the shade at noon, and

The skin constantly renews itself, the lowermost layers of the epidermis producing fresh cells and the older cells giving way to the new. In washing we brush away dead cells from the surface.

near the oven or fireplace at night. The human body works with at least half a dozen different regulators. One of them is the sweat glands. The evaporation of liquid lowers the temperature of the body; the body could not exist without this mechanism, which regulates not only its temperature but also, to some extent, its salt content. The dog, an animal with no sweat glands whatever, must pant with its mouth open to evaporate water and control its body temperature. It is said that in the Middle Ages children who were painted with gold and lacquered to look like angels for religious ceremonies died; their bodies could not perspire and the poor "angels" died because of fevers they developed. If a person burned by fire or scalded by steam is unfortunate enough to lose more than half of his skin, he usually will not survive.

Sweat is not simply water, and yet it is not lymph. It is a salty fluid that bears some resemblance to urine, so that the skin has been called the third kidney, but it is not so efficient as the kidney for regulating the body's salt and water and getting rid of its waste. If we sweat profusely for a long period, as do men working in foundries or in the tropics, we can develop heat exhaustion and even heat stroke. This is due not only to loss of water but also to an excessive loss of salts. For treatment we need both water and sodium chloride. In serious cases the doctor may have to infuse water and salt directly into the victim's veins.

There are certain modified sweat glands in the body that no longer secrete simple watery sweat but more complex products; for example, glands in our external ear canals secrete wax, occasionally to such an extent that we have difficulty hearing and must have the wax removed. Even more interesting are modified sweat glands that become active only at puberty, when our sex glands begin to function. These glands are located in our armpits and navel and in our genital and anal areas. It is likely that these are vestigial remnants of the scent-producing glands of animals and once aided in sexual attraction. Children, lacking these glands, smell sweet even when they wash infrequently. In women, these glands reach the height of their activity just before the menstrual period. Today our deodorants and antiperspirants are directed mainly against the odors arising from these modified sweat glands.

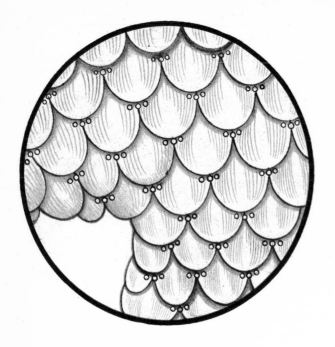
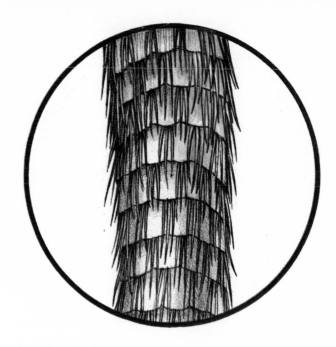

The Hair

The skin of the human body produces approximately 300,000 to 500,000 hairs. The hair is a product of the epidermis but penetrates deep into the dermis like grass into soil. Hair exhibits all the characteristics of the epidermis: it grows steadily and dies after a certain time, but the root lives on and grows new hair. Historically, human hair is supposed to have developed from the scales of prehistoric reptiles, and the first hairs grew in clusters of three. Every hair is bound in a network of lymph vessels that feeds the hair as though it were a blade of grass. It is also encased in several membranes. Just as hairs develop from primitive scales, so do our nails and the hooves of herbivorous animals.

The Sebaceous Glands

About midway in a hair's length the epithelial cells of the hair form a pair of glands that produce a fatty, oily product, sebum. The primary function of the sebaceous gland is providing oil for the hair and skin. Creamed hair stays smooth and is protected against dust, drying out and becoming brittle. Next to the sebaceous gland runs a muscle so placed that it can squeeze oil out of the gland; the muscles of the sebaceous glands are thus, so to speak, our built-in barbers. These muscles also make the hair stand up. If a draft passes over our skin, the muscles contract, the hair stands up and little bumps appear, called goose flesh. Fright, which affects the autonomic nervous system, also makes these muscles contract.

At intervals we tend, like all animals, to clean our skin. As civilized human beings we do not lick the skin but wash it with soap and water to dispose of the accumulated film of sebum, dust and dirt. In showering, we dissolve this film chemically with soap and then mechanically by rubbing the skin with a towel; the roughness of the towel stimulates the fresh production of skin and hair oil, and so we go through life with a skin that is constantly undergoing an oily rejuvenation. Shoes wear out, gloves get thin, dresses lose their shape, but our skin, with its elastic and resistant lower layer, the dermis, its self-rejuvenating upper layer, the epidermis, and its 400,000 sebum glands and their muscles, renews itself continually. Hail to our skin!

Ailments of the Skin

Ailments of the skin are so varied and so common that dermatology is a specialty in the practice of

From reptile scales to hair. *The hair covering our body probably traces back to the scales of primordial reptiles (far left). At first, hairs grew in clusters, as shown in the tail of a mouse (center), whereas in man each hair grows singly (left).*

(Below) A network of lymph vessels and capillaries surrounds the root of each hair.

medicine. The most remarkable fact about this field of medicine is how much there remains to be learned about it.

For instance, that plague of adolescence, acne, is not completely understood even today. Acne is an inflammation of the sebaceous glands. At puberty, when the sex glands become active, these glands begin to secrete more sebum than before. In some adolescents the openings of the glands become plugged up and the flow of sebum is interrupted. Then some of the bacteria on the skin, called microflora, which are our symbionts because ordinarily they do us no harm, attack the plugged-up sebaceous glands, and a full-fledged case of acne develops. It appears that some imbalance of the sex hormones is responsible, but for reasons still not understood patients who have ailments that require prolonged treatment with cortisone also develop acne. Fortunately, as we outgrow adolescence, we outgrow acne, usually without any harm. A few acne patients, however, develop pits and scars and treatment by a dermatologist is essential.

Parasites of the Skin and Allergies

Although the microorganisms we have been discussing are parasites, we called them symbionts

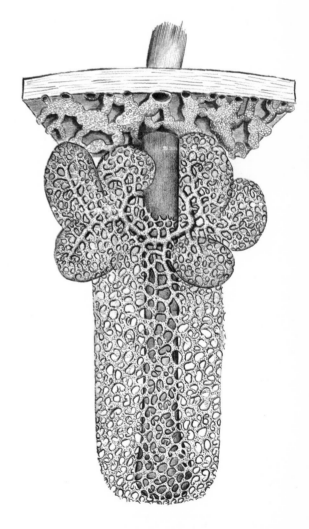

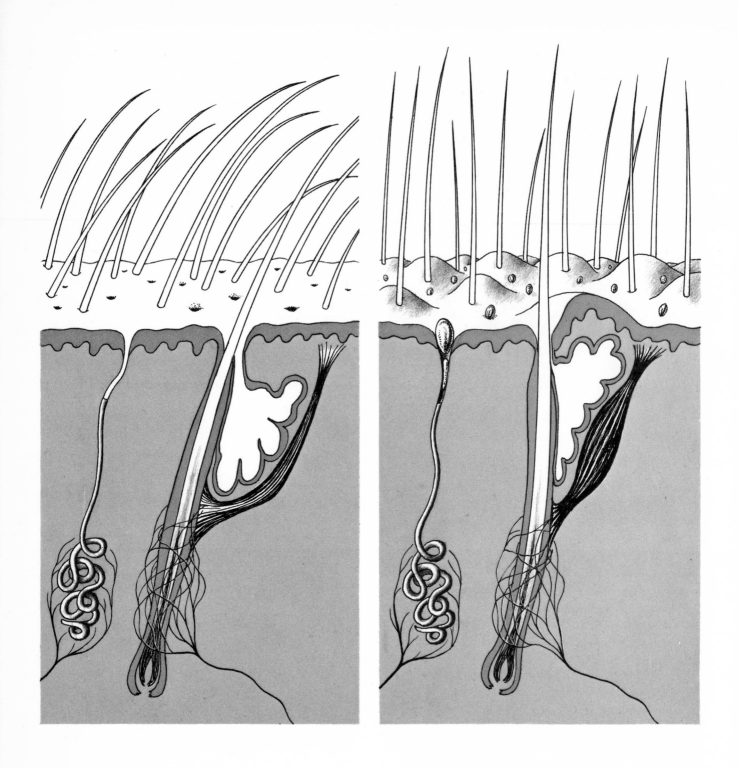

Each hair is equipped with a band of smooth muscle next to the sebaceous gland. When the muscle contracts, the hairs "stand on end" and the skin around the hair is raised, causing "goose flesh." The contraction also squeezes oil from the sebaceous gland, which lubricates the skin. Also shown is sweat oozing up from the sweat glands.

because they ordinarily live at peace with us; we reserve the term parasites for such creatures as fleas, lice, and mites, which visit and live on us from time to time and do us harm. The problem is further complicated by the fact that the flea that annoys man is different from a dog's flea, and both are different from a cat's flea. There are also a variety of lice: one lives in the hair of the head, another in the pubic hair. Then there are also microscopic mites that burrow through the horny layers of the skin, particularly of the fingers, and cause irritation, itching and inflammation.

Dermatitis is not a specific illness but a general term for any inflammation of the skin. In the last few decades it has been found that a great many such inflammations are allergic reactions. The foreign proteins called allergens that cause these reactions are sometimes products of metabolism that appear after the intake of foods which the body is not accustomed to digesting. Among the most frequent offenders are such fruits as strawberries and certain proteins from such seafood as crabs and lobsters. A typical case results from a dinner which begins with an appetizer of crabmeat and ends with strawberry shortcake for dessert. At midnight the family is awakened by five-year-old Mary. Her body is covered with a rash. She has had this reaction before: it comes from strawberries. The mother powders the child's body, gives her some warm milk, and the child falls asleep. Two hours later it is the poor mother herself who becomes ill. She should not have eaten the crabmeat. She has an attack of diarrhea, a natural way for the body to get rid of the crabmeat; the mother may also develop a rash.

These are mild cases; an allergic reaction can be serious and even fatal. It can produce asthma, closing down the breathing tubules, the bronchioles. We know the symptoms, and we give an impressive name, allergic shock, to them. The well-informed person even speaks knowingly of a specific protein, histamine and antihistamine, but the true causes are still unknown and, of course, not simple. The body tries to keep out all foreign or dangerous elements. Only after a careful quarantine are digested foodstuffs allowed to pass through the intestinal walls and into the blood stream; at the liver there is another squad of customs guards and all foods are investigated again before they are allowed to become part of the body.

The body also has another defense, the lympho-epithelial system, including the spleen and the host of lymph glands in all parts of the body. This intricate defense system reacts against imports that are considered contraband. It manufactures antibodies against allergens. Antibodies may be deposited in the skin, in which case the skin acts as the shock organ and may develop a rash if the allergen is ingested. Or the antibodies may be deposited by the body in the bronchioles, and if the allergen is pollen, inhaling the pollen will cause asthma. If the shock organ is the nose, the allergy will be called hay fever. One victim gets gastritis, a second has a skin reaction, and a third may get an inflammation of the eyes, a migraine or some other reaction. This diversity is typical of allergy.

In summary: skin diseases constitute only a small percentage of skin ailments. The skin is an excretory organ; it secretes sweat and sebum. It helps control the body temperature. It protects the inner body from the outer world. It serves the body as a faithful policeman. The ailing skin—on its tombstone should be carved the epitaph: "It died in the service of its country."

25

Touch

One of the most complex of our senses is that which registers such sensations as pressure, pain, warmth, cold, tickling and sexual contact.

It is the skin that makes the contact of the body with the outside world. The various kinds of apparatus that register these contacts are called sense organs. The child learns in school that we have five senses: sight, hearing, taste, smell, and touch, or feeling. On growing up we learn that the fifth sense is not a single or simple sense but a complex one which registers not only pressure but also such sensations as tickling, pain, heat, cold and many more. Certain kinds of skin sensations are connected with the excitation of the sexual zones and culminate in the high point of sexual passion that we call an orgasm. But we should not make the mistake of thinking that the so-called "lower senses," such as pain, are simple, or that we know more about them. The few investigators who have tried to arrive at a clear understanding of pain or of the difference between heat and cold have been unable to achieve satisfactory answers even after many years of research.

The epidermis with its half-dead horny cells contains no nerves. With a few exceptions the nerves end below the base layer of the epidermis. Experimenters using fine needles have found that we feel only at about three million points. These points register pain, touch, heat and cold. The sensations are carried through the afferent, or sensory nerves to special centers in the brain.

Sense Organs of the Dermis

In the layers of the dermis investigators have found various mechanisms for reacting to sensations. Their structure is sometimes elaborate, sometimes simple. These mechanisms, which seem to serve as a contact apparatus, are located directly under the arches of the papillae. Like an electric buzzer they announce that someone is touching you. Deeper in the dermis are structures that seem to react to greater pressures. These platelike corpuscles consist of fine membranes, like layers of onion skin, around a central nerve fiber. They are found not only in the dermis but also occasionally in the capsules that enclose the joints, in the covers of muscles, and in the peritoneum, the cover of the intestine. We assume that in the latter they signal a movement of the bowels. A few are found in the walls of the great arteries.

(Facing page) The "fifth sense." The sense of touch is complex, embracing such sensations as tickling, pain, heat, cold, pressure and others. Specialized nerve endings for registering these sensations are embedded in the dermis. Shown here are the nerve endings believed to register (1) pain and (2) heat, as well as the corpuscles stimulated by (3) cold and (4) pressure.

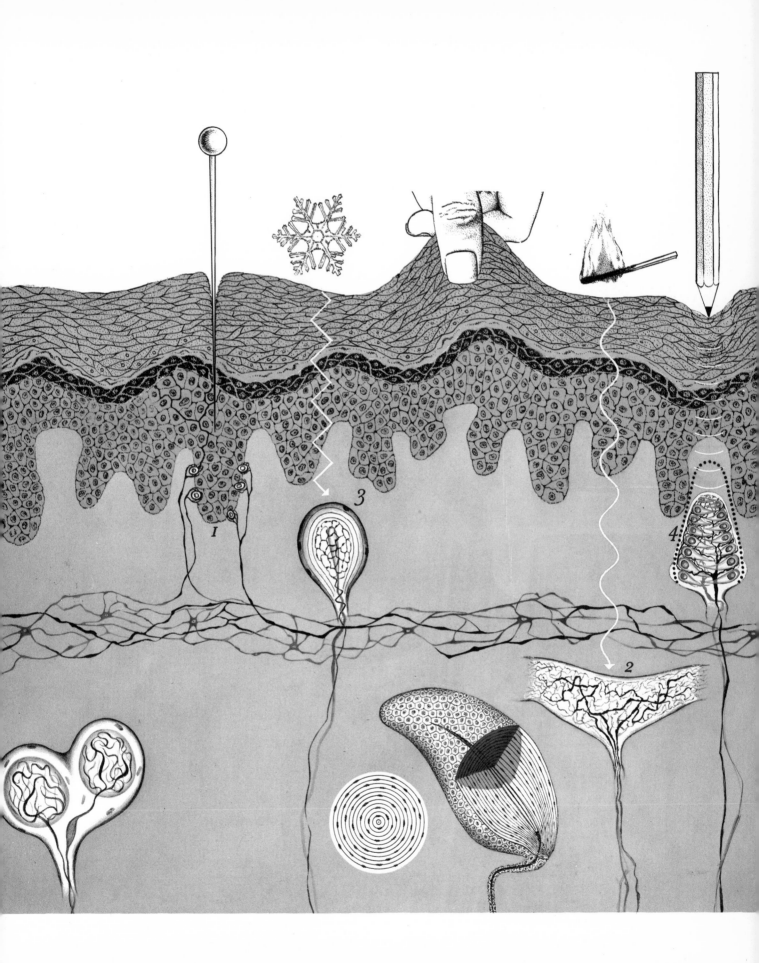

Drafts and Thermal Changes

A distinctive sensation of the skin is that caused by a draft. The roots of the hairs are encased in sensitive nerve endings not unlike the wire mesh we put around newly planted trees. These nerves tell us when a draft touches the hair. A prolonged draft may occasionally cause harm, such as an attack of lumbago or a stiff neck, but there is no reason to fear every draft as if it were deadly.

Other distinctive skin sensations result from heat and cold and pain. They are apparently perceived by separate mechanisms and only at certain points. All we know about them is that the points sensitive

(Right) Hot and cold points. Experimenters using fine needles have discovered that the body feels such sensations as hot and cold only at certain points, and that heat is felt in different areas from cold.

(Below) The mechanism registering sensations seems to operate like an electrical circuit. The brain is informed of a sensory stimulus once a switch is closed, thus permitting a flow of current.

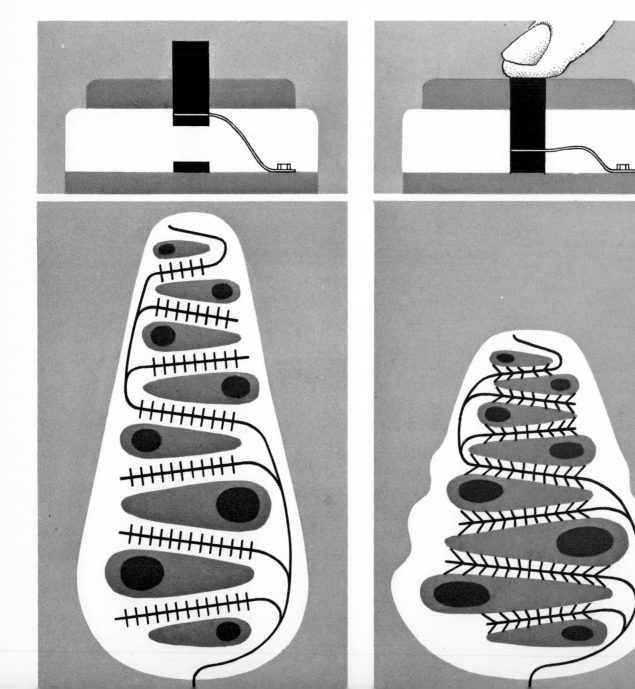

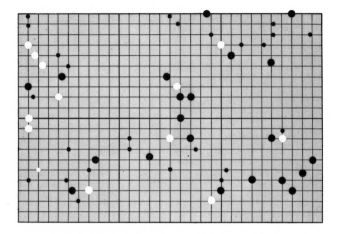

to cold are quite different from those sensitive to heat. All over the skin there are more spots sensitive to heat than to cold.

The Sense of Touch

We have a very acute tactile sense which we use almost from the first hour of life. Among the first sensations the child experiences is that of the touch of its mother's breast. Every animal is born with the instinct to get to the mother's breast and suck on it. Through this sucking the child gets its food and its almost uncanny relationship to the mother.

As everyone knows, the blind achieve the highest development of the tactile sense. It is most strikingly demonstrated in the Braille system, in which the reader depends entirely on his sense of touch.

The Pleasure Senses

In this category we include all those sense organs of the skin that seem to be intended to give us pleas-ure. One of the first kinds of play we indulge in with infants is tickling them. We tickle the baby lying in its crib and we are delighted by its pleasure. This seems to be a characteristic peculiar to this pleasure—the fact that we delight in giving it as well as receiving it. This is especially true in sexual play, where the lover, whether male or female, knows no greater delight than giving greater and greater pleasure to the partner.

The whole subject of the pleasure sensations has been too little explored and we will touch only on one aspect of it here. That is the effect of rhythmic stroking; the hypnotist uses such stroking as a means of putting his subject to sleep. We also know how cats, dogs and other animals respond to rhythmic petting; the most familiar response to this is the purring of cats.

Apparently the sensory organs are electrical mechanisms, and sensations such as cold, pain and pleasure are electrical phenomena. The triggering action is the contact. But as in the world of physics, electricity may be transmitted not only through contact but also through induction. Every individual appears to live in a specific atmosphere with a characteristic charge. We call it "personality" and speak of one individual's "strong" personality or another's "weak" one. If we react to a person's "electromagnetic field" positively we speak of having a sympathetic reaction. If we feel repelled, we speak of an "antipathy." Lovers can sit for hours hand in hand without speaking. That is in part, perhaps, an electrical phenomenon. Of a person with a strongly charged field we say that he is a radiant or magnetic personality. Of a sexually attractive woman we say that she is "hypnotic." Through her "charm" the Countess Kowalewska did more for Poland in the struggle against Napoleon than any army. And there has been more than one leader in history, such as Napoleon himself, whose extraordinary power has been ascribed to an "electrifying" or "supercharged" personality.

26

Taste and Smell

Tiny taste buds mainly on the tongue tell us whether our food is salt, sweet, bitter or sour. Similarly, a group of cells high up in the nose enables us to distinguish countless odors.

(Facing page) The tongue is covered with tiny projections, or papillae. Within cracks in these projections lie the sensitive taste buds. Secretions of the mucous glands of the tongue help form the saliva in which food dissolves. Food must be in solution before it can stimulate the taste buds.

The history of the organs of taste is fascinating. Human beings taste by means of tiny little buds located mostly in the lining of the tongue. Some of the buds are also present in the wall of the throat and in the soft palate of the roof of the mouth. These are apparently the oldest types of sensory organs, basically unchanged for at least a billion years. They can be found in the oldest forms of polyps, in such worms as the common earthworm and in many other invertebrates. Insects have the buds on their legs; flies, for example, have them on their front legs.

The construction of these buds is simple: a number of cells form a bulb, with an opening, a taste pore, leading to the surface of the tongue or palate. From the base of the bulb, nerves lead to the brain. Fine hairs protruding from the surface of the cells register the onslaught of the molecules of the outer world. This chemical sensitivity to the bombardment of molecules gives us the sensation of taste. And this sensation has remained the same through the ages. What a span from a seaworm in the stream of plankton to the gourmet savoring his glass of Burgundy—with the same kind of taste buds! The buds are the same, but the brain has changed. In lower animals, up to the fishes, taste buds are distributed over wide areas of the skin: if you sprinkle salt on the tail of a fish it reacts with a vigorous flapping of the tail. Land vertebrate animals taste only with the tongue and associated areas in the mouth.

The taste buds of human beings are concentrated on the tongue. But man is a poor taster. The number of his taste buds is about 1,000; a hog has 5,000, a cow 90,000!

The taste buds do not lie on the surface of the tongue, but in the walls of countless cracks in the surface. The salivary glands fill the cracks with the necessary fluid to allow the molecules of food to dance around freely. Unless food is in solution, the taste buds cannot react. When we take in salty food, the minute molecules of salt disperse quickly and enable us to say immediately: "It tastes salty." On the other hand, a complex molecule like that of malt sugar dissolves slowly and we need considerably longer to identify it.

There are four kinds of taste buds, one each for salt, sweet, and bitter, and probably a separate kind for sour. The buds for sweet are on the tip of the

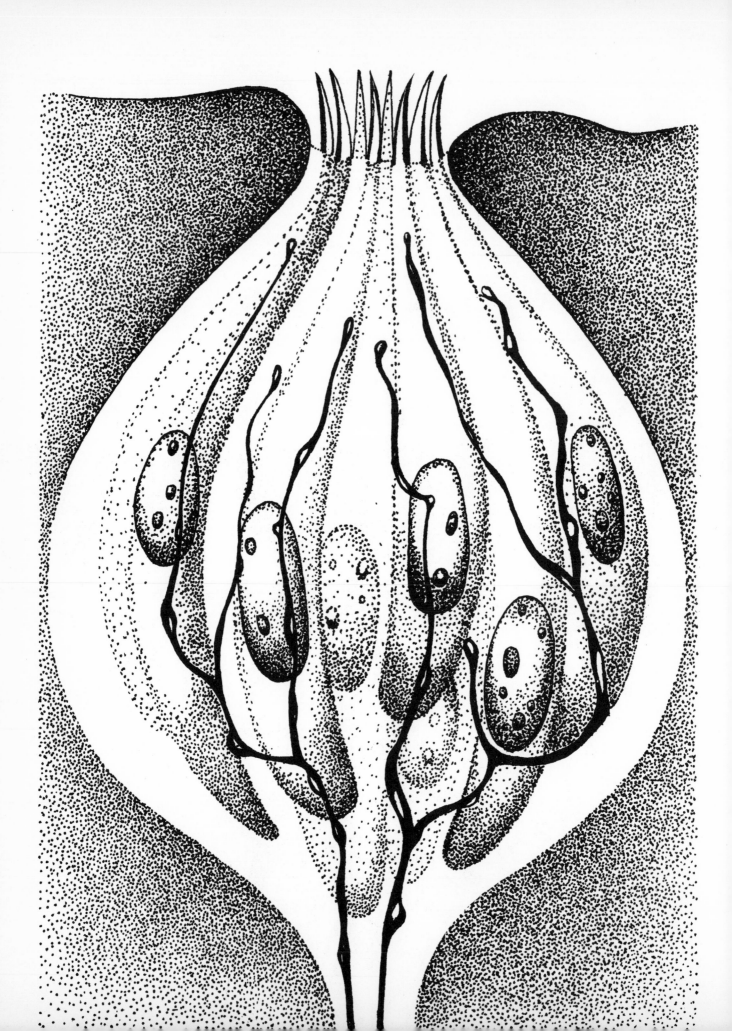

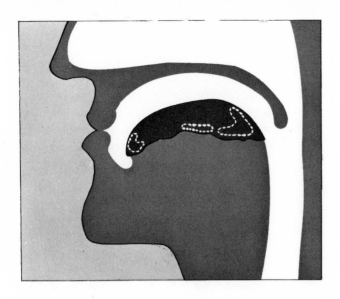

Four kinds of taste buds. Sweet and salty tastes are registered by various buds at the tip of the tongue, sour at the sides of the tongue, and bitter at the back.

(Left) Anatomy of a taste bud. A taste bud is formed by groups of taste cells; these cells end in protrusions, the taste hairs, that come into contact with foods in solution. This stimulation is relayed to taste centers in the brain by nerve endings (in black lines) in each taste bud.

tongue, the buds for salt on the sides and tip, the buds for sour on the edges, and the buds for bitter on the back. The child who is given a lollipop licks it with the tip of his tongue: the man who wants to savor a vermouth brings it into contact with the back of his tongue. Wines are never gulped; contrariwise, a beer drinker would never think of sipping beer. The taste of sweet passes quickly, that of bitter lingers in the narrow canyons of the tongue's cracks.

The relations between the chemical structure of a substance and its taste are not completely known. Acids like citric acid or acetic acid taste sour; this is probably due to the hydrogen ions. Chlorine, bromine and iodine ions in solution have a salty taste. Quinine is bitter and for that reason is added to certain drinks and aperitifs. Most alcohols taste sweet, like sugars.

All measures that slow down the movement of molecules blunt the sharpness of taste. Molecules that move around freely in clear water are slowed up by syrup or fat or gelatine; thus, the addition of cream softens the bitter taste of coffee. Egg white smooths the taste of bouillon. The culinary art is the art of playing on a thousand taste bulbs without overworking some and neglecting others. The undisputed masters of this art of the kitchen are the French. Brillat-Savarin, one of the few of his class who survived the holocaust of the French Revolution, includes in his famous *Physiology of Taste* an elegy for all those poor creatures who had to live in the days before modern gastronomy was developed:

> "Poor Odysseus! Circe could not have offered you a sauterne of Mont Barsillac... O Hercules, Denera could not cook for you a lobster thermidor... Poor Henry IV, you promised all the citizens of France a chicken on Sunday... but you never tasted *Pâté de Strasbourg*.... And never a praline, that marvellous creation of Mme de Pompadour.... Poor mankind of ancient times!"

In a scientific sense taste is the stimulus we register in the taste bulbs of the tongue. But in a culinary sense it is much more than that. The dish we enjoy exerts a whole symphony of sensations on our sensory organs. We see the dish with our eyes; we smell its flavor; we feel its temperature. Toast evokes a very different sensation in the mouth from a pudding; the taste of chocolate lingers, that of

243

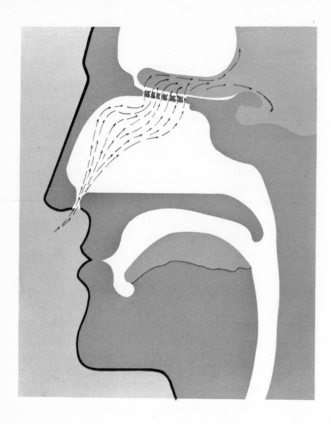

Smell. Molecules of a substance with an odor reach the nose through the air we breathe but must first go into solution in secretions in the roof of the nose. Olfactory cells in a small area of the roof of the nose are stimulated by the dissolved molecules, and nerve fibers then pass through fine holes in the bony roof. The olfactory nerve finally carries the stimulus to the brain.

celery passes quickly. In certain dishes or beverages—such as wine, coffee and tea—we depend so much on the sense of smell that we hardly know whether taste or smell is more important in our enjoyment of them. Professional tasters do not drink cognacs but only put a few drops on hot water and smell them. And when we catch a cold and the nasal passages are clogged we all know how much this can affect the sense of taste: at such a time tasty foods are wasted on us.

Smell

Our organ of smell is located in the mucous membrane of the nasal cavity. Since it is high in the cavity, we tend to sniff when we are trying to capture a smell, and all our domestic animals do the same. Compared with other animals man has a poor sense of smell but nevertheless it takes far fewer molecules to affect the sense of smell than to arouse the sense of taste.

The closer we are to the source of an odor, the more molecules reach our nose, and the stronger the smell. When we walk past a dead animal our small children object to the smell more than we do. Bend over so that your nose is as close to the source of the smell as a child's nose and you will appreciate the reason for this. Insects lack noses, but they use their antennae and feelers instead, and can detect odors at incredible distances. If we have breakfast in a garden on an autumn morning and open a jar of marmelade, it will take no more than minutes for a wasp to come from a distance of miles. Most birds, on the other hand, have little or no sense of smell; neither is their sense of taste very strong.

The olfactory area is darkened by pigment, the sensory areas having a yellowish or brownish-yellow color. The olfactory cells are contained in an area about three quarters of a square inch in size. Each cell has six to eight pigment granules and each granule sends a fine hair out of the surface of the cell. The base continues as a nerve fiber which forms part of the olfactory nerve leading directly to the brain. Some animals have an incredibly acute sense of smell—to detect food and to warn them of the approach of enemies—and their brain is mainly an organ for the appreciation of odors.

The olfactory membrane is covered by a layer

of wet mucus in which the molecules of odoriferous substances dissolve. Without this humid mucous layer, the ability to smell is reduced. Wetness in general heightens a smell. The aroma of forests and meadows is richest after rain, and hunters and police put their dogs on the trail in the humid hours of early morning.

The ability to smell, like the ability to see or to hear, differs from person to person. Some individuals are gifted with an acute sense of smell, and since smell is closely associated with taste, such persons often become professional tasters of wines or smellers of perfumes. Famous for his extraordinary sense of smell was the French novelist Emile Zola; so was his contemporary, the poet Baudelaire, who wrote poems about the aroma of his mistresses. A famous pediatrician of Leipzig, Dr. Heim, was once brought by a mother to her ailing child. Halfway up the stairway to her apartment he turned around, saying, "The boy has scarlet fever. I don't need to go any farther." Blind persons rely on their sense of smell much more than do ordinary persons with sight. They become experts in smelling. On entering an apartment a blind person can generally determine by smell who is in it. He may even be able to do so through a closed door.

The Chemistry of Smell

The odorous substances consist mostly of complicated molecules. Simple molecules, like those of the elements, generally do not give off an odor. Such substances as sulphur or iodine, which we regard as having a strong odor, do not themselves have an odor; what we smell are the compounds they form with hydrogen. The atomic groups that have odors are called the odor-carriers, or osmophores. The osmophoric groups are found mostly in the broad family of the benzene ring, but we do not yet know the principles underlying such groups. At present we distinguish the following groups: aromatic odors such as camphor, bitter almonds, cloves and lavender; flowery smells such as roses and violets; burning odors as of tobacco, roasted coffee, burning feathers; ethereal smells such as fruits, beeswax, ethers; putrescent smells such as excrement, decaying meat and vegetable matter; goat odors, such as sweat and ripe cheese; garlic odors, as of garlic and onions; ambrosial odors, as of musk and ambergris.

Since smelling is a chemical and atomic process, the amount of substance necessary for a reaction is incredibly minute. Up to the close of the 19th century the most common perfume used in low-class bars was musk. Its smell is so strong that once it is used on curtains or upholstered furniture, getting rid of it is practically impossible. A piece the size of a lump of sugar is sufficient to perfume the contents of thirty million bottles of fluid. The odor of mercaptan is twice as strong.

In classical Japan the social form of expressing friendly feeling was by touching the noses and smelling. Kissing with the lips was regarded as obscene, and when films from the Western world were first introduced, kissing scenes had to be cut out of them.

Just as the sense of taste is bound up with a symphony of other sensations, so is the sense of smell. It can evoke old memories most powerfully; such a novelist as Marcel Proust made great use of it in his famous *Remembrance of Things Past*.

27

Hearing and Balance

In the ear one delicate mechanism registers air waves and translates them into sounds; another helps us maintain our equilibrium.

After the first reptile left the mud of the warm primordial swamp and became the earliest terrestrial vertebrate, its clumsy skull with its long jaws rested on the ground. It perceived the first terrestrial vibrations as a tremolo through its jaws, and the posterior parts of the upper jaw became the "hearing bones." The more demanding the task of hearing became, the more delicate these bones grew until they were the three of the most finely wrought bones of the skeleton, each not much larger than a letter or two on this page. They are connected with each other by tiny joints and held by the smallest ligaments and muscles in the body.

The "ossicles," as the bones are called, bridge the less-than-pea-sized cavity of the middle ear and act as a transmission belt, reducing the relatively large air waves of the atmosphere to the approximately twenty times smaller waves that oscillate inside the ear. Because of their shapes, the ossicles are called the hammer, the anvil and the stirrup. The space they occupy is the middle ear. Beyond the ossicles is the inner ear, where the true organ of hearing, the cochlea, is located. The cochlea coils around an axis and contains a lymph fluid that is set in vibration by the attached ossicle. The cochlea also carries the nerves that transmit acoustic sensations to the brain. The nerve fibers are in contact with specialized auditory cells which have small bristles on their surface that serve as sensory hairs.

The acoustical apparatus of the cochlea basically resembles that of a piano, but a piano shaped like a snail's shell and having 24,000 strings. Like a piano, the cochlea is an instrument of resonance. Sounds come to us through the air waves; when they reach the eardrum at the entrance to the middle ear, the vibrations of the air are transformed into vibrations of the ossicles. The ossicles transmit these vibrations to a second, inner drum, a membrane in the wall of the cochlea, and thence to the lymph that fills the cochlea. The 24,000 fibers form a resonating structure and different parts are set to vibrating by the vibrating lymph—short fibers by high frequencies, long fibers by low frequencies. These vibrations are picked up by the auditory cells, thus stimulating the nerve fibers; so we do not hear air waves as such but a mosaic of vibrations in a column of lymph in the cochlea.

A grand piano has a range of seven-and-a-half octaves. The human ear has a greater range: from

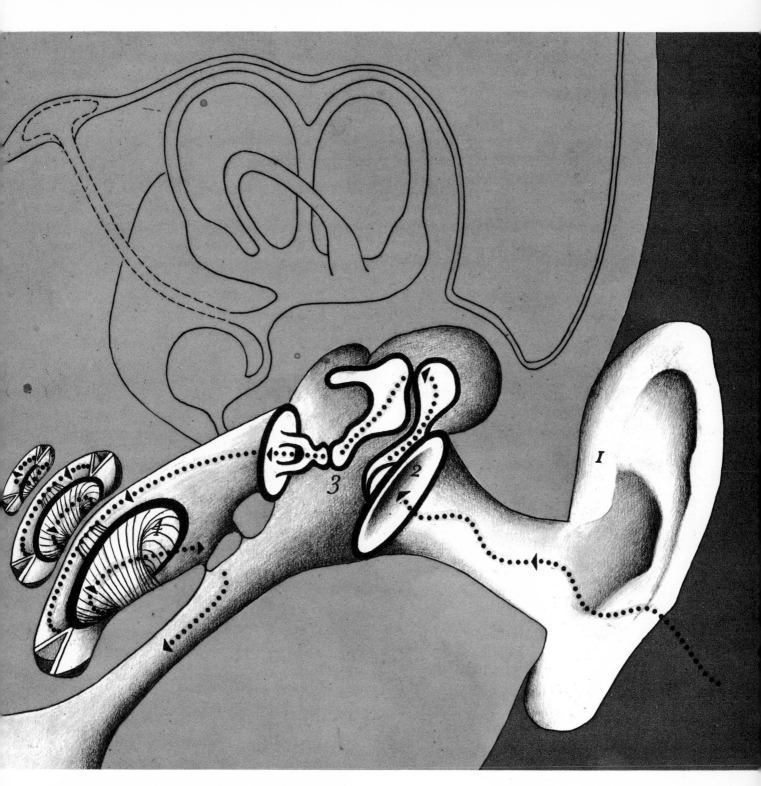

The ear. Sounds enter the outer ear (1) as air waves. On reaching the eardrum (2) they set three tiny interconnected bones, the ossicles (3), to vibrating. The innermost ossicle passes the vibration to the lymph within the cochlea of the inner ear (4).

one octave lower to four octaves higher. The range narrows with age: an average child of seven can detect twenty thousand vibrations per second; at the age of thirty the average range is fifteen thousand; a person of fifty hears only up to thirteen thousand vibrations.

We may use the ear for hearing, but in reality we hear with the brain. Like seeing, hearing is not a physical act but a psychological experience. Beethoven became deaf in his thirties; but he later composed and conducted his symphonies. At the end of his last performance he could not hear the applause of the public behind his back. He stood on the podium entirely lost. One of the singers ran up to him and turned him around; when he saw the audience applauding he wept.

The Mechanism of Balance

The human ear is not only an apparatus for hearing but also for balancing. To balance itself, every animal, whether it lives in water, air or earth, needs a mechanism that will inform it of its position and thus help it maintain its equilibrium. A very simple embodiment of this mechanism is the medusa, a jellyfish that floats about in the open sea and therefore is in constant need of a gyroscopic device. Utilizing salts from the sea, the medusa forms inside itself little balls lined with sensitive hairs. The rolling of the balls lets the medusa know its position in space. The principle of this mechanism applies to the balancing apparatus of all animals.

In little cavities within the bones of the skull, man has semicircular canals, containing lymph fluid, that extend in three directions from a central point approximately at right angles to each other. These tell him in which of these directions he is moving. Together with the cochlea and connecting parts they make up the inner ear. Each canal corresponds in structure and function to the balance balls of the medusa. The little "stones" in man's balancing apparatus are not loose but are covered with a jelly-like material spread on a base like butter on a slice of bread. Each "stone" consists of a group of cells with fine bristles, and when we move our heads the lymph fluid in the semicircular canals stimulates the bristle cells. Sensitive nerve fibers in contact with the bristle cells are stimulated and

(Above) The cochlea. A cross section of this main organ of hearing shows the basic spiral of bony structure. The individual compartments of the spiral are filled with lymph and contain rows of sensitive cells (detail at right) with hair-like processes on their surfaces. Fluid waves in the lymph stimulate the hair cells, which pass on the impulses to the nerve of hearing.

(Below) The hearing center. We hear with the brain rather than the ears. The hearing receptors relay impulses to the auditory area of the cerebral cortex by means of nerve fibers, most of which cross over to the opposite side of the brain.

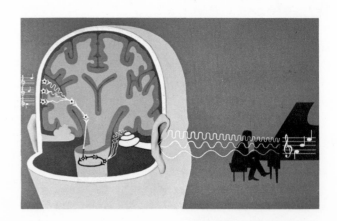

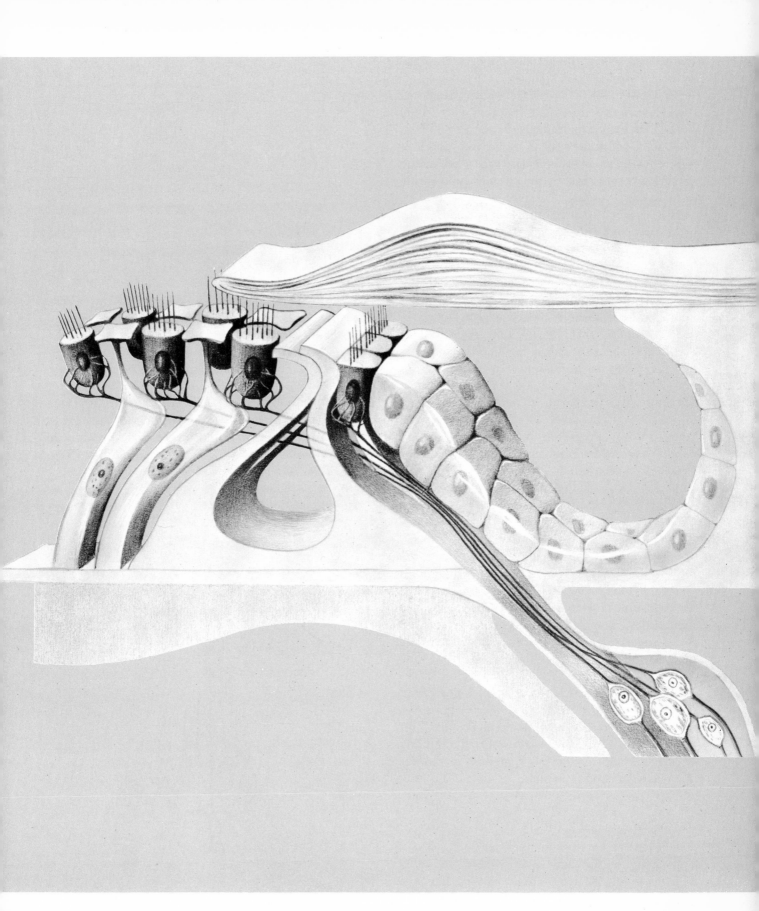

immediately notify the brain of the position of the head.

An injury to the inner ear, such as may be caused by a blow on the head, often results in a loss of the sense of balance. The victim reels; the world seems to whirl, and walls appear to become floors or ceilings. A disease of the inner ear, such as Ménière's disease, causes vertigo, buzzing sounds and hearing disturbances.

Motion sickness is another disturbance of the inner ear. It is caused by a constant and prolonged shifting of direction—and velocity—on many levels. Psychological factors often play a considerable part in this; some individuals fall sick before a plane, a car or a ship even starts to move. Together with dizziness, there is nausea and a feeling of malaise. During World War II, when many soldiers had to be moved by ship, it became important to find a remedy for seasickness. Fortunately, drugs have been discovered which act on the center of the brain that responds to changes in position. If, for example, dramamine is taken just before and during a voyage, those who are sensitive to motion sickness can generally escape the more unpleasant effects of an attack.

The External Ear

The external ear, attached to the outside of the head, is the most spectacular piece of cartilaginous sculpture. This outer ear is peculiar to the primates; its prehistoric model was an ear like that of the present-day monkey known as a macaque. The muscles that enabled monkeys to move their ears degenerated in the course of history. Man can now make only insignificant movements with his ears—regardless of how hard schoolboys try. The ear of the macaque ended in a tip, which is still recognizable and is called the "point of Darwin." In time, the rim of the ear folded inward. To this day some of the old ape-fur is still visible on the ear of a newborn child.

Middle Ear Infection

The cavity of the middle ear where the three auditory ossicles vibrate is connected with the back

(Right) Balance in the medusa. Every animal has a balance mechanism. From sea salts the jellyfish medusa forms tiny balls lined with sensitive hairs; the rolling of the balls informs the medusa of its position. This is in principle similar to the balance mechanism in the human ear.

(Below) The canals of the inner ear. With each movement of the head, the lymph in the semicircular canals moves a jelly-like mass within the canals. Tiny bristle cells are in turn stimulated, and nerve fibers then carry details of the head's position to the brain.

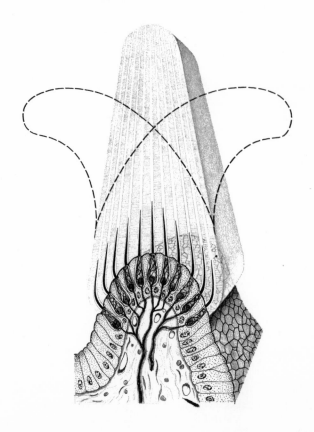

250

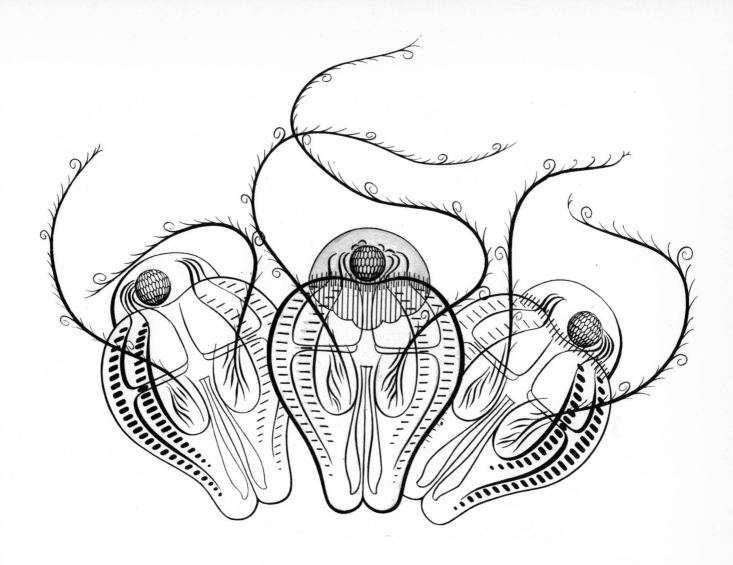

of the mouth through the Eustachian tube. As we swallow, or as we descend from a height, we can feel the air in the mouth passing through this tube to equalize the pressure against the ear drum. When tonsils become infected, a condition particularly dangerous in children, the bacilli or viruses invade the Eustachian tubes. If the bacteria ascend into the cavity of the middle ear, an inflammation of the fine mucous lining causes the very painful condition known as otitis media. Pus collects and before antibiotics a doctor might have to perforate the eardrum to release the pus.

Deafness in Old Age

Progressive deafness is a common ailment in aging persons. Since the number of persons in the oldest age group is constantly increasing, senile deafness is becoming more frequent, and we encounter more and more aging persons who make use of hearing aids.

A hearing aid usually consists of a tiny transistor that is inserted in the external ear canal and serves to amplify the vibrations of the air. When deafness is caused by diminished functioning of the auditory apparatus, a hearing aid can be very effective in compensating for the loss.

Sometimes the ossicles in the middle ear become fixed in place, as though by a kind of arthritis, and are unable to transmit the vibrations of the eardrum to the lymph in the cochlea, thus causing deafness. Ear doctors today perform operations that free the tiny ossicles and make it possible for these sensitive bodies to perform their complex function once again.

251

28

Sight

A wonderfully sensitive mechanism, the eye, enables us constantly to register the lights, colors and shapes of the world.

(Facing page) The eye muscles. We can rotate the eyeball in all directions because of an intricate system of muscles connecting eyeball to socket. Tiny muscles also permit the raising and lowering of the eyelids.

Seeing is partly a psychological process. The eye is a photographic apparatus like a camera. But a camera does not see, and neither does the eye alone see. Seeing is the product of the brain of the person who uses his eyes. We "see" with a group of brain cells located in the back of the brain, deeply hidden in a canyon of cortex. If a man is so unlucky as to have this area destroyed, as, for example, by a bullet, he loses the ability to see, even though his eyes are unharmed.

There are three optical parts to the eye: the cornea in front, the lens in the middle, and the retina in the rear. There are also three parts that may be called nonoptical: the lids in front; in the middle, the apparatus for adjusting the lens; and in the rear, the muscles that control the movement of the eyeball.

The Cornea

The cornea is the curved film in front of the eye. It seems to be transparent and clear, but if we look at it through a microscope we are surprised to find that it is not clear at all but composed of connective tissue covered with epithelial cells. Even nerves and lymphatic vessels run through it, with lymph cells floating through the vessels; these do not disturb us because they are too close for us to see them. When a speck settles on the cornea, someone else can see it but we cannot—unless we look in a mirror. Equally surprising is the fact that if a splinter imbeds itself in the cornea, a doctor will not hesitate to anesthetize the eye and then scrape the splinter out of the cornea with a sharp instrument. He knows that the layer of epithelial cells has a remarkable ability to regenerate itself. First the cells bordering the injury flatten out and cover the defect. Then the deeper cells multiply by mitosis and complete the repair.

The next surprising fact is that the cornea and not the lens is the main organ of refraction in the eye. By this we mean that the cornea changes or bends the direction of a ray of light as it passes into the eye. We measure such refraction in diopters. A lens has a refraction of one diopter if it focuses an image of an object at a distance of one meter behind the lens, and of two diopters if the image appears half a meter behind it; that is, the greater the

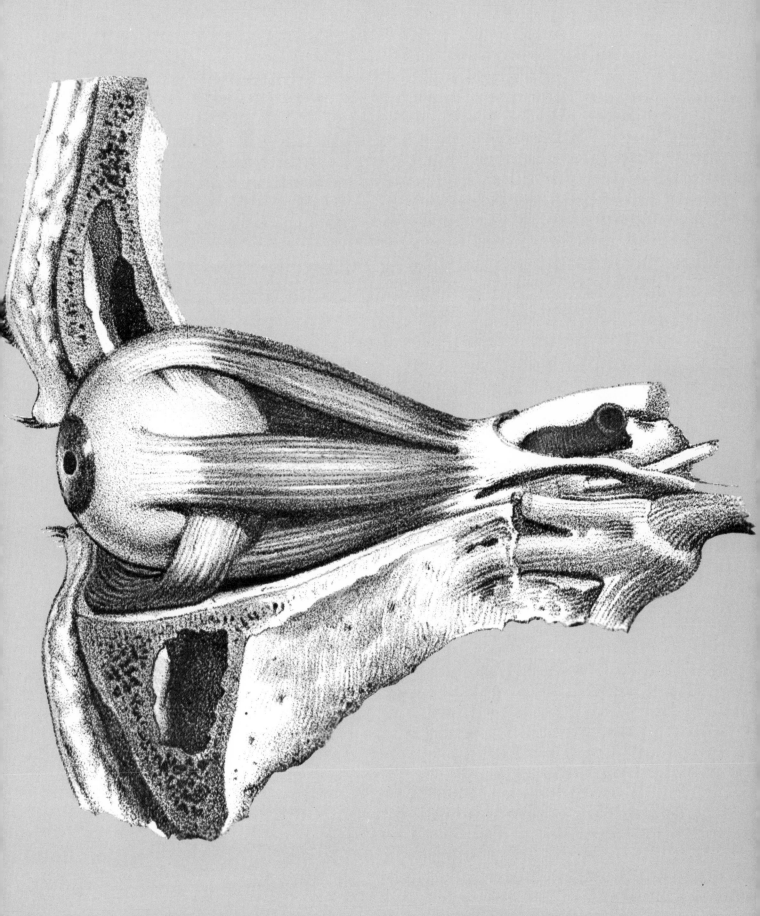

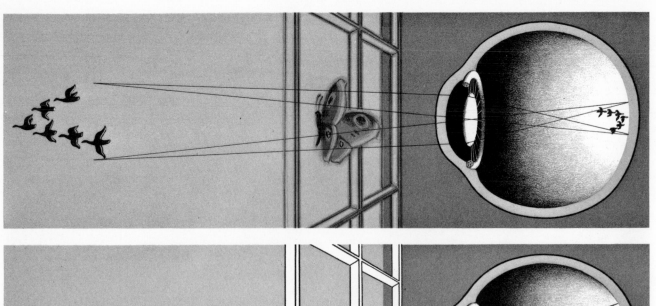

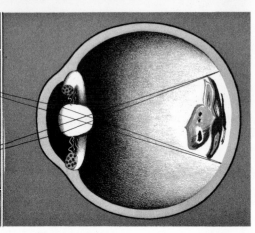

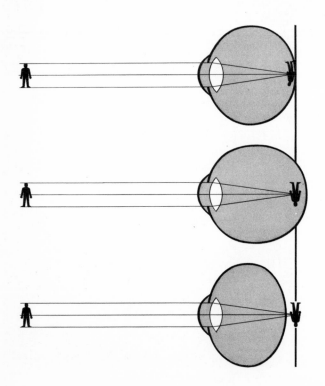

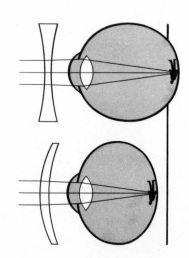

(Left) Lens accommodation. We can focus on both near and distant objects because the lens of the eye can change its shape. When we gaze at birds outside a window, the image is easily refracted and falls in sharp focus on the retina. To focus on a butterfly on the windowpane itself, the lens must assume a more spherical shape.

(Left below) Near-sightedness and far-sightedness. Normally, the image of a distant object comes into focus upside down on the retina (top). In near-sighted persons, the eye ball is too deep (center), and the image comes into focus in front of the retina. By means of a concave eyeglass lens the image can be carried farther back so that it focuses on the retina. In far-sightedness the eyeball is too shallow, and the image comes into focus beyond the retina (bottom). A convex eyeglass lens will bring the image forward.

(Right) Binocular vision. The image registered by the brain is the product of the overlapping fields of vision of our two eyes. In the diagram, light rays from the plant reach the retina of each eye while rays from the figure on the left focus only on the retina of the left eye and those from the figure on the right only on the right eye. Half the fibers of the optic nerve from each eye cross before they enter the brain, the crossing fibers coming from the inner half of each retina. The rays from the plant fall on the outer halves of the retinas. As a result, the plant is "seen" by both halves of the brain, whereas light from the white figure focuses only on the inner half of the retina of the left eye and is "seen" only by the right brain. Higher visual centers in the brain integrate both these images so that a final fused image, corresponding with reality, forms.

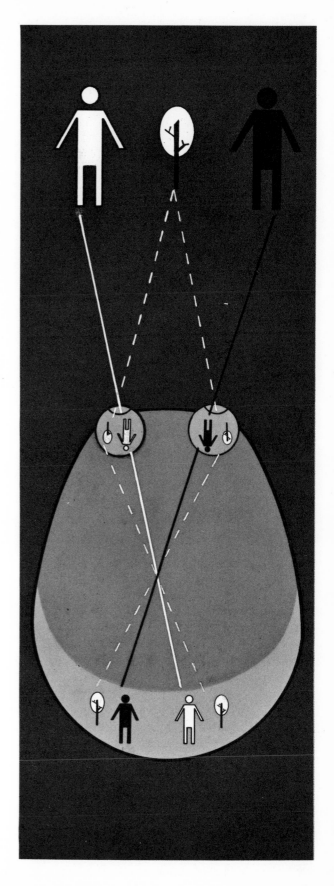

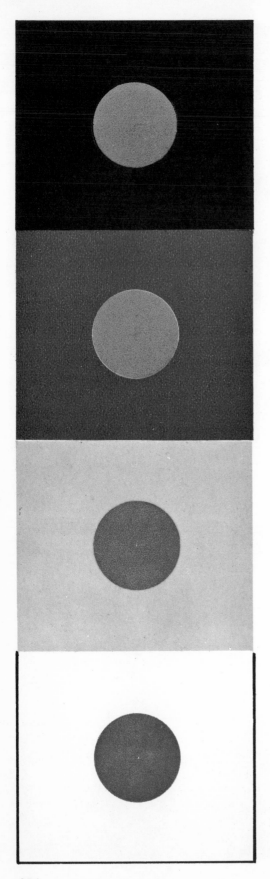

refraction of the lens, the closer behind the lens will it focus an image. Since the eye is about two centimeters, or less than an inch deep, it needs a refraction of about fifty diopters to produce images of the outer world on its light-sensitive background. Of these fifty diopters the cornea provides forty and the lens ten, so that the cornea is actually the main refracting piece of the human eye. The importance of the cornea in refraction is not the result of its special refractory power or construction but of its position; that is, the light rays are first bent when they pass from the atmosphere into the cornea at the front of the eye.

Near-Sightedness, or Myopia

If an individual's eye is too deep, the image of a distant object passing through the cornea and lens will not strike the screen of the retina exactly but will focus perhaps a millimeter, or about four hundredths of an inch, in front of it. To get the picture on the screen, so to speak, this individual must use an eyeglass lens that will focus the image farther back. If the eye is too shallow he must use a lens that will focus the image farther forward.

In the last quarter of the 19th century in Europe, mass examinations of school children showed that a high percentage suffered from defects of vision, principally near-sightedness; that is, their eyes were so deep that images of distant objects focused in front of the retina. Near-sightedness was recognized as a widespread problem and great efforts were made to find its causes, but without success. Near-sightedness is inborn and is apparently a hereditary trait.

Thoughtful investigators have even raised the question of whether near-sightedness is really a shortcoming. In some respects the near-sighted person is not handicapped: for example, a man who must constantly read fine print or work with fine mechanisms.

The Lens

The lens is, like hair and nails, the product of the epithelial layer of the embryologic skin. It has long been known that the lenses of men who blow glass

(Above) The blind spot on the retina is insensitive to light because the optic nerve enters at that point. To find your blind spot hold this book about a foot from your eyes, close the right eye and focus the left eye on the cross at the right. Then turn the head from side to side until the circle at the left disappears. The farther away objects are, the larger the blind spot: at three feet the circle will appear as large as an apple.

(Facing page) The illusion created by contrast. The gray circles in the center of each of these four panels are identical but appear to become darker as the background becomes lighter.

lose their clarity because such men stare so much into the glare of fires. The loss of transparency of the lens results from the growth of what is called a cataract. The removal of a cataract is one of the oldest operations and is mentioned as early as the Egyptian papyrus *Eber,* a medical treatise of the epoch of Moses. The removal was performed with a needle having a curved point similar to those that women use in crocheting.

The lens is wrapped in an elastic cover or capsule that protects it from lesions. It is made of epithelial cells of which the oldest are in the center of the lens and the youngest in the periphery. The cells elongate into the form of fibers. By means of ligaments surrounding it the lens is attached to the wall of the eyeball close behind the cornea. Muscle fibers are present in this area and when they contract the ligaments relax, permitting the biconvex lens to become more spherical. This increases its refractive powers and makes it possible to focus on very close objects. The entire process is called accommodation.

Accommodation

The accommodation mechanism thus holds the lens in position and changes its shape according to the distance of the eye from the object it is focusing on. The story of this mechanism is one of the most exciting in the voluminous book of evolution and

257

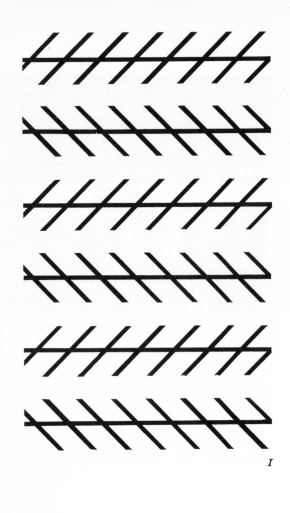

1

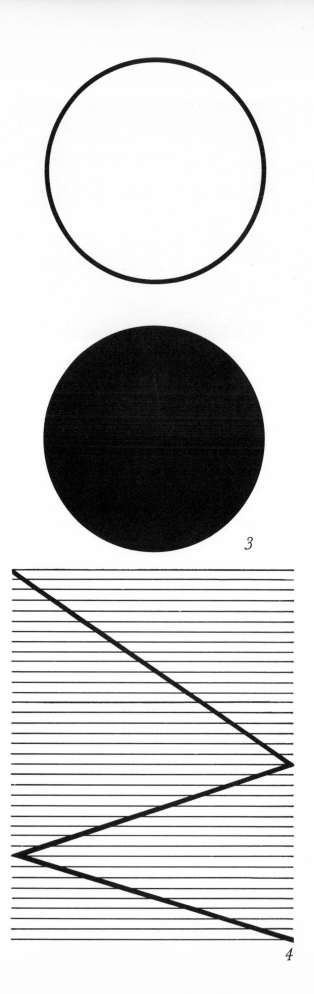

3

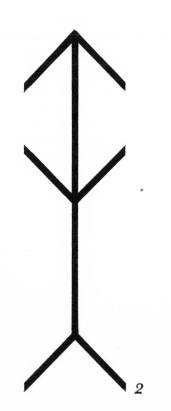

2

4

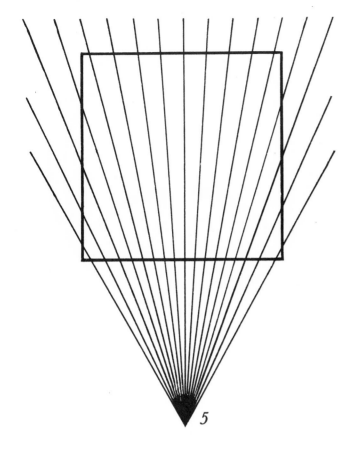

5

is one of the wonders of nature. The complexity of the accommodation solutions developed by various animals is overwhelming. Fishes have intricate devices for shifting the lens forward and backward or they have retinas that are built like the wings on our theatre stages. The human lens hangs in the center of a circular muscle like Saturn in the midst of its rings.

Accommodation involves muscular contraction and is therefore fatiguing. If we read small print hour after hour we feel this fatigue. It is a relief to interrupt the reading and look out of the window into the distance. If we read at night in bed and become sleepy, the print loses its sharpness and becomes blurred.

With advancing age, the lens loses its elasticity. This hardening process actually begins in the school years, but in the early stages it does not make itself felt. Generally when an individual approaches forty years of age the loss of elasticity of the lens becomes so great that its shape cannot be changed by the muscles of accommodation and eyeglasses must be introduced.

By the time the average person reaches sixty he needs the help of eyeglasses, especially for reading. Another common sign of weakening eyesight occurs in the older woman who finds that she is having difficulty threading a needle.

The Retina

The third major part of the eye, the background, is called the retina, meaning net. This is the equivalent of the film on which the picture is formed in a camera. It has two layers, an inner one of nervous tissue and an outer one of pigmented cells. After leaving the brain the optic nerve passes through the rear of the eye and the pigmented layer of the retina. It then sprays out like a fountain in the form of "drops"—that is, cells—forming the nervous layer of the retina and its light-sensitive receptors. These appear in two forms, one long and narrow, called rods and the other somewhat shorter and bottle-shaped, called cones. Altogether there are about ten million retina cells registering the incoming light waves.

Since each retina cell is a single receptor of light, we see the world as a collection of separate points

1. Illusion of the random parallels. All the longer lines are parallel but appear to run in different directions because the many short lines cut through them at different angles.

2. Arrowhead illusion. The upper half of the line appears shorter because the "arrows" at each end close in on it, while those around the lower half run outward.

3. The circle vs. the disc. The black disc seems smaller since the eye wanders quickly over a black field. It takes a greater effort for the eye to pass around the periphery of the white circle, thus we have the impression of a larger object.

4. "Broken" diagonals. The diagonals appear to be broken because each parallel line deflects our gaze.

5. The distorted square. The square appears distorted because the surrounding lines disturb our vision.

or dots. By means of a psychological process in the cortex of the brain we compose or fuse these points into a coherent image. Pictures are printed in much the same way, as collections of dots, but the brain fuses the dots into a coherent picture.

The rods and cones are specialized forms of light-sensitive receptors. The cones are receptors for color and for sharp vision. They are concentrated around the center of the retina, so that we use this area when we focus sharply. Since the cones are also color sensitive, we focus our eyes so that the area of color we intend to judge is seen with the center of the retina. The cones are not particularly sensitive to dim light because we must have strong light to enjoy and to judge colors. If we are trying to decide on the color of a fabric in a shop we move toward the nearest window in search of maximum light.

The farther out they are from the "conal" center of the eye toward the periphery, the greater is the number of rods that mingle with the cones until in the peripheral area we only with rods. Rods are sensitive to light but not to color. With the cones we see colors and contours—especially in strong light. If the light is faint we use the light-sensitive rods of the periphery. Some persons use the rods more than the cones. They may be said to get a misty, impressionistic view of things. Dürer, whose vision was preternaturally sharp, was a "coner." The Romantic landscape painters of the 19th century with their shaded scenes were "rodders." Another user of the rods was Rembrandt; in his paintings the colors are almost obscured. Nocturnal animals, such as owls, see with the rods. Song birds and chickens see with cones, and go to sleep at sunset. Hens are not blind but simply night blind.

We do not, moreover, see any colors at night. "By night," we say, "all cats are gray." And everyone knows that all ghosts are white; the idea of a ghost in color makes us laugh. After sunset the colors of the landscape disappear in a specific order, beginning with the red of flowers and ending with the blue of the sky. The rods are weak in perceiving colors but useful in perceiving movement. We notice a fly on the periphery of our visual field before we recognize the shape or the color of the insect. We "feel" that something is moving; but only after focusing the center of the eye on the thing can we describe it.

(Above) Deceptive shadows. If you turn the picture upside down you will no longer see the lines of a cross. The deception is created by perspective lines.

(Facing page) Dominance of bright objects. The crescent seems larger than the rest of the circle because it is brighter. Hold a ruler up to a flame and it appears curved. We overestimate the size of bright objects because light stimulates the retina beyond the area truly affected.

Having cones and rods in our retina and being able to rely more on the center during the day and more on the periphery at night, we have a dual camera, one for daylight and a second for night light. The first is color film; the second is black and white. This is the human eye—a double instrument.

The Blind Spot

When a physician looks into the eye with an instrument called an ophthalmoscope, the spot where the "cable" containing the million nerve fibers of the optic nerve enters the eye is seen on the retina as a white disk. This spot is blind because at that point the retina has no light-sensitive cells and does not register light. It is therefore called the "blind spot." It was detected by a keen observer, the monk Scheiner, around 1600. It is not difficult to find this blind spot and test it by means of the experiments in the accompanying diagrams.

The pupil of the eye is formed by the iris suspended between the cornea and the lens. It is attached to the wall of the eye by the ligaments of the lens. The pupil is a thin, circular, colored disk containing pigment cells and two sets of smooth muscle fibers: circular muscles and radiating muscle fibers. The circular muscle fibers narrow or constrict the pupil. The radial muscle fibers enlarge or dilate the pupil. When bright light enters the eye, the circular muscle fibers react as a reflex and the pupil is narrowed. In dim light the radial muscle fibers react automatically and the pupil is dilated.

The Windshield of the Eye

The front of the eye is furnished with a mechanism called the lid, which is astonishingly similar to the windshield on a car. The lids develop as double folds of skin strengthened by fibrous tissue. Layers of muscle fibers raise and lower them; the lowering protects the cornea from drying out. We lower the lids, that is, we blink, at frequent intervals.

The lids lubricate the front of the eye. To do so they have twenty to thirty sebaceous glands which open on the margin of the lids. To protect the cornea against drying out, each eye carries on its

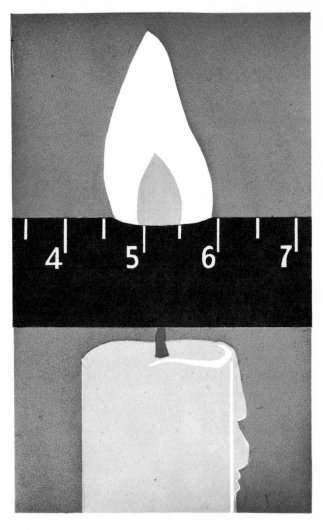

outer edge a lacrimal gland, which produces tear fluid. The tears flow through the sievelike openings in the lid as it passes over the surface of the eyeball. After being spread over the surface of the eye by the lid, the tears drip through a tube, the naso-lacrimal duct in the inner corner of the eye, and thence into the nose.

Eye Muscles and Binocular Vision

Needless to say, an apparatus that is so complex as the eyeball requires an intricate system of muscles and nerves to control its various movements. One of the muscles runs through a "hook" to roll the eyeball in an oblique direction, much the way the coachman uses the reins to guide his horses into a turn. Special layers of muscle also fan out in the upper lids to regulate the raising and lowering of the lids. The nerves of the muscles of the eye are not prominent among the maze of fibers. But if we look for them and study them we become aware of the existence of a network of lines, centers and

Bridging the gap. If the illustration is brought very close to the eye, the separate fields of vision of the two eyes fuse, closing the gap between the two halves of the bridge.

(Right) Contrast effect. The influence of the black background causes the areas where the white bars intersect to appear to be gray.

262

relays no less intricate than those of our telephone or computer systems.

All vertebrates have binocular vision, that is, they see with two eyes. A bird has its two eyes so widely separated that its two fields of vision are independent and the bird can look around itself in a complete circle. The field of vision of the human eye is entirely different. If we close the right eye, we see only the visual field of the left eye, that is, as much as can be seen to the left and over the ridge of the nose. If we then open the right eye, we see the two visual fields superimposed, which is our normal way of seeing things. At a middle point between the eyes, approximately in the region of the nose, we see nothing. There we have what is called a blind area. We can easily test this by trying to focus on a finger approaching the nose; when it comes close to the nose it will become unclear. To see the finger clearly it must be moved out to about four inches or more.

If we tie a string to a fixed point and raise the free end to the tip of our nose, we do not see one string but two strings crossing at that point where we focus. If we shift the focal point, the strings will cross at a different point. If there is a fly on a window pane and we gaze through the window at a passing airplane, the fly will appear as double. If we focus on the fly, the airplane will double. Such an experience makes us aware of one of the tyrannizing laws of the world of vision: we see clearly only the object we focus on; other objects appear double. If we try to look at a cigarette between our lips, we see two cigarettes. We hold only one match to our cigarette, but we see two. These double-images are out of focus in relation to the distance between them and our eyes.

Once we become aware of the problems, we realize that seeing clearly is not an automatic or even an easy task. The newborn child needs months of daily training to learn where things are placed in space. It must learn where to grasp a rattle, how to handle a fork, how to replace a cup on a table. It is in the first year of life that we learn the art of seeing.

29

Male and Female

The primary difference between the two sexes is present at birth; the secondary differences—in size, hair, breasts, voice, skin and muscles—begin to appear at puberty.

The life of the individual starts when the egg cell of the mother and the sperm cell of the father unite to form the single cell of the embryo. The embryo cell multiplies by division into many cells. At first these cells all look alike but soon they develop into epithelial cells, connective fiber cells, nerve cells and others.

The embryo cells also differentiate into body cells and sex cells. At a time when the embryo is a ball of not more than a dozen cells, a fourth of them become sex cells. They wait about ten to thirteen years until the body of the child is sufficiently developed before they begin to function. Then these cells awaken. The sex glands of the boy secrete sperm cells which are ejected from time to time. The girl begins to menstruate each month, in a cycle which begins with the production of an ovum, or egg cell. Besides the sex cells the glands produce the sex hormones, which determine the secondary sex traits of man and woman.

The sex hormones of male and female are chemically very similar. In their fundamental atom structure they are basically alike; they differ only in a few of their hydrogen atoms and one CH_3 group. The difference is no greater than that between two decorated Christmas trees where one tree has twenty-three candles and the other twenty-four. But this seemingly insignificant difference is sufficient to form one child into a woman, another into a man. The female develops all the traits of femininity. She remains smaller and has less muscular strength; fat fills the connective tissue; and the breasts form. The hair on her head grows into a full silky mantle, the voice becomes higher and the skin is soft and hairless. Biologically her desire is to love and be loved, and her urge is to bear children.

And the other sex, the male? As soon as his sex glands start to produce sperm and the male hormone, his muscle fibers proliferate, and the urge for activity enlivens them. Hair sprouts on his face and his chest. He has less fat pads than the female and his voice is deeper.

All these distinctions between the two sexes result from that incredibly minute difference in the atomic configuration of the female and male sex hormone, one tiny group more or less of CH_3. This is one of the wonders of the world, manifested in the biology of the human body.

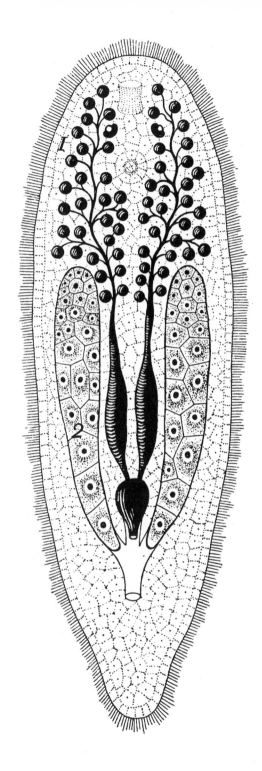

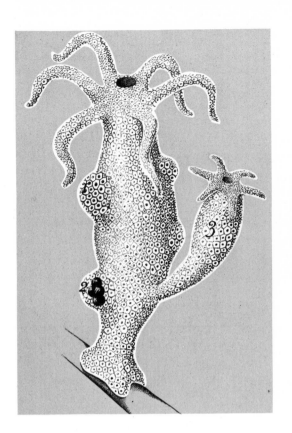

The sexes. In some species each creature is a hermaphrodite, functioning as both male and female. The parasitic worm (above) and the simple hydra (right) each has tiny glands for the production of sperm (1) as well as eggs (2). The hydra young (3) are thus offshoots of a single creature. The human embryo itself begins life as a hermaphrodite.

The separation of the two sexes is in many species a development that takes place late in life. The embryo begins as a hermaphrodite, that is, combining both male and female. The human sex gland in its early stages also contains cells of both sexes. Under normal conditions the cells of the one sex soon dominate and the embryo becomes male or female.

When in the later years of life the sex gland loses some of its power, the traits of the other sex begin to display themselves. In a senile woman the hair of a man's beard appears on the face, and the voice becomes deep and rough. "Tell me," the Chinese sage asks the girls; "tell me, you many pretty girls, whence come all the ugly women?" The girls only giggle, but we know the answer: humans are all, in some degree, bisexual. In the rare cases of true hermaphroditism, the body glands are actually half male and half female. An individual raised as a boy may during puberty develop female breasts as well as female traits, or vice versa. More frequently, a boy will develop certain feminine characteristics or a girl certain mannish qualities. When these become extreme, and individuals have intimate relations with their own sex, the men are called homosexuals and the women are known as lesbians (after the Greek poetess, Sappho of Lesbos). When an individual of one sex wears the clothes of the other sex, such a person is known as a transvestite.

The male and female sex organs are not so different as they may seem. The central organ of both sexes is the gland that produces the sex cells. There are two sex glands in each person and they are situated symmetrically. Both originate in the embryo near the kidneys. The female glands, the ovaries, descend but remain inside the abdomen; the male glands move down until they hang as testes outside the body cavity. In their early embryonic stages, the external organs of both sexes look alike. At the beginning, the meeting point of the two legs is an open slit. The slit is walled by two lips. Where the lips meet in the front they form a mound or knob which is rich in sensitive nerves. The excitation of these nerves produces an agreeable sensation of a voluptuous kind. This "pleasure knob" is in a man the glands of the penis, in a woman the clitoris.

In the male as well as in the female the area of excitability is padded by so-called cavernous tissue; this tissue is a major portion of the penis. The cavernous tissue is a spongelike system into which arteries and veins open. This tissue ordinarily contains little blood because involuntary smooth muscle fibers in the walls of the spaces keep them closed. But if the genital area is aroused by direct titillation or psychological stimulation, the normal tonus of the smooth muscle fibers in the walls diminishes, the closed-off cavernous spaces fill with blood, and the rings of smooth muscle guarding the exits contract and prevent the blood from leaving. The organ becomes rigid. The penis, which ordinarily hangs loose, becomes erect, and can be thrust into the vagina of the female. The entrance into the vagina, which contains cavernous tissue, also becomes tumescent, that is, swollen with blood, and holds the shaft of the penis tightly, so that the motion of one within the other produces a stimulating sensation.

Venereal Diseases

Among the most troublesome of man's diseases have been those that come from sexual intercourse. Fortunately modern medicine has been quite successful in combating these maladies, including the most common, gonorrhea and syphilis. Gonorrhea is caused by the gonococcus, which was identified only at the very end of the 19th century. Syphilis results from an active spiral organism called a spirochete. It must be identified while it is alive and motile.

Gonorrhea causes a discharge from the male organ and painful urination; it also causes an inflammation of the sexual organs in both sexes. If not treated in time it may become chronic and impair the ability to bear children. Once difficult to treat, acute gonorrhea can now be cured by a single injection of penicillin.

Syphilis is a more serious matter. It first appears as an ulcer, called a chancre, on the penis of the male. In the female the chancre may be hidden. Even when not treated, the chancre disappears in from two to six weeks but then a rash appears, which is called secondary syphilis. This too heals spontaneously, but after an interval, perhaps of years, syphilis of the nervous system, and indeed every part of the body, shows up. Fortunately syphilis can also be cured by penicillin injections, but such treatment must be undertaken well before the nervous system, heart and blood vessels have been involved.

Up to recently doctors believed that the venereal diseases would be eradicated through the use of penicillin. But there has been a resurgence of the diseases, particularly in young people and homosexuals. Doctors believe this increase could be checked if patients would seek treatment promptly.

30

The Sexual Function in Man

When sexually aroused, the male ejaculates semen containing sperm cells capable of fertilizing the egg cells of the female.

Unlike all other glands, the sex glands of the male, the testicles, hang outside the body. Why the testicles of some of the higher mammals migrated to this unprotected position is still an unanswered question.

Like the ovaries, the testicles produce both the sex cells and the male sex hormones. Sometimes the testicles do not descend from the abdomen. Undescended testicles secrete the sex hormone but the higher temperature within the body apparently makes it impossible for the sperm cells to develop. If a child has undescended testicles, it is important at puberty to bring the testicles out of the abdomen and down to the scrotum, the bag which normally contains them.

The Sperm

A testicle is a package of about a thousand thread-like tubes, whose combined length is about two hundred and fifty yards. These tubules are lined with cells that become the sperm cells, the principal element in the secretion called semen. The tubules are wound in spirals but join to form one collective tube. This tube meanders along in the back of the testicle, like a vine in a rain forest, and is here called the epididymis. Uncoiled, the canal of the epididymis would extend to fifteen or twenty feet. In relation to the minute size of a single sperm cell, this is a tremendous distance. The tube from each of the two testicles returns to the abdominal cavity through the inguinal rings and enters the urethra, the tube leading from the bladder into the penis. Although urine and semen flow through the same tube, they ordinarily remain strictly separated. Before entering the urethra, each sperm tube goes through the prostate gland which surrounds the urethra close to the bladder. The prostate gland, which is shaped like a chestnut, contains, besides muscle fibers, glands that produce a milklike secretion. When a man is sexually aroused and his penis comes to erection, the muscle fibers of the prostate compress the urethra, thus closing off the bladder, so that no urine can infiltrate the semen.

After a man reaches fifty, the prostate tends to become less flexible and to increase in size, and he cannot empty his bladder as easily as before. A certain amount of urine remains in the bladder after urination and the man may be disturbed by the feeling of not having fully emptied his bladder. If the disturbance becomes acute or if it becomes impossible for the man to empty his bladder at all, the prostate can be removed by an operation.

Two little glands, the seminal vesicles, add to the semen a viscous yellow fluid containing gray globules, the function of which is not clear. This fluid mixes with a secretion of the prostate to form the product of the male sex organ known as semen, a milky fluid with an odor like fresh mushrooms. In this fluid wriggle the sperm cells—as many as two hundred million of them in one ejaculation.

A great spectacle, equal in its way to the first sight of the Alps or the Grand Canyon, is one's first view under a microscope of sperm—millions of spermatozoa, each of them miraculously capable of becoming a human being.

The Penis

The penis is a cylinder of flesh that normally is pendulous and limp. Its tip is covered by a ring-shaped fold of flesh called the foreskin. Although originally the cutting away of this foreskin, called circumcision, may have been a part of ancient rituals, it is today practised by many peoples for sound hygienic reasons.

The act of fertilization begins when a man inserts the penis in a state of erection into the female vagina. In erection, which is stimulated either by stroking or by erotic thoughts, the arteries of the penis fill with blood, the folds expand and the penis stiffens and swells to many times its ordinary size. When the sexual excitation reaches a peak, semen is ejaculated. The ejaculation is the result of a spasmodic contraction not unlike the act of sneezing. It affords relief for an almost unbearable urgency. The penis returns to normal size and both partners in the act experience a sense of relaxation and the desire to sleep.

Impotence

An inability to achieve an erection of the penis is called impotence. A nerve center in the lumbar

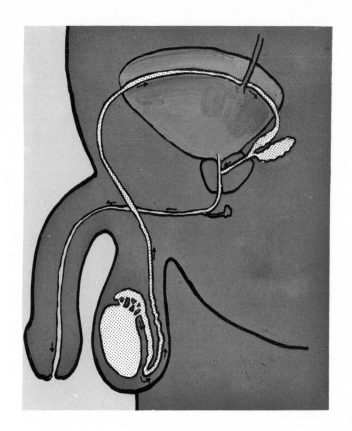

(Above) From sperm to semen. Sperm cells from the testicles travel along a tube which returns to the abdominal cavity. After passing behind the bladder, it is joined by the duct of the seminal vesicle and enters the prostate portion of the urethra.

(Right) Spermatozoa. The seminal fluid of one ejaculation may contain upward of 225 million spermatozoa. Any one of these cells may fertilize the female egg cell and produce a unique human being. (Preparation by Dr. J. A. G. Rhodin, New York Medical College)

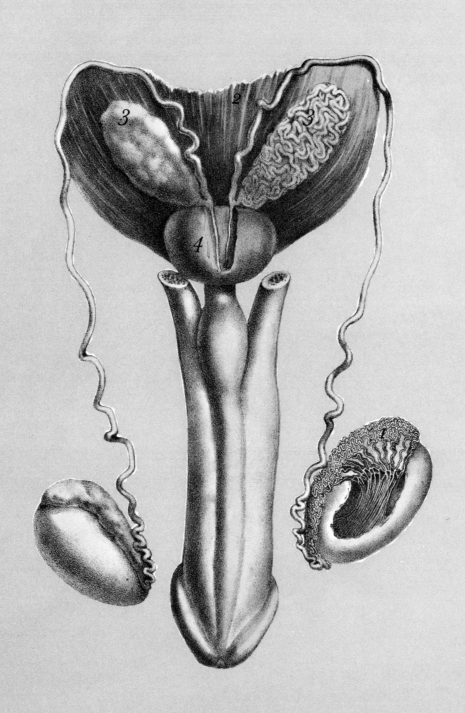

region of the spinal cord gives the nerves leading to the sex organs the stimulus that sets the arteries and valves of the erection mechanism in motion. The control of this complex arrangement is in the cortex of the brain. Impotence is a symptom of aging. It is premature if a man in his thirties or forties loses his capacity to have an erection.

The development of impotence from truly organic causes is relatively rare. Generally it is brought on by psychological inhibitions resulting from fears, whether of sin or the possibility of making a girl pregnant or of not being adequate. Often the man is impotent only during the period of sexual intercourse; he goes to a doctor but realizes when he arrives that he is responding normally again. This kind of impotence often occurs on the wedding night. The bridegroom is overexcited, looks on the act as a test and cannot perform. Psychological impotence of course requires a psychological treatment—the restoration of the self-confidence that is natural in any physically healthy male.

The testicles. Within the scrotum are the sperm-producing testicles, each composed of about a thousand threadlike tubes (1). These join in a single tube which returns to the abdominal cavity (2) through the inguinal rings and enters the urethra. Fluids from the seminal vesicles (3) and the prostate gland (4) are secreted with the sperm during an ejaculation. The seminal fluid passes out of the body by way of the urethra and the penis.

31

The Sexual Function in Woman

The ovaries of the female produce ova, or eggs, one of which, when fertilized by the sperm of the male, will develop into the embryo.

The sex organs of the female (color portfolio plate 32) are not so different from those of the male as they may seem on the surface. Their basic arrangement is the same. The two sex glands in woman, called ovaries, paralleling the testicles in the male, produce sex cells called ova, or eggs. The vagina is like the finger of a glove and serves as a receiver of the penis and the ejected semen of the male.

The Ovary

The egg cell of the female starts its growth in the epithelial lining of the ovary. It does not evolve as a solitary cell but induces the cells around it to multiply and thus acquires a staff of cells, a kind of entourage of "ladies in waiting," with the ovum in the center. A space forms between the "ladies in waiting" and the ovum, and the space fills with liquid. This liquid-filled ball with the egg cell in the middle is called a follicle. The follicle grows until it reaches the outer cover of the ovary and pierces it. The egg splashes out through the break. This is the normal beginning of the human egg. The ovary does not have an excretory duct attached to it; it is tightly enclosed on all sides, and our first adventure in life is a daring escape. But after the escape comes another surprise: no friend awaits the fugitive outside. There is a rescue brigade with a life net, whose purpose is to help the fugitive on his way to liberty and life; but there is no certainty that the brigade will catch the fugitive as he plunges to freedom.

Each ovary at birth contains four hundred thousand or more eggs, but of this vast number only about four hundred are destined to mature and be discharged. The rest atrophy.

The Oviducts

In the center axis of the body, deep within the pelvis hangs a pear-shaped organ called the uterus. Like the ears on a head, two oviducts, or ova-carrying tubes, are attached to the uterus; each is about as thin as a pencil and as long as a finger. The tubes have a ciliated lining and a fringed opening which catches the ovum as it leaves the ovary. The cilia

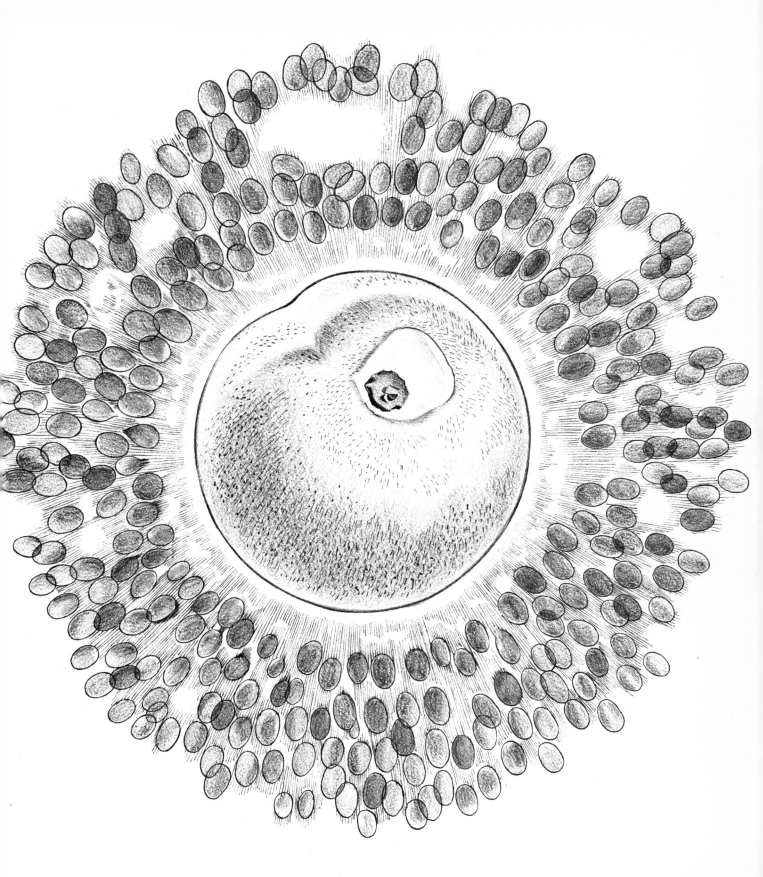

The egg cell is surrounded, during development in the ovary,
by a host of smaller satellite cells essential to its growth.

then wave the ovum slowly along toward the uterus. The sperm cell of the father will unite with the egg cell of the mother in the oviduct. And this is where the creation of the individual takes place—where the chromosomes combine to form the essence of our personality. It is here in the oviduct that the dice of destiny are cast. Which one of the approximately two hundred million spermatozoa will win the race? What combination of the twenty-three pairs of chromosomes will we have as the underlying formula of our personality?

The uterus is the central organ of the female sex apparatus—in a sense, of the total woman. Ancient peoples actually regarded the uterus as an independent being, symbolizing it as a toad. Women brought toads of clay, silver, or even of gold as offerings to the altars of the gods and goddesses. In medieval times these offerings were brought to the Madonna in the hope of warding off sterility or ailments of the womb.

The Uterus and the Monthly Cycle

After fertilization, the egg cell immediately begins subdividing and multiplying and floats into the cavity of the uterus. The uterus has a dual purpose: first it serves as a muscle organ to hold and later to expel the child. Secondly, it is an instrument to nurse the growing child (color portfolio plate 33). Its cavity is lined with a mucous membrane with deep glands.

As we have said, when the egg cell inside the ovary ripens, the cells around the egg form a ball, the follicle. After rupture and escape of the egg cell the follicle produces a hormone, progesterone, which stimulates the uterus to prepare for the arrival of a fertilized egg. The glands of the mucous membrane of the uterus become active, increasing in size, and the membrane is described as "blooming." The mucous membrane of the uterus becomes thicker and softer and the arteries and veins in it are enlarged. When a woman has not had relations with a man, the egg arrives without fertilization, the follicle atrophies, the progesterone diminishes and the blooming membrane withers and is ejected from the uterus. The discarded membrane floats as a mass of fluid and blood through the neck of the uterus, called the cervix,

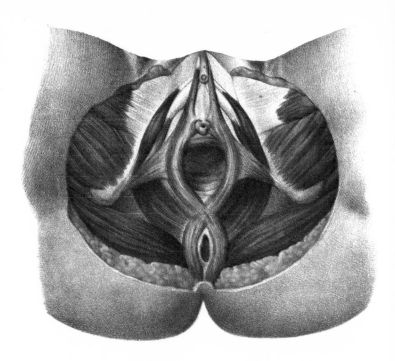

(Above) External female genitals, showing the clitoris, the urethral orifice and the vaginal opening.

(Right) Female sex and excretory organs (side view): (1) the bladder; (2) the ovary; (3) the uterus; (4) the vagina and (5) the rectum.

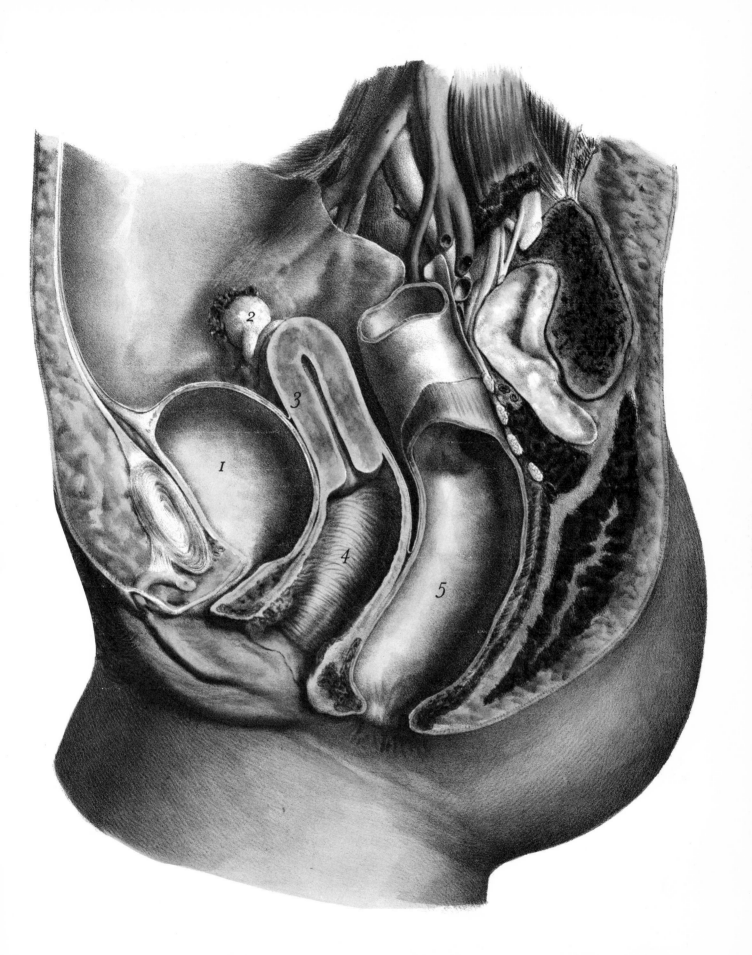

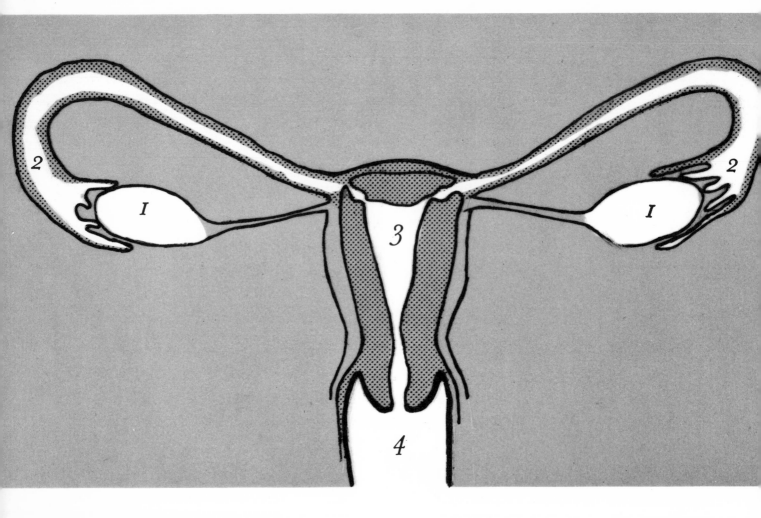

and then through the vagina and out of the body in the course of menstruation.

If the egg has been fertilized by a sperm, the multiplying cells sprout roots. These roots form a network of blood vessels, and processes called villi implant themselves in the mucous membrane of the uterus to help form the placenta that feeds the embryo. The ruptured follicle continues to develop and secrete progesterone, which is necessary for the development of the placenta, and becomes the corpus luteum or "yellow body" of pregnancy. As the placenta develops, it takes over the secretion of progesterone as well as estrogen and other hormones that foster the pregnancy. While progesterone is being secreted, the ovary will not discharge any other egg cells. Progesterone thus frees the embryo from the competition of another embryo. It is the protector of the unborn child.

We have so far ignored the controlling role of the

Female sex organs. Shown here are (1) the egg-producing ovaries; (2) the Fallopian tubes where the egg is fertilized; (3) the uterus where the embryo develops and (4) the vagina.

pituitary gland. The ovary is not independent; it acts at the command of the pituitary gland. The pituitary gland secretes two hormones: one stimulates the immature follicles of the ovary to secrete estrogen, which controls the development of the secondary sex characteristics. The other is, as we have noted, progesterone, which is needed to make the uterus receive the fertilized egg and then to protect the embryo. These pituitary hormones are also secreted in the male, one stimulating the formation of sperm and the other stimulating the cells between the sperm cells in the testis.

Contraception

More and more often we hear the phrase "population explosion." It refers to the fact that hygiene, preventive medicine, improved diet and housing have reduced the death rate and increased the survival rate, and thus threaten the world with overpopulation. There are fewer epidemics and famines and more and more the deadly diseases are being controlled by vaccines, serums and so forth. The danger is that the day will come when there will be more people than the earth can support. An answer that has been suggested to this problem is "planned parenthood." One method of achieving this is the administering of a hormone, such as progesterone, which will temporarily prevent ovulation or egg cell maturation and production just as it does in a pregnant woman. This is currently very widely used, being taken in the form of pills containing primarily progesterone, and some estrogen as well.

Another method is the use of what is known as the rhythm method in intercourse. Menstruation is a monthly process, occurring about every twenty-eight days, and lasting for three to five days. A follicle in the ovary matures and ruptures between the fourteenth and sixteenth days of the cycle. Since a sperm cell after intercourse is capable of fertilizing the egg for about two days, the twelfth to eighteenth days of the cycle are fertile days. Intercourse on the other days is generally safe and this is called the safe period.

Artificial methods of contraception are also available. For example, a woman may wear a diaphragm, which closes off the cervix so that the sperm cannot enter. Or the male may wear a sheath over the penis, preventing the ejection of the sperm into the vagina.

The Cervix

The uterus and vagina together have the shape of a pear that—unlike a pear on a tree—hangs with its smaller part, the vagina, downward. The cervix, the narrow neck of the uterus, tightly closes off the uterus from the vagina, which, like our mouth, swarms with microorganisms.

The semen of the man is ejaculated against the rear wall of the vagina. Here the mobile spermatozoa wriggle into the opening of the cervix, a canal hardly wider than a knitting needle. The cervix contains mucus that is, in contrast to the acid vaginal fluid, alkaline. Since the spermatozoa abhor acids, they flee, like eels, out of the acid vagina into the alkaline mucus of the cervix and migrate upward through the uterus, into the oviducts, and toward the egg cell. Certain substances emitted by the egg cell act as a bait to attract the sperm cells.

In childbirth, the tissue of the cervix permits the widening of the uterine door and thus the issuance of the child. During the final weeks of pregnancy the normally firm tissue of the cervix becomes as porous as a sponge and during the hours of the mother's labor this spongy tissue is flattened into a membrane as thin as paper. The canal of the cervix stretches first to the diameter of a dime, then a half dollar, and finally to a width sufficient to allow the head of the child to pass.

The Vagina

The vagina is an elastic sheath capable of accommodating the male penis in erection. Its membrane continuously sheds cells and a watery fluid containing glycogen, which feeds a host of microorganisms, the flora of the vagina. The most common in a healthy vagina is the Döderlein bacillus.

Cells of the cervix are also discharged into the vagina. A modern Greek physician, George Papanicolaou found that if he took smears of cells from the vaginal wall and from a scraping of the cervix, he could determine whether the cervix was cancerous. This has become a very important method of detecting cancer of the cervix before it begins to bleed or has spread.

The Vulva

The exterior opening of the vagina is called the vulva and is an area of sexual pleasure. Indeed, satisfaction in the love relation and consequently in matrimony requires that a man and woman be acquainted with the form and function of this organ.

The entrance to the vagina, is protected by a double fold of flesh comparable to the lips at the entrance to the mouth. The outer and fuller fold is covered by the pubic hairs, which transmit fine tactile sensations. Just inside the apex of the opening of the labia, or lips, hangs the clitoris, the "penis" of the female. It is like a nipple or button made up of tissue that, like the penis, fills with blood during sexual excitation. As it becomes erect, the clitoris comes out of its recess and exposes itself to the titillation of the male penis, a sensation considered to be the most exquisite of bodily pleasures.

The external opening of the vagina, lying between the inner lips of the vulva, is partly closed by a ring of connective tissue called the hymen. This is generally ruptured during the first act of intercourse and the slight bleeding that takes place is considered evidence of virginity. It can, however, be ruptured accidentally at an earlier time.

3² Sleep

Most individuals spend about eight of every twenty-four hours in a state of semiconscious, generally restful repose; but the mind often continues to be as active as ever.

Sleep is a recurrent loss of consciousness. Normally it lasts for about eight hours and is apparently connected with the rhythm of day and night. It is not a state peculiar to human beings but is characteristic of all living things. Even plants periodically alternate between activity, which we describe as being awake, and passivity, which we call sleep. The rhythm varies: the hen sleeps during the night and is awake during the day, and the owl does the opposite. Concerning fishes we are not so sure what the rhythm is, although we do know that among the creatures of the sea some are active during the night and others during the day. Many animals, such as cats, seem to be independent of the rhythm of day and night. They tend to rely on naps, but they will adapt to the family with which they live.

We human beings are also very adaptable, with great individual differences in the time of going to sleep and of rising and in the number of hours of sleep required. The average person sleeps about eight hours of every twenty-four, or a third of his life. The need for sleep diminishes from infancy to maturity. The newborn baby sleeps twenty hours, the child of four about twelve hours, and the child of ten about ten hours. Thereafter each person develops his own pattern. There is no rigid rule: the optimum amount may be six, eight or ten hours, or it may be several naps. Night workers do not suffer from having to sleep during the day. Orderly sleeping habits are not necessarily conducive to good health or to great productivity. Great inventors and artists often keep irregular hours. Thomas Edison is a famous example of a man who required little sleep, taking only about four hours a day, generally in the form of hour-long naps in his workshop.

The Deep Sleeper

The secret which enables some persons to get along on very little rest is their capacity for deep or restful sleep. General Townsend, famous during the period of British colonization, paid little attention to sleep. Once during a night conference he fell asleep for a few minutes and awakened as completely refreshed as if he had slept eight hours. Alexander the Great was also an example of a deep sleeper. He could work long into the night, then creep into his sleeping-bag and sleep so deeply that his aide, General Parmenio, had to make three attempts to awaken him before he succeeded. During the battle of Wagram, Napoleon slept amidst the sound of galloping horses and thundering cannon.

Perhaps the capacity for deep sleep is associated with brief periods of sleep. It may be that the art of deep, brief sleep will eventually become the accepted form of sleep. Man is a clever animal, able to justify both sides of a question. The brief sleeper will say: "Sleep half as long and your waking life will be twice as long." The long sleeper says: "Sleep twice as long and you will feel doubly refreshed and enjoy life twice as much." Each must decide for himself.

Brain Activity in Sleep

A sleeping person is like an automobile that is standing still with its motor running, or, as we say, "idling." All parts of the brain do not become inactive.

The brain is like an office with departments or divisions on three floors. The top division is the gray surface of the cortex. This is the sphere of feeling, action and thought, the sphere in whose cells are stored our memories and whatever we have learned in life. It is the director of our ideals, religious beliefs, morals, and conscience, the source of our individual personality.

The middle section is less peculiar to the individual and more common to the entire species. In human beings it is the sphere of such semi-automatic actions as weeping, experiencing pain, idly playing a piano or driving on familiar roads. Below these two spheres is that deep sphere which is the center of such automatic biological activity as the heartbeat, breathing, digestive and bladder movements, the reactions of the pupils of the eye and the body's thermal mechanism. These vital activities are almost entirely independent of our personalities. The vast majority of individuals cannot exert any control over them. Among the alleged exceptions to this is the Roman senator Cato, who is said to have committed suicide by holding his breath. Also the yogis of India are reported to be able to control and direct many of these automatic body activities.

In normal sleep the activity of the upper cortex of the brain is very greatly reduced, that of the middle sphere is much reduced, while that of the deepest sphere is hardly affected. The activity of the upper sphere manifests itself as dreams. Dreams are the product of a brain working without the control of what are called the "higher centers," without direction, so to speak, of the forces of government, law or education. We are educated and trained to control the activities of our cortical brain just as a dog is trained to behave according to certain rules. The dreaming brain behaves like a dog who has broken his leash and is roaming about haphazardly. Because dreams are not controlled by our conscious selves, they reveal much about the driving forces in the deeper layers of the personality. That is why the analysis of dreams plays such an important part in modern psychology and psychoanalysis. Regrettably, our recollection of our dreams is often very fragmentary, and we unconsciously falsify and censor our reports on our dreams because we do not wish to acknowledge some of the things we feel and do in them. With modern methods of measuring the brain waves and the movements of the pupils of the eyes, a new science of dreams and sleep has developed, and we are able for the first time to perceive the exciting direction that future exploration may follow.

Sleep and Consciousness

Sleeping is not a loss of being. Many a mother never "sleeps"; she can hear in the midst of sleep the slightest restlessness in her slumbering child. Sleep is a kind of marking time in the daily life of the individual, but it is not actually a complete loss of consciousness. It is sleep.

In contrast to sleep, such a narcotic as ether or an excessive quantity of an intoxicant such as alcohol produces a true loss of consciousness. You do not instantly awaken from them. But even these, properly administered, do not stop respiration, the heartbeat, the action of the smooth muscle fibers and so forth. They continue under the direction of the deep centers at the base of the brain, the medulla. If, however, the narcotization reaches the deep layers of these centers, life is endangered and the sleep may become the last sleep of all—death.

33
Death

The life span of the average individual has increased greatly over the centuries. Today it stands at about sixty-five.

A living being is like a watch: the spring is wound up at birth and it runs for what we call the span of life. Except in so-called backward areas the normal span is the biblical three score and ten. In exceptional instances, individuals have lived much longer. The oldest man on reliable record was Thomas Parr, an English farmer who was more than one hundred and fifty years old when he died. King George took him into his palace, but the royal diet was too much for the countryman's stomach and the following year Parr died. The leading anatomist of the time made an autopsy and was surprised at the excellent condition of the old man's organs.

The fertility of living creatures far exceeds the earth's capacity to support all their progeny. It is a very sad and sobering fact, but the survival of living things depends on the consumption or slaughter of other living things. The whale lives by drinking a soup of teeming plankton—five million tiny creatures disappearing at every gulp. The song with which a bird greets the dawn is a funeral song for hundreds of insects that it will eat before the day is over.

The average life span of a newborn babe in the 15th century was about thirty years. In the past century there has been a spectacular rise in life expectancy and the figure now stands at about sixty-five. This of course is only an average. Many factors have contributed to increasing the average life span: improvements in housing, food and water supply, cleanliness, medical care and remarkable drugs, retirement plans and pensions, and so forth. A hundred years ago the main causes of death were tuberculosis, syphilis, malaria, scurvy, childbirth fever and the infectious diseases of childhood. Such deadly diseases as these have by now almost completely disappeared. Today the majority of children grow into adulthood. The composition of the population has consequently changed; where in 1800 the majority of the population were children, and really old people were rare, the majority in advanced countries today are past middle age. The leading causes of death are no longer the diphtheria of childhood or the tuberculosis of adolescence, but the diseases of the aged—arteriosclerosis, heart failure, cancer, diabetes, pneumonia. A man dies because he has lived his life. This is the death of modern man.

The Signs of Death

In most cases there is no doubt as to whether a person is dead. The signs are many:

1. *Cessation of breathing*. This is an obvious sign. If there is any doubt about it, a mirror or a feather held over the lips will usually settle the question.

2. *Cessation of the heartbeat*. This can be tested by seeing whether the arteries in the wrists or, better, those alongside the windpipe, the carotids, pulsate.

3. *Reaction of the pupils*. The pupil of the eye will not contract even if a flashlight is shined on it.

4. *Corneal reflex*. If the very sensitive surface of the eye, the cornea, is touched, the body will show no reaction.

5. *The Hypostatic spots*. After death, the blood begins to sink in the vessels as a result of gravity, and shows up as bluish spots, especially in those areas pressed by the weight of the corpse.

6. *Rigor mortis*. Several hours after death the body becomes stiff. This state, called rigor mortis, represents the last contraction of the muscles. After a day or so the muscles soften again. When the Cid, the hero of the Spanish legend, died, his soldiers made use of rigor mortis to tie him upright on his horse, so that the Moors would think he was still alive and leading his army.

When these signs are present, we know that the spring in the clock of life has unwound and that the most remarkable of all engines has stopped.

Index

Numbers with asterisks indicate color plates; those in italics indicate pages on which black and white illustrations appear.